Introduction
to Mathematics
for College Students

KENNETH C. SKEEN   Diablo Valley College
Concord, California.

CHARLES W. WHEELER   Diablo Valley College
Concord, California

ADDISON-WESLEY PUBLISHING COMPANY
Menlo Park, California · Reading, Massachusetts
London · Don Mills, Ontario

Preface

Introduction to Mathematics for College Students is designed to provide both a review of skills and an extension of concepts. We recognize that effective skills are an essential foundation to the everyday use of mathematics. With this fact in mind, we have provided thousands of exercises which can be used in the development of good computation. However, we further recognize that skills and understanding go hand in hand. On a given day the student who has some skill and recognizes a particular problem type may do very well in solving a dozen or more problems of this kind. But if he fails to comprehend this problem type in terms of the patterns of mathematics, he may very probably be unable to solve such a problem on another day in another part of his course.

Hence we have included a spiral development of structure in both the exposition and the exercises. In exposition, generalizations of properties are developed from numerical examples. In the exercises, generalizations are reinforced throughout the book with discovery-type problems.

Definition, as well as the role of definition in mathematics, is stressed throughout. From the beginning of Chapter 1 the terminology of mathematics is introduced and applied. Consider these terms from the first three sections: *one-to-one correspondence, inequality symbols, numerical expression, order relations, base, factor, exponent,* and *polynomial in ten.* The concept of a variable is introduced early in Chapter 1.

In the use of language, care has been taken to avoid compartmentalization of terms. For example, a concept usage is most frequently illustrated first in simple number situations and then with variables. However, it seems pedagogically and mathematically desirable to avoid naming one illustration "arithmetic" and the other "algebra." Rather, the goal is progress toward a basic mathematical background.

Mathematical structure, skills, and problem solving are interwoven to develop understanding on the part of students. To this end the arithmetic of whole numbers and fractions is presented in Chapters 1 and 2. The decimals and percent are combined as a unit in Chapter 3. The percentage formula is presented as the fundamental pattern, and its usage is encouraged in many applications throughout the book. Following an elementary discussion of geometry in Chapter 4, graphing and statistics are combined in Chapter 5. Hence, the working tools of a basic course are provided in Chapters 1 through 5. Within the work of applications that follow, new topics are developed (such as sequences, series, compound interest, the trigonometric ratios, and the negative numbers). But the groundwork for the study of these topics is essentially completed in the earlier chapters. Chapters 6 through 8 include extensive applications, as well as an introduction to new topics which can be treated with the tools of earlier chapters.

The textbook may be adapted according to course patterns. Because of the abundance of material, some selection will be necessary for most courses. For example, the first five chapters may provide an ample short course.

The material in this book has been classroom tested, and we appreciate the contribution of those who took part in this test. In addition, we wish to thank Robert Herrera, Los Angeles City College, and Thomas Southard, California State College at Hayward, for their critical evaluation of the manuscript as it was being written. We further express appreciation to the staff of Addison-Wesley for editorial assistance.

K. C. S.

C. W. W.

Contents

v

3 DECIMAL FRACTIONS AND PERCENT

4 GEOMETRIC CONCEPTS AND MEASUREMENT

5 INTERPRETATION OF DATA; COORDINATES

6   THE ARITHMETIC OF FINANCE

7   INDIRECT MEASUREMENT

8 NEGATIVE NUMBERS AND OPERATIONS

APPENDIX

SELECTED ANSWERS

INDEX

1 Sets, Numbers, and Operations

1-1 COUNTING

As soon as man began to gather possessions, he had a need for keeping some account of them. It seems likely that he did this by using sticks or stones for **counters.** Later, he may have used scratches on the wall for the same purpose.

Suppose that an ancient caveman collected a number of clay pots of wild grain and used stones for counters in the following way. He placed a stone by each pot of grain. Then he placed the set of stones in the corner of his cave. As he collected more grain, the *number* of stones in his *counting* pile increased.

In Figure 1–1 note that a stone is placed by each clay pot. The stone is a **symbol** for a count of one. The figure shows a relationship of one stone for one clay pot. In mathematics we call the relationship shown a **one-to-one correspondence.**

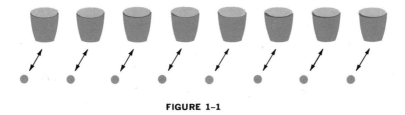

FIGURE 1–1

The early caveman probably did not understand the idea of *how many*, even in terms of very small numbers. However, he knew that

1

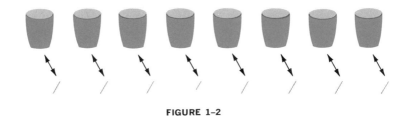

FIGURE 1-2

he had as many pots of grain as stones in his *counting* pile. Later, he
may have used a stick to mark tallies in the ground or a piece of
charcoal to mark tallies on stone walls. Here again, he was using a
one-to-one correspondence, as the figure indicates.

Exercises for Section 1-1

1. Which of the following sets of objects can be placed in a one-to-
   one correspondence?

   (a) $\triangle, \triangle, \triangle, \triangle$ (b) $\square, \square, \square, \square, \square$
   (c) $+, -, \times, \div$ (d) A, B, C, D
   (e) $\phi, \theta, \psi, \gamma, \beta$ (f) $\#, \$, \%, +, \cent$

2. A theatre has a full house for an evening. Name two sets of
   objects which can be placed in a one-to-one correspondence.

3. Suppose that you have a pile of coins. If you do not count them,
   how can you determine whether you have as many nickels as
   dimes?

4. The count of votes in an election is shown as $/\!/\!/\!/\!/ \ /\!/\!/\!/\!/ \ /\!/$.
   What one-to-one correspondence is suggested?

5. A turnstile at a ball park admits one person at a time. How does
   this show a one-to-one correspondence?

6. A player keeps his score in a card game by moving pegs along
   a series of holes in a board. How does this show a one-to-one
   correspondence?

■ 1-2 EGYPTIAN SYSTEM

As he gained more and more possessions, man found the tally system
to be tedious. Perhaps he shortened it by writing $/\!/\!/\!/\!/$ for five.
At some time in the development of civilization, man made significant

progress by letting one picture (symbol) stand for the number of objects in a set. One of the earliest forms of this was the Egyptian system.

A collection of objects is called a set. In expressing a set we enclose the list of objects in braces, { }. A capital letter is used to name a set. The set of Egyptian symbols for numbers was

$$E = \{\ /\ ,\ \cap\ ,\ ?\ ,\ \text{🌷}\ ,\ \nearrow\ ,\ \text{🐟}\ ,\ \text{👤}\ \}.$$

Notice that the symbols were taken from things in nature.

one = $/$, a stroke

ten = $\cap$, the heelbone

one hundred = $?$, a coil of rope

one thousand = 🌷 , a lotus flower

ten thousand = $\nearrow$, a pointing finger

one hundred thousand = 🐟 , a fish

one million = 👤 , an astonished man

We call the symbols above numerals. Thus $\cap$ and 10 are two different numerals used to stand for the same number of objects (in this case, ten).

To write larger numerals the Egyptians repeated the symbols and added the results. Thus if a man had twenty-six slaves, he represented this number as $\cap\ \cap\ //////$, which he evaluated by thinking of it as $\cap + \cap + / + / + / + / + / + /$. (We use the $+$ with today's meaning; it was not an Egyptian symbol.)

The following represent different numerical expressions:

$$6 + 5,\ \cap\ ////,\ \tfrac{1}{2} - \tfrac{1}{4},\ \cap + ? + /,\ ? - \cap\ .$$

The equals symbol, $=$, shows that the expression on one side of the symbol represents the same number as that on the other side. We use this symbol to show equality of expressions. For example,

$$\cap + \cap + \cap = \cap\ \cap\ \cap = \text{thirty},$$

$$? + ? + \cap + / + / = ?\ ?\ \cap\ // = \text{two hundred twelve}.$$

A basic property of numbers is that of order. We order the numbers of a set when we arrange them in order of size, from smallest to largest.

We show order relations among numbers by using inequality symbols, $>$ and $<$. For example, we write:

$$\cap \cap \; > \cap /// , \quad \text{and read,} \quad \text{“20 is greater than 13.”}$$

$$// \; < \; \cap , \quad \text{and read,} \quad \text{“2 is less than 10.”}$$

The symbol $>$ means *is greater than*; the symbol $<$ means *is less than*.

Notice that in the Egyptian system the relative positions of symbols has no influence on the value of the number represented. For example,

$$\cap \cap /// = \cap // \cap / = /// \cap \cap = 23.$$

However, Egyptian numerals probably were written with symbols for the larger groups appearing first, as in $\cap \cap ///$.

Exercises in this section involve some use of the four fundamental operations: addition, multiplication, subtraction, and division. The symbols $+$, $\times$, $-$, and $\div$ are used with their common meanings.

Exercises for Section 1–2

1–2 A

Write in Egyptian numerals:

1. 5	**2.** 10	**3.** 15	**4.** 20	**5.** 25
6. 30	**7.** 35	**8.** 40	**9.** 45	**10.** 50
11. 55	**12.** 60	**13.** 65	**14.** 70	**15.** 75

1–2 B

Write in Egyptian numerals:

1. 11	**2.** 21	**3.** 13	**4.** 23	**5.** 9
6. 22	**7.** 31	**8.** 101	**9.** 210	**10.** 333

1–2 C

Write in our system of notation:

1. $\cap + \cap + \cap + /$ **2.** $𝟃 + \cap + / + /$

3. $𝟃 + 𝟃 + \cap + /$ **4.** $\cap /$

5. $𝟃 \cap /$ **6.** $\cap //////$

7. $𝟃 \cap \cap$ **8.** $𝟃 \cap \cap \cap /$

9. $𝟃 \, 𝟃 \, \cap$ **10.** $𝟃 \, 𝟃 \, \cap \cap \cap ///$

11. $𝟃 \, 𝟃 \, \cap //////$ **12.** $𝟃 \cap \cap \cap \cap \cap /////$

1–2 D

If a statement is true, mark it true. If it is false, write a replacement for the symbol ($<$, $=$, $>$) to make it true.

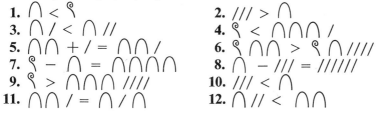

1. ∩ < ⟨
2. /// > ∩
3. ∩ / < ∩ //
4. ⟨ < ∩∩∩ /
5. ∩∩ + / = ∩∩∩ /
6. ⟨ ∩∩ > ⟨ ∩ ////
7. ⟨ − ∩ = ∩∩∩∩
8. ∩ − /// = //////
9. ⟨ > ∩∩∩∩ ////
10. /// < ∩
11. ∩∩ / = ∩ / ∩
12. ∩ // < ∩∩

1–2 E

If a statement is true, mark it true. If it is false, write a replacement for the part underlined to make it true.

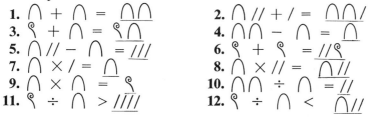

1. ∩ + ∩ = <u>∩∩</u>
2. ∩ // + / = <u>∩∩ /</u>
3. ⟨ + ∩ = ⟨ <u>∩</u>
4. ∩∩ − ∩ = <u>∩</u>
5. ∩ // − ∩ = <u>///</u>
6. ⟨ + ⟨ = <u>// ⟨</u>
7. ∩ × / = <u>∩</u>
8. ∩ × // = <u>∩ //</u>
9. ∩ × ∩ = <u>⟨</u>
10. ∩∩ ÷ ∩ = <u>//</u>
11. ⟨ ÷ ∩ > <u>////</u>
12. ⟨ ÷ ∩ < <u>∩ //</u>

1–2 F

In each exercise perform the operation or operations indicated. Write your answers in Egyptian notation.

1. ∩ + ∩ + ∩ //
2. ∩∩ + ∩ / + ⟨
3. ⟨ − ∩ + ∩ //
4. ⟨ + ⟨ ∩ + ∩ ////
5. ∩∩∩ //// ÷ //////
6. ∩∩ /// × ///
7. ⟨ × ⟨ × //
8. ∩∩∩ // × ////
9. ⟨ ∩∩∩ / × ///

1–2 G

In each exercise perform the operations indicated. Write your answers in Egyptian notation.

1. ∩ + ∩ + ∩
2. ∩ × ∩ × ∩
3. ∩ × ⟨ × //
4. ⟨ × ⟨ × ///
5. ⟨ ∩∩ ÷ ∩ //
6. ⟨ ∩∩∩∩ ÷ ∩ ////
7. ↟ × ↟
8. ↗ ÷ ∩
9. ↧ ÷ ↗

1–2 H

Find the value of each expression. Express your answer in our system of notation.

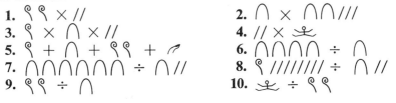

■ 1–3 ROMAN NUMERATION

The Romans devised a system of numeration similar to that of the Egyptians. Like the Egyptians, the Romans employed repetition and addition. However, the Romans also invented uses of subtraction and multiplication. The set of symbols used was

$$R = \{\text{I, V, X, L, C, D, M}\}.$$

The table below shows some Roman numerals and their equivalents in our system of numeration.

1	I	20	XX	200	CC
2	II	30	XXX	300	CCC
3	III	40	XL	400	CD
4	IV	50	L	500	D
5	V	60	LX	600	DC
6	VI	70	LXX	700	DCC
7	VII	80	LXXX	800	DCCC
8	VIII	90	XC	900	CM
9	IX	100	C	1000	M
10	X	110	CX	1900	MCM

Observe the following uses of addition, repetition, subtraction, and multiplication.

XXIII = X + X + I + I + I	Note addition and repetition.
IX = X − I	We subtract I from X.
XL = forty	We subtract X from L.
$\overline{\text{XL}}$ = forty thousand	The bar indicates that forty is multiplied by one thousand.

In general, numbers which do not appear in the table can be written as sums or products in this way:

$$19 = 10 + 9 = X + IX = XIX;$$
$$185 = 100 + 80 + 5 = C + LXXX + V = CLXXXV;$$
$$1492 = 1000 + 400 + 90 + 2 = M + CD + XC + II$$
$$= MCDXCII;$$
$$5000 = 1000 \times 5 = \overline{V};$$
$$10,000 = 1000 \times 10 = \overline{X}.$$

Notice that, in contrast to the Egyptian system, the order or position of the symbols does influence the value of the number represented. For example,

$$XI = \text{eleven and } IX = \text{nine, so } IX \neq XI;$$
$$XL = \text{forty and } LX = \text{sixty, so } XL \neq LX.$$

The symbol $\neq$ means *is not equal to*. We read $IX \neq XI$ as "nine is not equal to eleven."

The following rules were developed to avoid confusion when the subtraction principle is used. Only the symbols I, X, and C can precede symbols for larger numbers, and each one can precede only the next two symbols for larger numbers. Thus to show subtraction,

I can precede only V or X;

X can precede only L or C;

C can precede only D or M.

The Roman system of numeration was revised many times by other Europeans. It was in fairly common use as late as the sixteenth century.

Exercises for Section 1–3

1–3 A

Write in Roman numerals:

1. 5	**2.** 10	**3.** 15	**4.** 20	**5.** 25
6. 30	**7.** 35	**8.** 40	**9.** 45	**10.** 50
11. 55	**12.** 60	**13.** 65	**14.** 70	**15.** 75

1-3 B

Write in Roman numerals:

1. 4	**2.** 8	**3.** 12	**4.** 16	**5.** 20
6. 24	**7.** 28	**8.** 32	**9.** 36	**10.** 40
11. 44	**12.** 48	**13.** 52	**14.** 56	**15.** 60

1-3 C

Write in Roman numerals:

1. 142	**2.** 148	**3.** 149	**4.** 152	**5.** 158
6. 159	**7.** 187	**8.** 188	**9.** 189	**10.** 398
11. 399	**12.** 401	**13.** 798	**14.** 799	**15.** 801

1-3 D

Write in Roman numerals:

1. 909	**2.** 919	**3.** 929	**4.** 939	**5.** 949
6. 959	**7.** 969	**8.** 979	**9.** 989	**10.** 999
11. 1009	**12.** 1019	**13.** 1029	**14.** 1039	**15.** 1099

1-3 E

Write in Roman numerals:

1. 440	**2.** 940	**3.** 1940	**4.** 740	**5.** 840
6. 1840	**7.** 490	**8.** 590	**9.** 990	**10.** 220
11. 450	**12.** 660	**13.** 880	**14.** 1760	**15.** 3520

1-3 F

Write in Roman numerals:

1. 1000	**2.** 2000	**3.** 3000	***4.** 4000
5. 5000	**6.** 7000	**7.** 8000	**8.** 9000
9. 10,000	**10.** 50,000	**11.** 60,000	**12.** 70,000

Note: Remember to use the bar, as in $\overline{XL} = 40,000$; $\overline{VI} = 6000$.

1-3 G

Write in our system of notation:

1. XXIV	**2.** XCIX	**3.** LXXV
4. LXXXIV	**5.** XCII	**6.** CCIX
7. CLXXII	**8.** CCXL	**9.** CCCXL

1-3 H

Write in our system of notation:

1. CD	**2.** DC	**3.** XLI
4. LXI	**5.** CM	**6.** MC
7. CMII	**8.** MCII	**9.** MDCC
10. MDCCLXXVI	**11.** $\overline{\text{VI}}$	**12.** $\overline{\text{XXX}}$

1-3 I

If a statement is true, mark it true. If it is false, write a replacement for the symbol ($>$, $=$, $<$) to make it true.

1. LXI $>$ LIX	**2.** XL $<$ XXXIX
3. LXXII $<$ LXIX	**4.** XCIX $>$ CII
5. C $+$ D $=$ D $+$ C	**6.** XLII $=$ 52 $-$ 10
7. LXXVI $=$ 70 $+$ 6	**8.** MCM $=$ 1000 $+$ 900
9. DXL $>$ DL	**10.** CDIV $>$ DIV

1-3 J

1. In writing whole numbers,
   (a) how many different symbols did the Egyptians use?
   (b) how many different symbols did the Romans use?
   (c) how many different symbols do we use in our system?

2. Why do you suppose that neither the Egyptians nor the Romans had a symbol for zero?

3. When we write 10, we use the symbol 1 to represent *ten*. Did the Egyptians ever use the symbol / to represent *ten*? Did the Romans ever use I to represent *ten*?

4. When we write 30, we use 3 to represent 3 *tens*. Did the Egyptians ever use /// to represent 3 *tens*? Did the Romans ever use III to represent 3 *tens*?

5. The Egyptians used four symbols to write *twenty-two*: ∩∩//. How many symbols did the Romans use to write *twenty-two*?

6. The Egyptians used eleven symbols to write *twenty-nine*: ∩∩/////////. How many symbols did the Romans use to write *twenty-nine*?

7. By what device were the Romans able to write *twenty-nine* with fewer symbols than the Egyptians?

8. How many symbols did the Egyptians use to write *forty-nine*? How many did the Romans use?

1-3 K

All of these statements written in Roman numerals are false. In each case move one match to make a true statement. Stay within the Roman system of notation.

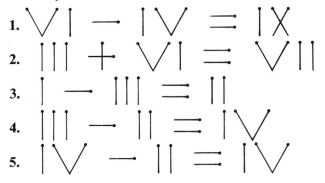

1. $\bigvee | \longrightarrow | \bigvee \;=\; | X$
2. $||| + \bigvee | \;=\; \bigvee ||$
3. $| \longrightarrow ||| \;=\; ||$
4. $||| \longrightarrow || \;=\; | \bigvee$
5. $| \bigvee \longrightarrow || \;=\; | \bigvee$

■ 1-4 THE HINDU-ARABIC NUMERATION SYSTEM

The collection of symbols and the system of notation used by most of the world today is called the *Hindu-Arabic system*. The symbols, or pictures, used are called **digits.** They are members of the set

$$D = \{0, 1, 2, 3, 4, 5, 6, 7, 8, 9\}.$$

This system makes use of two simple but highly effective ideas: **positional notation** and **addition.** In the numeral 35

the 3 stands for 3 tens,

the 5 stands for 5 ones.

Now consider the numeral 350:

the 3 stands for 3 hundreds;

the 5 stands for 5 tens;

the 0 stands for no ones.

Notice that in both cases (35 and 350) the 3 has the same digital value. But in 35 the 3 stands for 3 tens: $10 + 10 + 10$. In 350 the 3 stands for 3 hundreds: $100 + 100 + 100$. In general, the value represented by a digit depends upon the position it holds.

In all cases these digits are used to represent a number of units. For example, the digit 3 can stand for this many triangles, △△△, or this many pots of grain, ⋃ ⋃ ⋃ .

The zero was the last of the digits to be invented. In our positional notation this symbol is a necessity. Suppose that we need to write 100, 102, and 120 *without a symbol for zero*. We might leave positions vacant in this way:

$$1 \quad , \quad 1 \quad 2, \quad \text{and} \quad 12 \quad .$$

On the other hand we might use such symbols as boxes to show empty positions:

$$1\square\square, \quad 1\square2, \quad \text{and} \quad 12\square.$$

Also, we might use dots in this manner:

$$1\cdot\cdot, \quad 1\cdot2, \quad \text{and} \quad 12\cdot .$$

You can see that a symbol was needed to denote the empty set. Also, you can see that the Egyptians and Romans did not have such a pressing need, since their systems were not positional. For example, we can very easily, write 100, 102, and 120 in the Roman system without a zero:

$$C, \quad CII, \quad CXX.$$

The addition principle of our system is apparent when we write a numeral in expanded form. For example,

$$3709 = (3 \times 1000) + (7 \times 100) + (0 \times 10) + (9 \times 1),$$

that is,

$$3709 = \quad 3000 \quad + \quad 700 \quad + \quad 0 \quad + \quad 9.$$

In mathematics **parentheses,** ( ), are used as a form of punctuation to indicate the order of operations. By definition, we perform first the operations indicated within parentheses. Consider the expression $2 + 7 \times 3$. If we perform the operations in the order written, we have

$$2 + 7 \times 3 = 9 \times 3 = 27. \tag{1}$$

However, if we first multiply and then add, we have

$$2 + 7 \times 3 = 2 + 21 = 23. \tag{2}$$

In mathematics we use the word *unique* to mean "one and only one." Since a problem such as this must have a unique answer, we use parentheses to clarify our intention. For (1) we write

$$(2 + 7) \times 3.$$

For (2) we write

$$2 + (7 \times 3).$$

Hence

$$(2 + 7) \times 3 \neq 2 + (7 \times 3).$$

When two or more numbers are multiplied, we call each of the numbers a factor of the product. Since

$$4 \times 5 = 20,$$

4 and 5 are factors of 20. When a number appears more than once as a factor, we use a special notation. For example, we write

$$1000 = 10 \times 10 \times 10 = 10^3.$$

The expression 10^3 means that 10 is used as a factor 3 times; we call 10 the base and 3 the exponent. Hence

$$10^4 = 10 \times 10 \times 10 \times 10,$$
$$10^3 = 10 \times 10 \times 10,$$
$$10^2 = 10 \times 10,$$
$$10^1 = 10.$$

We read 10^1 as "10 to the first power"; 10^2 as "10 squared," or "10 to the second power"; 10^3 as "10 cubed," or "10 to the third power"; 10^4 as "10 to the fourth power."

Now making use of the exponent, we can write

$$6752 = (6 \times 10^3) + (7 \times 10^2) + (5 \times 10) + (2 \times 1),$$
$$23,475 = (2 \times 10^4) + (3 \times 10^3) + (4 \times 10^2) + (7 \times 10)$$
$$+ (5 \times 1).$$

In each case the expressions on the right are called polynomials in ten.

The following array gives the names, up to trillions, of the various positions in our system of numeration.

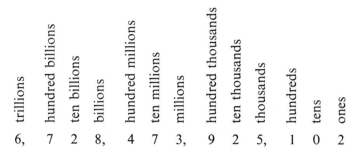

This numeral is read, "six trillion, seven hundred twenty-eight billion, four hundred seventy-three million, nine hundred twenty-five thousand, one hundred two." Notice that digits in this numeral are separated into groups of three by commas, and that each group carries the name of the last position to the right in the group. Thus in the above numeral the 925 is read nine hundred twenty-five thousand, since the 5 is in the thousands position.

Exercises for Section 1-4

1-4 A

Write as a polynomial in ten:

1. 38	**2.** 67	**3.** 98	**4.** 105
5. 345	**6.** 859	**7.** 3459	**8.** 9402
9. 6084	**10.** 45,783	**11.** 26,054	**12.** 213,459

1-4 B

Write in words:

1. 42	**2.** 78	**3.** 87	**4.** 182
5. 309	**6.** 853	**7.** 4530	**8.** 8056
9. 9006	**10.** 45,609	**11.** 78,005	**12.** 107,885

1-4 C

Write as a numeral (Example: $(7 \times 10^2) + (5 \times 10) + (4 \times 1) = 754$):

1. $(6 \times 10) + 7$ **2.** $6 \times (10 + 7)$
3. $(5 \times 10) + 9$ **4.** $5 \times (10 + 9)$

Exercises 1–4 C continued on page 14.

5. $(4 \times 10) + 7$
6. $(9 \times 10^2) + 5$
7. $(5 \times 10^2) + (6 \times 10) + 8$
8. $(6 \times 10^3) + (9 \times 10^2) + 5$
9. $(3 \times 10^3) + (2 \times 10) + 4$
10. $(8 \times 10^4) + (3 \times 10) + 9$
11. $(5 \times 10^3) + (6 \times 10^2) + (3 \times 10)$
12. $(5 \times 10^5) + (4 \times 10^4) + (2 \times 10^3) + (1 \times 10^2) + (8 \times 10) + 7$

1-4 D

Write in numeral form:

1. twenty-four
2. ninety-one
3. fifty-six
4. eighty-nine
5. fourteen
6. forty-four
7. one hundred twelve
8. one thousand four hundred two
9. six hundred seventy-five
10. ninety thousand, five hundred six
11. two million, four thousand, fifty
12. eight hundred thirty-two thousand, five hundred twenty-one

1-4 E

If a statement is true, mark it true. If it is false, write a replacement for the part underlined to make it true.

1. $\underline{235} = (2 \times 100) + (3 \times 10) + (5 \times 1)$
2. $\underline{235} = (2 \times 10^2) + (3 \times 10) + (5 \times 1)$
3. $\underline{1672} = (1 \times 10^3) + (67 \times 10) + (2 \times 1)$
4. $\underline{1672} = (1 \times 10^3) + (6 \times 10^2) + (7 \times 10) + (2 \times 1)$
5. $\underline{5000} = (5 \times 10^3)$
6. $\underline{703} = (7 \times 100) + (3 \times 10)$
7. $\underline{703} = (7 \times 10^2) + (0 \times 10) + (3 \times 1)$
8. $\underline{1000} = 10 \times 10^2$
9. $\underline{1000} = 10^2 + 10$
10. $\underline{4763} = 4000 + (7 \times 10^2) + 60 + (3 \times 1)$
11. $\underline{4763} = [(4 \times 1000) + 3] + (7 \times 10^2) + (6 \times 10)$
12. $\underline{4763} = (3 \times 1) + (4 \times 10^3) + (7 \times 10^2) + (6 \times 10)$

Order of Operations

You have seen how parentheses are used to make clear the order of operations. However, we often do not use parentheses. Then by definition, we first multiply and divide; next, add and subtract. For example,

$$2 + 7 \times 3 = 2 + 21 = 23.$$

In writing formulas we frequently use letters for numbers. Thus we represent the distance around a room by $2L + 2W$. Here, $2L$ means $2 \times L$; $2W$ means $2 \times W$. No parentheses are used, even though two multiplications and one addition are indicated. Do we find $(2 \times L) + 2$ and then multiply by W? Do we find $2 \times L$ and $2 \times W$ and then add? We follow the definition above:

$$2L + 2W = (2 \times L) + (2 \times W).$$

Remember, we now do the operations in parentheses first.

Now consider a number d of dimes and a number q of quarters. We may write a formula for the value in dollars:

$$\frac{d}{10} + \frac{q}{4}.$$

In the formula $d/10$ means $d \div 10$; $q/4$ means $q \div 4$. By the rule above, it is clear that

$$\frac{d}{10} + \frac{q}{4} = (d \div 10) + (q \div 4).$$

Thus if $d = 20$ and $q = 4$, we have

$$\frac{20}{10} + \frac{4}{4} = 2 + 1 = 3.$$

1-4 F

Use the rule in the box on Order of Operations to find:

1. $3 + 9 \times 5$ 2. $\frac{6}{2} + 3$ 3. $5 \times 4 + 7$
4. $7 + \frac{12}{2}$ 5. $6 \times 3 + 8$ 6. $\frac{18}{9} + 2$

Exercises 1–4 F continued on page 16.

If $p = 2L + 2W$, find p when:

7. $L = 4, W = 9$ **8.** $L = 12, W = 18$ **9.** $L = 60, W = 20$

If $V = \dfrac{d}{10} + \dfrac{q}{4}$, find V when:

10. $d = 20, q = 8$ **11.** $d = 40, q = 12$ **12.** $d = 60, q = 16$

■ 1-5 SETS

The language of sets is useful in expressing mathematical ideas. We denote sets by capital letters. Thus we choose to call the set of whole numbers W and the set of natural numbers N:

$$W = \{0, 1, 2, 3, 4, \ldots\},$$
$$N = \{1, 2, 3, \ldots\}.$$

In each set the three dots show that the set continues without end in the manner indicated. We read, "N is the set whose members are 1, 2, 3, 4, and so on." Also, "W is the set whose members are 0, 1, 2, 3, and so on."

We can perform operations with numbers, such as addition and multiplication. We can also perform operations with sets. Two such operations are intersection and union. The intersection of two sets, say H and B, is a new set containing all members, and only these members, that belong to both H and B. We symbolize this by writing

$H \cap B$, which is read, "H intersection B."

The union of two sets H and B is a new set containing those members, and only those members, that belong to either H or B. We symbolize this by writing

$H \cup B$, which is read, "H union B."

For example, suppose H is the set of letters in the word *history*. Then
$$H = \{h, i, s, t, o, r, y\}.$$

Suppose B is the set of letters in the word *botany*. Then

$$B = \{b, o, t, a, n, y\}$$

and

$$H \cap B = \{o, y, t\}.$$

The only letters common to both H and B are o, y, and t. However the *union* of these two sets gives us

$$H \cup B = \{h, i, s, t, o, r, y, b, n, a\}.$$

The letters belonging to either H or B are h, i, s, t, o, r, y, b, n, and a. Note that in $H \cup B$ we do not repeat elements such as o, y, and t, which appear in both sets H and B.

The set containing no members is called the **empty set** and is symbolized by $\emptyset$ or $\{\ \}$. Thus if

$$A = \{2, 4, 6\} \quad \text{and} \quad B = \{1, 3, 5\},$$

then

$$A \cap B = \{\ \} = \text{the empty set} = \emptyset.$$

Sets like A and B, which have no members in common, are called **disjoint sets.** Notice that in this case A union B contains all of the members in each set; that is,

$$A \cup B = \{1, 2, 3, 4, 5, 6\}.$$

Addition can be defined as the operation which gives the number of objects in the union of two disjoint sets. Therefore when $n(A)$ means the number of elements in set A and $n(B)$ means the number of elements in set B, we write

$$n(A) = 3,$$
$$n(B) = 3.$$

Then

$$n(A) + n(B) = 3 + 3 = 6.$$

Also,

$$n(A \cup B) = 6.$$

Two sets are **equal** if they have exactly the same elements. Thus if $C = \{a, b, c\}$ and $D = \{b, a, c\}$, then $C = D$.

Now if $E = \{r, s, t\}$ and $F = \{r, s\}$, then $E \neq F$; that is, E is not equal to F. However, we write $F \subseteq E$, meaning that F is a **subset** of E. A set F is a subset of a set E if each member of F is a member of E.

Set F is not a subset of E if any member of F is not a member of E. Consider these sets:

Sets	Statements About the Sets
$P = \{a, b\}$	
$Q = \{a\}$	$Q \subseteq P$
$R = \{b\}$	$R \subseteq P$
$S = \{b, a\}$	$S \subseteq P$ and $S = P$
$\emptyset = \{\ \}$	$\emptyset \subseteq P$

By definition, the empty set $\emptyset$ is a subset of every set. Also, every set is a subset of itself.

In a given situation we define the set of all objects to be considered as U, the **universal set** or the **universe**. For example, in most of this chapter $U = W$; that is, the universal set is equal to the set of whole numbers.

We can illustrate the meaning of union and intersection with pictures, called **Venn diagrams**. In each figure below U is the set of points inside the large circle; A and B are subsets of U. The set $A \cap B$ is the doubly shaded area in each picture.

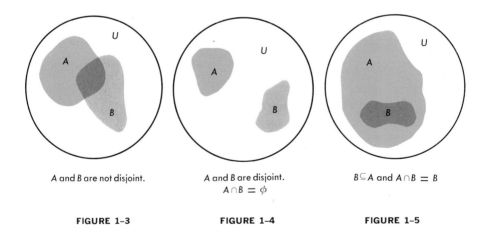

A and B are not disjoint.	A and B are disjoint. $A \cap B = \phi$	$B \subseteq A$ and $A \cap B = B$
FIGURE 1–3	**FIGURE 1–4**	**FIGURE 1–5**

In each figure on the next page U is the set of points inside the large circle; A and B are subsets of U. The set $A \cup B$ is the shaded area in each picture. Note that in Figure 1–8 $A \cup B = A$.

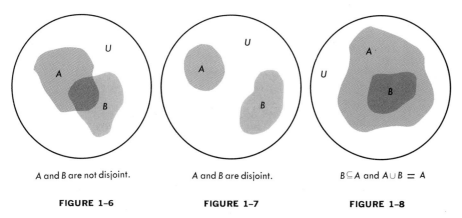

A and B are not disjoint.

A and B are disjoint.

$B \subseteq A$ and $A \cup B = A$

FIGURE 1-6   FIGURE 1-7   FIGURE 1-8

Exercises for Section 1-5

1-5 A

In these exercises you are given the sets

$$N = \{1, 2, 3, \ldots\},$$
$$W = \{0, 1, 2, \ldots\},$$
$$A = \{1, 2, 3, 4, 5\},$$
$$B = \{3, 4, 5, 6, 7\},$$

and the empty set $\emptyset$. Find the sets:

1. $A \cap B$	**2.** $A \cup B$	***3.** $A \cap N$	**4.** $A \cup N$
5. $A \cap W$	**6.** $A \cup W$	**7.** $A \cap \emptyset$	**8.** $A \cup \emptyset$
9. $B \cap A$	**10.** $B \cup A$	**11.** $B \cap N$	**12.** $B \cup N$
13. $B \cap W$	**14.** $B \cup W$	**15.** $B \cap \emptyset$	**16.** $B \cup \emptyset$

Note: In Exercise 3 A is a subset of N; hence $A \cap N = A$.

1-5 B

Consider the sets given in 1-5 A. Find the set:

1. $A \cap A$	**2.** $A \cup A$	**3.** $B \cap B$
4. $B \cup B$	***5.** $(A \cap B) \cap B$	**6.** $(A \cup B) \cup B$
7. $(A \cap N) \cap N$	**8.** $(A \cup N) \cup N$	**9.** $(B \cap W) \cap W$
10. $(B \cup W) \cup W$	**11.** $B \cup (W \cup W)$	**12.** $(A \cap B) \cap \emptyset$

Note: In Exercise 5 perform the operation in parentheses first; that is, $(A \cap B) = \{3, 4, 5\}$. Now find $\{3, 4, 5\} \cap B$.

1-5 C

Consider the sets

$$A = \{a, b, c\},$$
$$B = \{d, e, f, g\},$$
$$C = \{g, h, i, j, k\},$$
$$D = \{l, m, n, o, p, q\}.$$

You may consider the letters of the alphabet as the universal set, U. Hence A, B, C, and D are subsets of U. Find the following numbers:

1. $n(A)$
2. $n(B)$
3. $n(C)$
4. $n(D)$
5. $n(A) + n(B)$
6. $n(A) + n(C)$
7. $n(A) + n(D)$
8. $n(B) + n(C)$
9. $n(B) + n(D)$
10. $n(C) + n(D)$
11. $n(A) + n(B) + n(C)$
12. $n(A) + n(B) + n(C) + n(D)$

1-5 D

Consider the sets A, B, C, and D of 1–5 C. Find the following numbers:

1. $n(A \cup B)$
2. $n(A \cup C)$
3. $n(A \cup D)$
4. $n(B \cup C)$
5. $n(B \cup D)$
6. $n(C \cup D)$
7. $n(A \cup \emptyset)$
8. $n(B \cup \emptyset)$

1-5 E

Consider the sets

$$A = \{a, b, c, d, e\},$$
$$B = \{a, b, d, e\},$$
$$C = \{b, d, e\},$$
$$D = \{a, c, e\}.$$

Mark each statement true or false:

1. $B \subseteq A$
2. $C \subseteq A$
3. $C = A$
4. $D \subseteq A$
5. $C \subseteq B$
6. $C = D$
7. $D \subseteq B$
8. $\emptyset \subseteq A$
9. $\emptyset \subseteq B$

1-5 F

Consider the sets

$$A = \{1, 2, 3, 4, 6, 12\}, \text{ the factors of } 12;$$
$$B = \{1, 2, 4, 5, 10, 20\}, \text{ the factors of } 20;$$
$$C = \{1, 3, 7, 21\}, \text{ the factors of } 21.$$

We call 2 a common factor of 12 and 20 since it is an element of set A and of set B.

1. Find $A \cap B$, the set of common factors of 12 and 20.
2. Find $A \cap C$, the set of common factors of 12 and 21.
3. Find $B \cap C$, the set of common factors of 20 and 21.
4. Find the set of common factors of 24 and 40.
5. Find the set of common factors of 24 and 15.
6. Find the set of common factors of 40 and 15.
7. Find the set of common factors of 12 and 40.
8. Find the set of common factors of 15 and 21.
9. Find the set of common factors of 21 and 24.
10. Find the set of common factors of 12, 15, and 24.
11. Find the set of common factors of 12, 20, and 21.

■ 1-6 ADDITION OF WHOLE NUMBERS

Addition can be defined as the process which assigns, without counting, a number (the sum) to the total number of objects in two groups (sets). If one shelf contains three books and another shelf contains six books, we say that the number of books on the two shelves is nine. We can obtain this answer by starting with "six," and counting the other three, one at a time: "seven, eight, nine." This system of adding by counting becomes almost impossible when larger numbers of objects are being considered.

Addition requires the memorization of the basic combinations of our ten digits, taken two at a time.

For example, when we see the combination 8 + 9, then 17 should be our immediate response, without counting. The numbers to be added are called addends.

Below, we find the addends 56 and 23 written in the usual pattern, (1). Patterns (2) and (3) show more clearly what we mean in (1).

$$\begin{array}{r} 56 \\ 23 \\ \hline 79 \end{array} \tag{1}$$

$$\begin{array}{r} 56 \\ 23 \\ \hline (6+3) \quad \text{ones} \\ +\ (5+2) \quad \text{tens} \end{array} \tag{2}$$

$$\begin{array}{r} 56 \\ 23 \\ \hline 3+6=9 \\ 50+20=70 \\ 70+9=79 \end{array} \tag{3}$$

From (1), (2), and (3), we see that

$$56 + 23 \text{ means } (5+2) \text{ tens} + (6+3) \text{ ones.} \tag{4}$$

From (4), we generalize in mathematics and write as in I.

I. $\qquad (a \times c) + (b \times c) = (a + b) \times c$

We call I the **distributive property.** When we let letters, such as a, b and c, represent numbers, we call the letters **variables.** As an example of I, consider

$$5 \text{ tens} + 2 \text{ tens} = (5+2) \text{ tens,}$$

where $a = 5$, $b = 2$, and $c = $ ten.

Examples 1 and 2 lead to carrying.

Example 1. Find $2357 + 628$.

thousands	hundreds	tens	ones
2	3	5	7
	6	2	8
2	9	7	15

Example 2. Find $3856 + 578$.

thousands	hundreds	tens	ones
3	8	5	6
	5	7	8
3	13	12	14

Thus we have: Thus we have:

$$
\begin{array}{r}
2970 \\
15 \\
\hline
2985
\end{array}
\qquad
\begin{array}{r}
3000 \\
1300 \\
120 \\
14 \\
\hline
4434
\end{array}
$$

Examples 1 and 2 show why we carry. The problems are normally written as

$$
\begin{array}{r}
23\overset{1}{5}7 \\
628 \\
\hline
2985
\end{array}
\qquad
\begin{array}{r}
\overset{1}{3}\overset{1}{8}\overset{1}{5}6 \\
578 \\
\hline
4434
\end{array}
$$

If we add any two whole numbers, we always get another whole number. That is, the sum of any two members of set W is a member of set W. This property is called **closure.** We say that the set W of whole numbers is *closed* under addition, and we write

II. $a + b = c$

where a, b, and c are whole numbers.

In set language we use the symbol $\in$ to mean *is an element, or member, of.* For example, we write $x \in \{a, x\}$, which reads, "x is an element of $\{a, x\}$." So by the closure principle, if a and b are whole numbers, then

$$(a + b) \in W.$$

An **ordered pair** of numbers is indicated in mathematics as (a, b). Some examples are $(2, 5)$, $(7, 4)$, and $(0, 1)$. The word *ordered* is used since the order matters; that is, $(4, 7)$ is a different ordered pair from $(7, 4)$.

Example 3. In the formula $n = 2r + s$, find n when the values for (r, s) are: (a) $(7, 4)$ (b) $(4, 7)$.

$$
\begin{aligned}
\text{(a)} \quad n &= 2r + s \\
n &= 2(7) + 4 \\
n &= 18
\end{aligned}
\qquad
\begin{aligned}
\text{(b)} \quad n &= 2r + s \\
n &= 2(4) + 7 \\
n &= 15
\end{aligned}
$$

In Example 3(a) we have replaced r with 7 and s with 4. In Example 3(b) we have replaced r with 4 and s with 7. Note that the order, $(7, 4)$ or $(4, 7)$, makes a difference: in (a) we find $n = 18$; in (b) we find $n = 15$.

In Example 3 we have used the following axiom in substituting numbers for letters.

Substitution Axiom. A quantity may be substituted for its equal in any expression.

An axiom is a statement which we assume is true without proof.

Since the expression $3 + 8$ yields the same result as $8 + 3$, we can say that

$$8 + 3 = 3 + 8 = 11.$$

For any pair of numbers, the sum is the same in either order. We call this the commutative property of addition and write it as in III.

$$\textbf{III.} \qquad a + b = b + a$$

When we have three numbers to add, we can add any two of them first; then to this sum we add the third number. For example,

$$3 + 6 + 7 = (3 + 6) + 7 = 9 + 7 = 16;$$

or

$$3 + 6 + 7 = 3 + (6 + 7) = 3 + 13 = 16.$$

This property is called the associative property of addition and is written as in IV.

$$\textbf{IV.} \qquad a + b + c = a + (b + c) = (a + b) + c$$

As a check on addition, approximation is very valuable. For example, using the symbol $\approx$, read "is approximately equal to," we write

$$397 + 223 + 465 = s,$$
$$400 + 200 + 500 \approx s,$$
$$1100 \approx s.$$

We have used these approximations to estimate s: $397 \approx 400$, $223 \approx 200$, and $465 \approx 500$. Actually, $s = 1085$, so our approximation 1100 is quite close.

Exercises for Section 1-6

1-6 A

Perform the following by inspection:

1. $5 + 2 + 4$	**2.** $7 + 9 + 2$
3. $8 + 8 + 3$	**4.** $6 + 4 + 4$
5. $9 + 6 + 7$	**6.** $9 + 8 + 5$
7. $8 + 5 + 4 + 7$	**8.** $7 + 4 + 9 + 1$
9. $4 + 7 + 8 + 5$	**10.** $8 + 9 + 8 + 6$
11. $9 + 6 + 7 + 5$	**12.** $9 + 9 + 8 + 8$

1-6 B

If $27 + 41 = x$ tens $+ y$ ones, then we see that $x = 2 + 4 = 6$, and $y = 7 + 1 = 8$. In each exercise find x and y, where x is the number of tens and y is the number of ones.

1. $68 + 31$	**2.** $43 + 24$
3. $57 + 21$	**4.** $23 + 32$
5. $12 + 14$	**6.** $25 + 52$
7. $84 + 24$	**8.** $32 + 46$
9. $62 + 17$	**10.** $41 + 48$
11. $88 + 11$	**12.** $99 + 11$

1-6 C

Solve for n:

1. $64 + 17 + 8 = n$	**2.** $75 + 49 + 9 = n$
3. $5 + 88 + 99 = n$	**4.** $67 + 59 + 13 = n$
5. $55 + 82 + 7 = n$	**6.** $77 + 8 + 48 = n$
7. $44 + 167 + 34 = n$	**8.** $8 + 1564 + 98 = n$
9. $678 + 45 + 29 = n$	**10.** $6089 + 52 + 9 = n$
11. $563 + 529 + 4 = n$	**12.** $345 + 409 + 523 + 680 = n$

1-6 D

Approximate n; then find its true value by addition.

1. $19 + 19 + 19 = n$	**2.** $51 + 51 + 51 = n$
3. $39 + 31 + 41 = n$	**4.** $67 + 62 + 63 = n$
5. $94 + 95 + 96 = n$	**6.** $54 + 60 + 63 = n$
7. $489 + 129 + 434 = n$	**8.** $661 + 334 + 100 = n$
9. $1090 + 48 + 991 = n$	**10.** $808 + 178 + 220 = n$
11. $750 + 850 + 950 = n$	**12.** $135 + 165 + 205 = n$

1-6 E

Add:

1. 26	**2.** 88	**3.** 567	**4.** 500
43	33	209	718

5. 490	**6.** 668	**7.** 67	**8.** 75
835	874	35	75
		94	75

9. 565	**10.** 805	**11.** 89	**12.** 781
821	155	48	600
909	772	22	313
		76	178
			842

1-6 F

Approximate n; then find its true value by addition.

1. $n = 356 + 709 + 188$ **2.** $n = 601 + 661 + 701$
3. $n = 760 + 239 + 611$ **4.** $n = 227 + 337 + 447$
5. $n = 557 + 667 + 777$ **6.** $n = 1009 + 4532 + 6099$
7. $n = 1100 + 1300 + 1500$ **8.** $n = 2300 + 2600 + 2900$
9. $n = 4415 + 4515 + 5015$ **10.** $n = 6700 + 7800 + 8819$

1-6 G

Add:

1. $6 + 1005 + 48$ **2.** $13{,}270 + 68 + 101$
3. $686 + 2355 + 20$ **4.** $1004 + 2 + 17 + 84$
5. $108 + 21{,}365 + 9$ **6.** $13 + 4953 + 27 + 100$
7. $18 + 27 + 4 + 1060$ **8.** $975 + 34 + 13 + 715$
9. $28 + 135{,}208 + 11 + 125$ **10.** $100{,}000 + 10{,}000 + 1000 + 1$

1-6 H

Add:

1. 809	**2.** 659	**3.** 438	**4.** 472
156	428	606	462
450	109	770	669
			606

5. 6720	6. 4592	7. 67,800	8. 8009
1142	1406	34,622	2331
		67,808	1006
		45,732	8992

9. 13,492	10. 23,407	11. 56,002	12. 23,407
11,005	24,581	20,016	11,415
			26,789

1-6 I

1. Palmer played 18 holes of golf each day for 5 days. His scores were 68, 71, 69, 72, and 68. What was his total for the 5 days?

2. Miss Brown had 980 pages of history to read in 1 week. She read 134 pages the first day, 104 the second day, 230 the third day, 200 the fourth day, and 318 the fifth day. Did she complete the assignment?

3. A professional bowler was offered $150 if in 5 games he scored between 1001 and 1100, $350 if he scored between 1101 and 1150, $750 if he scored between 1151 and 1200, and $1200 if he scored over 1200. What was he paid if his game scores were 250, 225, 216, 238, and 194?

4. If the bowler in Exercise 3 played another 5 games and scored 228, 198, 246, 272, and 261, what did he earn?

5. A trucker's route in California goes from San Francisco to Sacramento, a distance of 84 miles; from Sacramento to Fresno, 172 miles; from Fresno back to San Francisco, 185 miles. If he makes two such round trips a week, how many miles does he cover?

6. In their first year of business a national tire company sold 4650 tires in New York, 2683 in Atlanta, 1987 in Portland, and 5376 in several smaller cities. Find their total sales for the year.

7. A baseball player got 25 hits in April, 34 hits in May, 31 in June, 27 in July, 18 in August, and 32 in September. How many hits did he get for the season?

8. Find the total number of days in May, June, July, August, and September.

9. During a home stand, the Yankees had the following attendance at games: 14,275; 30,265; 28,460; 9270; 7460; and 8973. What was the total attendance?

10. Write each pair of whole numbers whose sum is 19.

1-6 J

1. Suppose that a man accepted a job on which his pay was $1 for the first day, $2 for the second, $4 for the third, and so on. For each day after the first, he was paid twice the previous day's pay. How much did he earn for the first 6 days?
2. In Exercise 1 find the man's total pay for the second 6 days.
3. A clock strikes once at 1:00, then once at 1:30, twice at 2:00, once at 2:30, three times at 3:00, once at 3:30, and so on, until it strikes twelve times at 12:00 and then starts the sequence over again. How many times will it strike from 2:30 P.M. to 11:30 P.M.? (Count the strikes at 2:30 and 11:30.)
4. In Exercise 3 how many times will the clock strike during a full 24-hour day?
5. The set $D = \{1, 3, 5, 7, \ldots\}$ is called the set of odd numbers. Find the sum of the first 8 odd numbers.
6. The set $E = \{0, 2, 4, 6, \ldots\}$ is called the set of even numbers. Find the sum of the even numbers from 8 to 24, inclusive.

●1-6 K

The Greek capital letter Σ (sigma) is used in mathematics to mean the *sum of.* Suppose that n is a natural number; then

$$\sum_{n=1}^{n=5} n$$

is read, "find the sum of the natural numbers from 1 to 5." Below and above the Σ there are numbers which indicate *how many* or *which* members of n to add. Thus

$$\sum_{n=1}^{n=5} n = 1 + 2 + 3 + 4 + 5 = 15$$

$$\sum_{n=1}^{n=5} (n + 3) = (1 + 3) + (2 + 3) + (3 + 3) + (4 + 3) + (5 + 3)$$
$$= 30$$

Find the following:

1. $\displaystyle\sum_{n=1}^{n=8} n$
2. $\displaystyle\sum_{n=3}^{n=10} n$
3. $\displaystyle\sum_{n=6}^{n=13} n$

4. $\sum\limits_{n=2}^{n=18} n$ 5. $\sum\limits_{n=4}^{n=20} n$ 6. $\sum\limits_{n=1}^{n=17} n$

1-6 L

In the formula $A = I + P$ we can find A when we know I and P. For example, if the ordered pair (I, P) is $(2, 15)$, then $A = 2 + 15 = 17$. Find A for each ordered pair (I, P):

1. (5, 17)	2. (3, 20)	3. (2, 18)
4. (4, 28)	5. (27, 48)	6. (8, 75)
7. (10, 100)	8. (10, 350)	9. (17, 485)
10. (6, 244)	11. (10, 1000)	12. (20, 2475)

1-6 M

1. Is the set E of all even numbers closed under addition? (*Note:* $E = \{0, 2, 4, 6, \ldots\}$.) Now if s is the sum of any two of these, is s a member of E?

2. Is the set of all odd numbers closed under addition?

3. Is the set of all numerals ending in 0 closed under addition?

4. In the numeral 4549 what do the two 4's have in common as symbols? How do they differ because of their position in the numeral?

5. Name the property of addition used in writing

$$38 + 56 + 49 = 38 + 105 = 94 + 49.$$

6. Name the property of numbers shown in

$$7 \times 498 = (7 \times 400) + (7 \times 90) + (7 \times 8).$$

7. Consider the two numerals 475 and 4750. Compare the numbers named by the two 4's. By the two 7's. By the two 5's.

8. Does $(4 \times 2) + 3 = 4 \times (2 + 3)$? Why do we use parentheses in expressions of this kind?

9. Does $4 + (2 + 3) = (4 + 2) + 3$? Do we need parentheses in expressions of this kind? What property of addition applies here?

10. Solve for n:

  (a) $(7 + n) + 8 = 7 + (3 + 8)$
  (b) $(3 + 4) + 9 = (n + 4) + 9$
  (c) $(11 + 7) + n = 11 + (7 + 3)$

■ 1-7 MULTIPLICATION OF WHOLE NUMBERS

Multiplication of whole numbers may be thought of as a process for finding the sum of a number of like addends, without carrying out the addition. Note that

$$8 + 8 + 8 = 24; \text{ also, } 3 \times 8 = 24; \tag{1}$$

$$5 + 5 + 5 + 5 = 20; \text{ also, } 4 \times 5 = 20. \tag{2}$$

As in (1) and (2), we can multiply any pair of whole numbers by adding; for example, $7 \times 9 = 9 + 9 + 9 + 9 + 9 + 9 + 9$. However, this addition becomes tedious. For practical use, you must memorize $7 \times 9 = 63$.

Multiplication requires the memorization of the basic combinations of our ten digits, taken two at a time.

The problem 6×38 can be thought of as

$$6 \times (30 + 8) = (6 \times 30) + (6 \times 8) = 180 + 48 = 228.$$

We say that *multiplication is distributive over addition*, and write the distributive property presented in Section 1-6 in this order:

$$a \times (b + c) = (a \times b) + (a \times c),$$

or

$$a(b + c) = ab + ac.$$

Now consider the meaning of multiplication in the following example.

Example 1. Find 6×248.

$$
\begin{array}{r}
248 \\
\times\ 6 \\
\hline
48 \\
240 \\
1200 \\
\hline
1488
\end{array}
$$

$6 \times 8 = 48$ ones $= 4$ tens $+ 8$ ones
6×4 tens $= 24$ tens $= 240$
6×2 hundreds $= 1200$

Using the distributive property, we can show the product in Example 1 in this way:

$$6 \times 248 = 6 \times (200 + 40 + 8)$$
$$= (6 \times 200) + (6 \times 40) + (6 \times 8)$$
$$= 1200 + 240 + 48$$
$$= 1488.$$

Usually we write:

$$\begin{array}{r} 248 \\ \times\ 6 \\ \hline 1488 \end{array}$$

The method changes very little when we have a two-digit multiplier.

Example 2. Find 36×248.

$$
\begin{array}{r}
248 \\
\times\ 36 \\
\hline
48 \\
240 \\
1200 \\
240 \\
1200 \\
6000 \\
\hline
8928
\end{array}
$$

This part is the same as in Example 1.

3 tens $\times$ 8 = 24 tens = 240
3 tens $\times$ 4 tens = 1200
3 tens $\times$ 2 hundreds = 6000

Usually, of course, we write Example 2 in this way:

$$
\begin{array}{r}
248 \\
\times\ 36 \\
\hline
1488 \\
744 \\
\hline
8928
\end{array}
$$

As in addition, the set of whole numbers is **closed** under the operation of multiplication; that is, the product of any two whole numbers yields another whole number.

Like addition, multiplication is commutative.   For example, $6 \times 8 = 48$ and $8 \times 6 = 48$. Symbolically, we write the commutative property of multiplication as in V.

$$\textbf{V.} \qquad a \times b = b \times a$$

Multiplication is also associative. For example, $6 \times 8 \times 2$ can be evaluated as $(6 \times 8) \times 2$, or as $6 \times (8 \times 2)$.

$$6 \times (8 \times 2) = 6 \times 16 = 96$$

$$(6 \times 8) \times 2 = 48 \times 2 = 96$$

The associative property of multiplication is symbolized as in VI.

$$\textbf{VI.} \qquad (a \times b) \times c = a \times (b \times c)$$

As a check for multiplication, approximation can be used in this manner:

$$(215 \times 478) \approx (200 \times 500) = 100,000.$$

Note that we use $215 \approx 200$ and $478 \approx 500$.   To approximate 34×75, we write

$$34 \times 75 \approx 30 \times 80 = 2400.$$

Exercises for Section 1–7

1–7 A

Perform the following by inspection:

1. 6×16	**2.** 8×19
3. 5×30	**4.** 7×15
5. 9×12	**6.** 3×15
7. 6×20	**8.** 7×24
9. 5×20	**10.** 5×18
11. 2×340	**12.** 3×110
13. 4×120	**14.** 6×104
15. 8×105	**16.** 5×104
17. 3×220	**18.** 2×245
19. 2×700	**20.** 7×103

1-7 B

Approximate; then find the products:

1. 18 × 18
2. 24 × 12
3. 32 × 40
4. 36 × 80
5. 75 × 24
6. 75 × 85
7. 54 × 52
8. 64 × 90
9. 36 × 14
10. 45 × 86
11. 40 × 50 × 60
12. 32 × 36 × 30
13. 68 × 65 × 40 × 20
14. 45 × 56 × 15
15. 56 × 12 × 28
16. 71 × 72 × 73

1-7 C

Approximate; then find the exact products:

1. 340 × 709
2. 569 × 204
3. 558 × 178
4. 884 × 129
5. 800 × 945
6. 567 × 850
7. 650 × 285
8. 125 × 125
9. 450 × 150 × 250
10. 138 × 148 × 158
11. 275 × 265 × 245
12. 490 × 480 × 470

1-7 D

Find the products:

1. 13 × 6709
2. 24 × 1455
3. 67 × 3419
4. 50 × 8730
5. 132 × 2488
6. 230 × 5600
7. 405 × 5081
8. 150 × 8925
9. 450 × 16,500
10. 600 × 45,650
11. 567 × 88,934
12. 895 × 91,369

1-7 E

Use the distributive property to find the products. For example,
7 × 758 = 7 × (700 + 50 + 8) = 4900 + 350 + 56 = 5306.

1. 6 × 850
2. 4 × 456
3. 8 × 755
4. 5 × 875
5. 3 × 680
6. 5 × 324
7. 4 × 480
8. 5 × 459
9. 8 × 124
10. 7 × 245
11. 9 × 178
12. 3 × 784

1–7 F

Find the products; then write a rule for multiplication by 10:

1. 10×23	**2.** 10×56	**3.** 10×98
4. 10×123	**5.** 10×456	**6.** 10×894
7. 10×4567	**8.** 10×2340	**9.** 10×1345
10. $10 \times 16,783$	**11.** $10 \times 45,782$	**12.** $10 \times 99,803$

1–7 G

Find the products; then write a rule for multiplication by 10^p, where p is any whole number:

1. 100×442	**2.** 100×345	**3.** 100×543
4. 1000×256	**5.** 1000×569	**6.** 1000×670
7. $10^3 \times 354$	**8.** $10^3 \times 780$	**9.** $10^2 \times 567$
10. $10^4 \times 34$	**11.** $10^4 \times 75$	**12.** $10^5 \times 36$

1–7 H

Name the property indicated in each problem:

1. $4 \times 5 = 5 \times 4$
2. $6 \times 367 = 367 \times 6$
3. $81 \times 56 = 56 \times 81$
4. $6 + 45 = 45 + 6$
5. $5 + 98 = 98 + 5$
6. $3 \times (8 + 5) = (3 \times 8) + (3 \times 5)$
7. $5 \text{ tens} + 3 \text{ tens} = (5 + 3) \text{ tens}$
8. $2 \times (3 \times 8) = (2 \times 3) \times 8$

1–7 I

1. Clark drove 55 miles per hour for 8 hours. How far did he travel?
2. If you save $45 per month for 17 months, will you have enough money to buy a used car valued at $765?
3. Fred decided to learn the meaning of 25 new words per week. If he persisted with his plan, by how much did he increase his vocabulary after 18 weeks?
4. If a race track is 6890 feet around (one lap), how long is a race which lasts 35 laps?
5. The average person consumes 3250 calories per day. How many will he consume in 31 days?

6. Jim worked for $23 per day, 5 days per week. How much did he earn in 48 weeks?

7. If 356 men counted the number of pennies in their pockets, was the total a number in the set *W* of whole numbers?

8. How many words are there on a page if there are 37 lines and the lines have an average of 13 words?

9. If a boat uses $37\frac{1}{2}$ gallons of fuel per day for 7 days, is the total number of gallons used a number in the set *W*?

10. A car travels at a steady speed of 66 feet per second. How far will it go in 3 minutes?

1-7 J

1. If it costs $7265 a year to keep a fighting man overseas, how much does it cost to keep 150 fighting men overseas?

2. On a job, a man earned $21 per day for 3 days, $16 per day for the next 6 days, and $18 per day for the last 9 days of the job. Find his total wage.

3. The Andersons plan to have linoleum laid on the floor of their kitchen and family room. They choose material which costs $6 per square yard and find that the cost of labor for installation is $120. If the area they wish to cover is 64 square yards, how much will the entire job cost?

4. Marysville has a population of 1365. A nearby city has a population 17 times this. Find the population of the larger city.

5. A playhouse has 36 seats in the front which sell for $4 per seat, 120 in the middle section which sell for $3 per seat, and 225 seats near the back which sell for $1 per seat. How much money is taken in when there is a full house?

6. The area of the state of Washington is approximately 68,200 square miles. Find the approximate area of Texas, which has nearly 4 times the area of Washington.

7. A farmer has 165 artichoke plants. He estimates that 1 plant should produce at least 12 good artichokes. How many artichokes will his whole crop produce?

8. To avoid outside work during his senior year in college, a student saved $250 for each of the 3 summer months before his junior year. During his junior year, he saved $85 each month for 9 months. If he then saved $280 for each month of the next summer, what was his total savings for his senior year?

1-7 K

Find the following:

1. 6×24 2. $6 \times (20 + 4)$ 3. 7×28
4. $7 \times (20 + 8)$ 5. 9×43 6. $9 \times (40 + 3)$
7. 13×46 8. $13 \times (40 + 6)$ 9. 24×57
10. $24 \times (50 + 7)$ 11. 37×98 12. $37 \times (90 + 8)$

1-7 L

Find the following:

1. 49×85 2. $49 \times (80 + 5)$
3. 7×423 4. $7 \times (400 + 20 + 3)$
5. 6×384 6. $6 \times (300 + 80 + 4)$
7. 4×275 8. $4 \times (200 + 70 + 5)$
9. 8×1234 10. $8 \times (1000 + 200 + 30 + 4)$
11. 3×4725 12. $3 \times (4000 + 700 + 20 + 5)$

1-7 M

Find the following:

1. $4 \times (25 + 3)$ 2. $8 \times (25 + 2)$ 3. $6 \times (20 + 3)$
4. $9 \times (30 + 4)$ 5. $11 \times (40 + 5)$ 6. $12 \times (50 + 1)$
7. $13 \times (50 + 2)$ 8. $14 \times (50 + 3)$ 9. $50 \times (20 + 2)$
10. $60 \times (30 + 3)$ 11. $70 \times (7 + 3)$ 12. $80 \times (6 + 4)$

1-7 N

Solve for n:

1. $2 \times (n \times 5) = 2 \times (3 \times 5)$
2. $7 \times (8 \times n) = (7 \times 8) \times 72$
3. $(12 \times 75) \times n = 12 \times (75 \times n)$
4. $3 \times n = 3 \times 134$
5. $64 \times 38 = n \times 38$
6. $19 \times 75 = 75 \times n$
7. $38 \times (n + 5) = 38 \times (7 + 5)$
8. $25 \times (n + 2) = 25 \times 8$
9. $47 \times (6 \times n) = (47 \times 6)$
10. $38 \times (5 \times n) = 38 \times 5$

1-7 O

In the formula $d = rt$ determine d for each ordered pair (r, t):

1. $(10, 3)$	**2.** $(15, 5)$	**3.** $(12, 6)$	**4.** $(18, 10)$
5. $(20, 7)$	**6.** $(30, 9)$	**7.** $(25, 8)$	**8.** $(35, 6)$
9. $(45, 10)$	**10.** $(55, 17)$	**11.** $(32, 12)$	**12.** $(88, 12)$

1-8 SUBTRACTION OF WHOLE NUMBERS

We use the inverse of an operation to "undo" the original operation. Thus $9 + 5$ is 14, and $14 - 5$ is 9; that is, adding 5 and then subtracting 5 yields the number with which we started, $9 + 5 - 5 = 9$.

Subtraction is the inverse of addition. For example, in the problem $14 - 5$ we seek an n such that $n + 5 = 14$. Since $5 + 9 = 14$, $n = 9$. The answer to subtraction, in this case 9, is called the difference.

Because subtraction depends on the basic addition combinations, it is necessary to have these combinations memorized.

For example,

$$6 + 2 = 8, \text{ so } 8 - 2 = 6 \text{ and } 8 - 6 = 2,$$
$$4 + 5 = 9, \text{ so } 9 - 4 = 5 \text{ and } 9 - 5 = 4.$$

Example 1. Find $947 - 825$.

$$
\begin{array}{r}
947 \\
825 \\
\hline
122
\end{array}
$$

Example 2. Find $923 - 578$.
The process is more involved. Since $923 = 910 + 13$, we have

$$
\begin{array}{ccc}
\text{hundreds} & \text{tens} & \text{ones} \\
9 & 1 & 13 \\
5 & 7 & 8 \\
\hline
 & & 5
\end{array}
$$

Also, $923 = 800 + 110 + 13$ so

$$
\begin{array}{ccc}
\text{hundreds} & \text{tens} & \text{ones} \\
8 & 11 & 13 \\
5 & 7 & 8 \\
\hline
3 & 4 & 5
\end{array}
$$

That is,

$$
\begin{array}{rrr}
800 + & 110 + & 13 \\
500 + & 70 + & 8 \\
\hline
300 + & 40 + & 5
\end{array}
$$

In Example 2 we cannot subtract 8 from 3 and get an answer in the set of positive whole numbers. We borrow one ten from the tens column. This increases the number of ones to 13. Then we have $13 - 8 = 5$. By the same routine, we borrow from the hundreds column. The problem is normally written as

$$
\begin{array}{r}
923 \\
578 \\
\hline
345
\end{array}
$$

This process of "borrowing" is based upon the concept of our notational system which makes the unit in any column ten times the unit in the column on its right.

Exercises for Section 1-8

1-8 A

Find the differences by inspection:

1. $9 - 3$	**2.** $8 - 1$	**3.** $7 - 4$	**4.** $9 - 2$
5. $8 - 5$	**6.** $11 - 6$	**7.** $13 - 6$	**8.** $19 - 4$
9. $17 - 7$	**10.** $18 - 3$	**11.** $16 - 4$	**12.** $19 - 7$
13. $13 - 8$	**14.** $13 - 9$	**15.** $15 - 6$	**16.** $17 - 7$
17. $19 - 8$	**18.** $23 - 9$	**19.** $21 - 8$	**20.** $24 - 9$

1–8 B

Solve for n:

1. $n = 18 - 15$	**2.** $n = 45 - 31$
3. $n = 23 - 17$	**4.** $n = 67 - 45$
5. $n = 78 - 66$	**6.** $n = 123 - 67$
7. $n = 129 - 89$	**8.** $n = 461 - 41$
9. $n = 349 - 98$	**10.** $n = 285 - 99$
11. $n = 4000 - 458$	**12.** $n = 3809 - 245$
13. $n = 1067 - 840$	**14.** $n = 6733 - 459$
15. $n = 8894 - 905$	**16.** $n = 4008 - 3219$

1–8 C

Subtract:

1. 47 22	**2.** 98 58	**3.** 73 41	**4.** 75 75
5. 82 66	**6.** 75 46	**7.** 91 56	**8.** 53 44
9. 171 80	**10.** 329 78	**11.** 708 49	**12.** 560 95
13. 452 428	**14.** 705 419	**15.** 300 178	**16.** 903 565

1–8 D

Subtract:

1. 780 560	**2.** 349 279	**3.** 800 467	**4.** 905 899
5. 777 669	**6.** 611 473	**7.** 5441 4331	**8.** 3900 1550
9. 7831 5094	**10.** 6731 5509	**11.** 4403 3774	**12.** 9842 7995

1-8 E

Subtract:

1. 1484
   984
	2. 3409
	   1855
		3. 1400
		    573
			4. 7333
			   4906

5. 5682
   5679
	6. 3225
	   1996
		7. 14,566
		   8,542
			8. 24,505
			  15,502

9. 78,000 49,000	**10.** 10,101 8,759	**11.** 23,905 18,927	**12.** 57,680 34,698

1-8 F

In the formula $P = S - C$ determine P for each ordered pair (S, C):

1. (175, 80)   **2.** (95, 22)   **3.** (205, 95)

4. (812, 76)   **5.** (98, 90)   **6.** (275, 183)

7. (905, 208)   **8.** (1000, 755)   **9.** (675, 498)

10. (975, 486)   **11.** (12,275, 9180)   **12.** (14,675, 11,986)

1-8 G

Solve for n:

1. $n + 9 = 20$ **2.** $n = 20 - 9$ **3.** $n + 18 = 20$

4. $n = 20 - 18$ **5.** $n + 102 = 347$ **6.** $n = 347 - 102$

7. $n + 519 = 600$ **8.** $n = 600 - 519$ **9.** $n + 206 = 400$

10. $n = 400 - 206$ **11.** $n + 787 = 903$ **12.** $n = 903 - 787$

1-8 H

1. A group of 6 men wishes to buy a plot of land worth $24,500. Members of the group put up the following amounts: $2570, $1850, $2345, $1670, $5680, and $3575. How much more do they need to collect?

2. A car that averages 24 miles per gallon at 35 miles per hour gets only 18 miles per gallon at 60 miles per hour. How much farther does it travel on 15 gallons of gasoline at 35 miles per hour than at 60 miles per hour?

3. A used car dealer bought a station wagon for $1375. He spent $125 for a new paint job and $25 for an engine tune-up. If he sold the car for $2298, how much profit did he make?

4. On a trip, a man left home and drove 65 miles per hour for 6 hours; then he drove 50 miles per hour for 4 more hours. If his destination was 798 miles from home, how much farther did he have to drive?

5. At the beginning of May, the balance in a checking account was $478. During the month, checks of $48, $125, $19, $24, and $65 were written. Find the balance after these checks were deducted.

6. A man calculated that if he drove steadily at 55 miles per hour for 12 hours, he could complete his trip. At the start, the odometer on his car read 37,875; but after 12 hours of driving, it read only 38,503. How many miles did he still have to drive to complete his trip?

7. A woman made a down payment of $105 on a coat which cost $356. In the months following she made payments of $55, $60, $48, $40, and $52. This completed her payments and included a carrying charge. How much was the carrying charge?

8. A city planner estimated that 2450 cars passed through a certain intersection in a week. As a check on his estimate, a count was taken. The daily totals were 550, 300, 325, 305, 280, 255, and 267. Find the error in his estimate.

9. The factors of 75 are 1, 3, 5, 15, 25, and 75. List the factors of 144. Which has more factors, 75 or 144? How many more?

10. Six years ago a family bought a home for $16,750 and added a room and an extra bath at a cost of $1921. If they sell the home for $21,375, by how much has its value increased?

1-8 I

Solve for n:

1. $n - 8 = 15$	2. $n - 7 = 12$
3. $n - 15 = 20$	4. $n - 15 = 5$
5. $n - 23 = 7$	6. $n - 7 = 23$
7. $n - 17 = 40$	8. $n - 32 = 105$
9. $n - 102 = 18$	10. $n - 49 = 75$
11. $n - 165 = 793$	12. $n - 83 = 256$

1-8 J

We prove that a general statement is false if we find one instance for which it is false. For example, consider statement (a).

(a) Each of the numerals represents a natural number:
0, 1, 2, 3, 4, 5, 6, 7, 8, and 9.

We prove (a) false by statement (b).

(b) Zero does not represent a natural number.

We call statement (b) a **counterexample.** In these exercises assume:

the set W of whole numbers is closed under subtraction; that is, for any two whole numbers a and b, $(a - b) \in W$.

Are there counterexamples in the exercises? If so, in which ones?

1. $8 - 3$	**2.** $9 - 5$	**3.** $11 - 6$
4. $8 - 2$	**5.** $158 - 63$	**6.** $614 - 92$
7. $803 - 71$	**8.** $906 - 77$	**9.** $2040 - 2038$
10. $2214 - 2241$	**11.** $4030 - 2939$	**12.** $6070 - 4231$

1-8 K

1. Is subtraction commutative; that is, does $a - b = b - a$, where a and b are whole numbers? Try a few examples, such as $7 - 4$ and $9 - 5$.
2. To find $782 - 497$, we write:

$$\frac{782}{497} = \frac{700 + 80 + 2}{400 + 90 + 7} = \frac{600 + 180 + 2}{400 + 90 + 7} = \frac{600 + 170 + 12}{400 + 90 + 7}$$
$$\overline{a \; + \; b \; + \; c}$$

Then we subtract to find a, b, c.

3. As in Exercise 2, show all steps to find $834 - 675$.
4. As in Exercise 2, show all steps to find $1324 - 875$.
5. As in Exercise 2, show all steps to find $2047 - 958$.
6. (a) Does $2 \times (5 - 3) = (2 \times 5) - (2 \times 3)$?
   (b) Does $4 \times (17 - 1) = (4 \times 17) - (4 \times 1)$?
   (c) Does $6 \times (12 - 3) = (6 \times 12) - (6 \times 3)$?
   (d) Does $(27 \times 5) - (27 \times 2) = 27(5 - 2)$?
7. Does $a \times (b - c) = (a \times b) - (a \times c)$? Assume $b > c$.

1-8 L

Consider the following exercises and mark each statement either true or false:

1. $7 - 4 - 1 = (7 - 4) - 1$
2. $7 - 4 - 1 = 7 - (4 - 1)$
3. $9 - 4 - 3 = (9 - 4) - 3$
4. $9 - 4 - 3 = 9 - (4 - 3)$
5. $15 - 7 - 2 = (15 - 7) - 2$
6. $15 - 7 - 2 = 15 - (7 - 2)$
7. $28 - 10 - 5 = (28 - 10) - 5$
8. $28 - 10 - 5 = 28 - (10 - 5)$

9. On the basis of the patterns in Exercises 1–9, mark each statement true or false:

   (a) $a - (b + c) = (a - b) + c$
   (b) $a - (b + c) = (a - b) - c$

In 1–8 J note that the set of whole numbers is *not* closed under subtraction.

In 1–8 K, Exercise 1, note that subtraction is *not* commutative.

In 1–8 L, Exercise 9, note that subtraction is *not* associative.

1-9 DIVISION OF WHOLE NUMBERS

Division is the *inverse* of multiplication. For example, in the problem $24 \div 3$ we seek a number n such that $3 \times n = 24$. Since $3 \times 8 = 24$, $n = 8$; that is, $24 \div 3 = 8$. We often write $24 \div 3$ as shown below. Notice that the names of the members of a division problem are also shown.

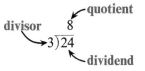

To solve a problem such as $24 \div 6$, we think, "What number multiplied by 6 yields 24?"

Again, we see how important it is to have the basic multiplication facts thoroughly memorized.

Division may also be thought of as repeated subtraction. In the example $24 \div 6$ we can subtract 6 from 24 repeatedly until we obtain a 0 remainder. Thus

$$24 - 6 = 18,$$
$$18 - 6 = 12,$$
$$12 - 6 = 6,$$
$$6 - 6 = 0.$$

Since we needed to make 4 subtractions, the answer is 4:

$$24 \div 6 = 4.$$

Consider a larger problem. If

$$n = 3689 \div 7, \text{ then } n = 527.$$

We do not memorize the multiplication tables as far as

$$527 \times 7 = 3689,$$

nor do we wish to subtract 7 from 3689, 527 times. The problem requires another approach.

$$
\begin{array}{r}
500 \\
7\overline{)3689} \\
3500 \\
\hline
189
\end{array}
\qquad 500 \times 7 = 3500; \text{ subtract 500 sevens.} \qquad (1)
$$

$$
\begin{array}{r}
20 \\
7\overline{)189} \\
140 \\
\hline
49
\end{array}
\qquad 20 \times 7 = 140; \text{ subtract 20 sevens.} \qquad (2)
$$

$$
\begin{array}{r}
7 \\
7\overline{)49} \\
49 \\
\hline
0
\end{array}
\qquad 7 \times 7 = 49; \text{ subtract 7 sevens.} \qquad (3)
$$

$$n = 500 + 20 + 7 = 527$$

We combine steps (1), (2), and (3) when we divide in the usual manner.

$$\begin{array}{r} 527 \\ 7\overline{)3689} \\ 35 \\ \hline 18 \\ 14 \\ \hline 49 \\ 49 \\ \hline \end{array}$$

In division we use approximation to estimate the final answer. Thus

$$\frac{17{,}995}{59} \approx \frac{18{,}000}{60} = 300.$$

We also use approximation to obtain partial quotients, as shown below.

Example. Find $17{,}995 \div 59$.

$$\begin{array}{r} 305 \\ 59\overline{)17{,}995} \\ 17\ 7 \\ \hline 29 \\ 00 \\ \hline 295 \\ 295 \\ \hline \end{array}$$

$\frac{179}{59} \approx \frac{180}{60} = 3$

We actually subtract 17,700.

$\frac{29}{59}$ will not give a whole number answer. Thus the partial quotient is 0.

$\frac{295}{59} \approx \frac{300}{60} = 5$

We subtract 295.

In the division problems discussed thus far the final subtraction performed yielded zero; that is, the remainder was zero. When the remainder in a division problem is zero, the dividend is said to be divisible by the divisor. We say that a is divisible by b if b is a whole number factor of a.

From your experience with division, you know that the following is true.

$$\text{If } \tfrac{15}{3} = 5, \text{ then } 15 = 3 \times 5. \tag{4}$$

$$\text{If } \tfrac{24}{4} = 6, \text{ then } 24 = 4 \times 6. \tag{5}$$

In fact, if $\dfrac{b}{a} = n$, then $b = a \times n$.

$$\text{If } 3 \times 6 = 18, \text{ then } 6 = \tfrac{18}{3} \text{ and } 3 = \tfrac{18}{6}. \tag{6}$$

$$\text{If } 7 \times 4 = 28, \text{ then } 4 = \tfrac{28}{7} \text{ and } 7 = \tfrac{28}{4}. \tag{7}$$

We define division in this way:

$$\textbf{If } a \times n = b, \textbf{ then } n = \frac{b}{a}, \; a \neq 0.$$

By $a \neq 0$ in the definition of division we point out that division by zero is impossible. For example, let us consider

$$n = \tfrac{5}{0}.$$

Suppose we guess that $n = 5$.

$$\text{Does } 5 \times 0 = 5? \text{ No.}$$

Let us try $n = 6$.

$$\text{Does } 6 \times 0 = 5? \text{ No.}$$

In fact, there is *no number n* such that $n \times 0 = 5$.
    Consider one more example:

$$n = \tfrac{0}{0}.$$

Suppose we guess that $n = 5$.

$$\text{Does } 5 \times 0 = 0? \text{ Yes.}$$

Now let us try other values for n. In this case we arbitrarily choose 6, 7, 8, and 9.

$$\text{Does } 6 \times 0 = 0? \text{ Yes.}$$
$$\text{Does } 7 \times 0 = 0? \text{ Yes.}$$
$$\text{Does } 8 \times 0 = 0? \text{ Yes.}$$
$$\text{Does } 9 \times 0 = 0? \text{ Yes.}$$

This suggests that there is no unique answer n. Hence we say that division by zero is undefined.

Exercises for Section 1-9

1-9 A

Find the quotients by inspection:

1. $16 \div 2$	**2.** $36 \div 6$	**3.** $18 \div 3$	**4.** $56 \div 7$
5. $72 \div 8$	**6.** $42 \div 6$	**7.** $48 \div 6$	**8.** $63 \div 7$
9. $39 \div 3$	**10.** $81 \div 9$	**11.** $15 \div 3$	**12.** $35 \div 7$
13. $45 \div 9$	**14.** $54 \div 6$	**15.** $75 \div 5$	**16.** $32 \div 8$
17. $64 \div 8$	**18.** $70 \div 7$	**19.** $72 \div 9$	**20.** $40 \div 5$

1-9 B

Find the quotients:

1. $4\overline{)256}$	**2.** $9\overline{)378}$	**3.** $8\overline{)248}$	**4.** $7\overline{)315}$
5. $3\overline{)615}$	**6.** $5\overline{)985}$	**7.** $5\overline{)2075}$	**8.** $4\overline{)6440}$
9. $7\overline{)6202}$	**10.** $8\overline{)7696}$	**11.** $4\overline{)8004}$	**12.** $6\overline{)7626}$

1-9 C

Find the quotients:

1. $5\overline{)8895}$	**2.** $2\overline{)9916}$	**3.** $6\overline{)9726}$	**4.** $9\overline{)3069}$
5. $7\overline{)1645}$	**6.** $8\overline{)9048}$	**7.** $5\overline{)17,095}$	**8.** $8\overline{)23,464}$
9. $4\overline{)40,832}$	**10.** $7\overline{)17,346}$	**11.** $9\overline{)72,495}$	**12.** $6\overline{)47,994}$

1-9 D

Approximate; then find the quotients:

1. $15\overline{)225}$	**2.** $13\overline{)169}$	**3.** $27\overline{)810}$	**4.** $32\overline{)288}$
5. $19\overline{)418}$	**6.** $28\overline{)868}$	**7.** $45\overline{)2970}$	**8.** $34\overline{)2822}$
9. $67\overline{)3015}$	**10.** $28\overline{)2072}$	**11.** $72\overline{)6552}$	**12.** $31\overline{)6355}$

1-9 E

Approximate; then find the quotients:

1. $18\overline{)1746}$	**2.** $35\overline{)2975}$	**3.** $73\overline{)4964}$	**4.** $88\overline{)7744}$
5. $16\overline{)2560}$	**6.** $38\overline{)2698}$	**7.** $42\overline{)3318}$	**8.** $71\overline{)6674}$
9. $50\overline{)9900}$	**10.** $97\overline{)2813}$	**11.** $85\overline{)6460}$	**12.** $76\overline{)5776}$

1-9 F

Approximate; then find the quotients:

1. $34\overline{)69,054}$ **2.** $18\overline{)12,960}$ **3.** $22\overline{)15,598}$ **4.** $19\overline{)10,735}$

5. $41\overline{)20,336}$ **6.** $78\overline{)47,814}$ **7.** $135\overline{)27,135}$ **8.** $109\overline{)35,425}$

9. $275\overline{)22,275}$ **10.** $305\overline{)90,890}$ **11.** $656\overline{)61,008}$ **12.** $735\overline{)540,225}$

1-9 G

The example shows that $87 \div 13 > 6$, since the remainder is 9. Thus if q is the true quotient, then $6 < q < 7$.

$$\begin{array}{r} 6 \\ 13\overline{)87} \\ 78 \\ \hline \textcircled{9} \end{array}$$

As in the example, find the quotient and circle the remainder.

1. $7\overline{)682}$ **2.** $9\overline{)1056}$ **3.** $5\overline{)342}$ **4.** $13\overline{)976}$

5. $24\overline{)707}$ **6.** $83\overline{)909}$ **7.** $126\overline{)2357}$ **8.** $206\overline{)7784}$

9. $495\overline{)1095}$ **10.** $684\overline{)13,750}$ **11.** $752\overline{)48,703}$ **12.** $919\overline{)90,946}$

1-9 H

In mathematics we show that a number is divisible by 9 if the sum of its digits is divisible by 9. Thus 7803 is divisible by 9 since

$$\frac{7 + 8 + 3}{9} = 2.$$

Which of these are divisible by 9? Check your answers by dividing.

1. 891   **2.** 337   **3.** 666   **4.** 1734

5. 1170   **6.** 1548   **7.** 12,384   **8.** 19,997

9. 34,506   **10.** 77,803   **11.** 132,408   **12.** 780,066

1-9 I

1. In checking the mileage on his new car, a man found that he got 320 miles on 16 gallons of gasoline. How many miles per gallon was this?

2. What number multiplied by 135 yields a product of 12,690?

3. In a social studies assignment a student had 420 pages to read. How many days did it take him to complete the assignment if he read 15 pages a day?

4. A man drives at a steady speed for 12 hours and travels for 744 miles. Find his speed.

5. At a bridge tournament 213 participants appeared. How many more will be needed to start the play if 4 are seated at a table?

6. A service club plans to make a $2000 contribution to a city park. The club has 395 members and only $420 in its treasury. How much should each member contribute in order to make up the difference?

7. A rocket traveled 65,100 miles in 62 hours. Find its average speed in miles per hour.

8. A workman's yearly wage was $9660 before deductions. If $117 was deducted per month, what was his monthly take-home pay?

9. A man died, leaving an estate valued at $27,335. His will indicated that his estate should be divided into 7 parts: 3 parts should be left to his son, 3 parts to his daughter, and the rest to his servant. How much did each person receive?

10. A housing contractor has $530,550 in capital. Using this money, how many homes can he build if he wishes to keep the cost per home at about $9850?

1-9 J

The **average**, or **mean**, of a set of measures is a statistic determined by dividing the *sum* of the measures by the *number* of measures. For example, a student's test scores are 85, 78, 82, 90, and 80. The average test score A is found as follows:

$$A = \frac{85 + 78 + 82 + 90 + 80}{5} = \frac{415}{5} = 83.$$

1. A student received scores of 80, 75, 73, 76, 72, and 74 on his history tests. Find his average.

2. The monthly sales for a store were $375, $482, $407, $422, $325, and $317. Find the average monthly sales during this period.

3. A professional golfer kept his scores for 7 rounds of golf. If his scores were 69, 70, 73, 68, 69, 73, and 75, find his average score.

Exercises 1–9 J continued on page 50.

4. There are 365 days in a year. How many more days would be needed to make a year if the average number of days per month were a whole number?

5. A bowler rolled scores of 168, 158, 149, 165, 137, 161, 169, and 181. Find his average score.

6. The men playing the front line of a football team weighed 200 pounds, 195 pounds, 196 pounds, 209 pounds, 193 pounds, 187 pounds, and 185 pounds. Find the average weight per man.

7. A manager wished to know the average weight per box of the tomatoes he was to haul. He selected 9 boxes at random and found that the weights were 52 pounds, 49 pounds, 52 pounds, 54 pounds, 52 pounds, 52 pounds, 53 pounds, 48 pounds, and 56 pounds. Find the average weight.

8. In mathematics Fred had test scores of 75, 78, 71, 80, 72, and 80. In psychology his test scores were 73, 72, 70, 73, and 77. Which average was better and how much better was it?

1-9 K

Solve for n:

1. $\dfrac{n}{4} = 17$ **2.** $\dfrac{n}{4} = 14$ **3.** $\dfrac{n}{4} = 12$

4. $\dfrac{n}{4} = 15$ **5.** $\dfrac{n}{7} = 7$ **6.** $\dfrac{n}{9} = 24$

7. $\dfrac{n}{8} = 45$ **8.** $\dfrac{n}{6} = 102$ **9.** $\dfrac{n}{5} = 24$

10. $\dfrac{n}{16} = 24$ **11.** $\dfrac{n}{18} = 42$ **12.** $\dfrac{n}{12} = 6$

1-9 L

Solve for x:

1. $\dfrac{x}{6} = 25$ **2.** $\dfrac{x}{8} = 40$ **3.** $\dfrac{x}{16} = 7$

4. $\dfrac{x}{18} = 5$ **5.** $\dfrac{x}{11} = 7$ **6.** $\dfrac{x}{22} = 8$

7. $\dfrac{x}{13} = 9$ **8.** $\dfrac{x}{24} = 24$ **9.** $\dfrac{x}{25} = 30$

10. $\dfrac{x}{35} = 30$ **11.** $\dfrac{x}{45} = 20$ **12.** $\dfrac{x}{75} = 125$

1-9 M

Solve for n:

1. $5n = 20$	**2.** $5n = 40$	**3.** $5n = 35$
4. $5n = 75$	**5.** $8n = 16$	**6.** $6n = 48$
7. $7n = 35$	**8.** $9n = 27$	**9.** $10n = 30$
10. $12n = 48$	**11.** $14n = 56$	**12.** $15n = 75$

1-9 N

Solve for n:

1. $4n = 124$	**2.** $7n = 245$	**3.** $8n = 256$
4. $11n = 121$	**5.** $24n = 576$	**6.** $18n = 648$
7. $17n = 51$	**8.** $19n = 57$	**9.** $25n = 450$
10. $21n = 357$	**11.** $36n = 1620$	**12.** $45n = 3915$

1-9 O

In the formula $r = \dfrac{d}{t}$ determine r for each ordered pair (d, t):

1. $(55, 5)$	**2.** $(24, 6)$	**3.** $(38, 2)$
4. $(45, 9)$	**5.** $(56, 8)$	**6.** $(64, 16)$
7. $(98, 7)$	**8.** $(125, 25)$	**9.** $(900, 30)$
10. $(640, 16)$	**11.** $(1296, 18)$	**12.** $(6096, 24)$

1-9 P

In Exercises 1–9 is n a member of W, the set of whole numbers?

1. $n = 10 \div 5$	**2.** $n = \frac{15}{3}$	**3.** $n = 24 \div 5$
4. $n = 64 \div 4$	**5.** $n = \frac{144}{9}$	**6.** $n = 1280 \div 5$
7. $n = 1350 \div 4$	**8.** $n = \frac{776}{26}$	**9.** $n = \frac{51}{17}$

10. Is the set W closed under division? (*Note:* See *counterexample*, page 42.)

1-9 Q

In Exercises 1–6 mark each statement true or false.

1. $\frac{14}{2} = \frac{10}{2} + \frac{4}{2}$	**2.** $\frac{36}{4} = \frac{28}{4} + \frac{8}{4}$	**3.** $\frac{60}{5} = \frac{40}{5} + \frac{20}{5}$
4. $\frac{123}{3} = \frac{102}{3} + \frac{21}{3}$	**5.** $\frac{248}{8} = \frac{200}{8} + \frac{48}{8}$	**6.** $\frac{981}{9} = \frac{612}{9} + \frac{369}{9}$

7. Does $\dfrac{a + b}{c} = \dfrac{a}{c} + \dfrac{b}{c}$? Assume both a and b are divisible by c.

8. Does $a \div b = b \div a$? Try some examples and state a conclusion about commutativity for division.

■ 1–10 A BASE SIX SYSTEM

Using the set of ten digits, $\{0, 1, 2, 3, 4, 5, 6, 7, 8, 9\}$, the idea of positional value, and the addition principle, we have developed a system of numeration. Since we use ten symbols, we call this the decimal system. The use of ten symbols probably comes from man's use of his ten fingers for counting.

We can use any member of the set $\{2, 3, 4, \ldots\}$ as the base for a numeration system. The Babylonians used sixty as their base and the Maya Indians used twenty.

The study of a system with a base different from ours leads to a better understanding of the operations and principles involved in a positional numeration system. We will now present a **base six** system. We shall use the set of symbols $S = \{0, 1, 2, 3, 4, 5\}$. The table below shows counting in base ten and base six.

Base ten	0	1	2	3	4	5	6	7	8	9	10	11	12	. . .
Base six	0	1	2	3	4	5	10	11	12	13	14	15	20	. . .

In order to indicate the base we write it as a subscript. Observe this usage in the table.

$$10_{six} = (1 \times 6)_{ten} + (0 \times 1)_{ten} = 6_{ten}$$
$$11_{six} = (1 \times 6)_{ten} + (1 \times 1)_{ten} = 7_{ten}$$
$$12_{six} = (1 \times 6)_{ten} + (2 \times 1)_{ten} = 8_{ten}$$
$$15_{six} = (1 \times 6)_{ten} + (5 \times 1)_{ten} = 11_{ten}$$
$$20_{six} = (2 \times 6)_{ten} + (0 \times 1)_{ten} = 12_{ten}$$

Consider the numeral 2013_{six}.

	6^3	6^2	6	1
Place value	two hundred sixteen	thirty-six	six	one
Numeral	2	0	1	3

So, $2013_{six} = (2 \times 216)_{ten} + (0 \times 36)_{ten} + (1 \times 6)_{ten} + (3 \times 1)$
$= 441_{ten}$.

To change from base six to base ten, we expand the numeral as a
polynomial in six and add the results. Thus

$$3451_{six} = (3 \times 6^3)_{ten} + (4 \times 6^2)_{ten} + (5 \times 6)_{ten} + 1$$
$$= (3 \times 216)_{ten} + (4 \times 36)_{ten} + 30_{ten} + 1$$
$$= 823_{ten}.$$

Changing from base ten to base six requires a different approach.
Suppose we wish to change 81_{ten} to base six.

	two hundred sixteens	thirty-sixes	sixes	ones
$81_{ten} =$	?	?	?	?

The result will be a three-digit numeral since $216_{ten} > 81_{ten}$. We
divide in base ten to determine the number of 36's, the number of
6's, and the number of 1's needed.

Example 1. Express 81_{ten} in base six.

```
36)81        (2
   72
 6) 9        (1     Thus (2 × 6²)ten + (1 × 6)ten + (3 × 1) = 81,
    6                              or 213six = 81ten.
 1) 3        (3
    3
   --
    0
```

Thus $(2 \times 6^2)_{ten} + (1 \times 6)_{ten} + (3 \times 1) = 81$,
or $213_{six} = 81_{ten}$.

Suppose we wish to change 585 base ten to base six. Since

$$585_{ten} < 1296_{ten} = 6^4,$$

we shall need only a four-place numeral; that is,

	1296's	216's	36's	6's	1's
$585_{ten} =$	0	?	?	?	? |$_{six}$

Example 2. Express 585_{ten} in base six. To fill in the other positions, we divide in base ten.

$$216 \overline{)585} \quad (2$$
$$\underline{432}$$
$$36 \overline{)153} \quad (4$$
$$\underline{144}$$
$$6 \overline{)9} \quad (1$$
$$\underline{6}$$
$$1 \overline{)3} \quad (3$$

This tells us that we need *two* 216's, *four* 36's, *one* 6, and *three* 1's for a total of 585.

Thus

$$585_{\text{ten}} = \begin{array}{|c|c|c|c|} \hline 2 & 4 & 1 & 3 \\ \hline \end{array}_{\text{six}}$$

with column labels 216's, 36's, 6's, 1's

$$= 2413_{\text{six}}$$

The operation of addition in base six is essentially the same as addition in base ten. However, there are fewer basic addition combinations, as shown in the table.

Addition Table for Base Six

+	0	1	2	3	4	5
0	0	1	2	3	4	5
1	1	2	3	4	5	10
2	2	3	4	5	10	11
3	3	4	5	10	11	12
4	4	5	10	11	12	13
5	5	10	11	12	13	14

Observe these addition problems in base six:

$$\begin{array}{r} 23_{\text{six}} \\ +32_{\text{six}} \\ \hline 55_{\text{six}} \end{array} \qquad (1)$$

$$\overset{1}{23}_{six}$$
$$\underline{25_{six}} \qquad (2)$$
$$52_{six}$$

In problem (1) we did not have to carry since the total in each column was less than six (10_{six}). In problem (2) the sum of the units column is $5_{six} + 3_{six} = 12_{six}$. We write down the 2 and carry the 1; that is, we carry one 6.

Check the following problems, referring to the table of addition facts, if necessary.

$$33_{six}$$
$$\underline{23_{six}} \qquad (3)$$
$$100_{six}$$

$$44_{six}$$
$$\underline{12_{six}} \qquad (4)$$
$$100_{six}$$

$$35_{six}$$
$$\underline{54_{six}} \qquad (5)$$
$$133_{six}$$

Exercises for Section 1–10

1–10 A

Change from base six to base ten:

1. 20_{six}	**2.** 25_{six}	**3.** 30_{six}	**4.** 35_{six}
5. 40_{six}	**6.** 45_{six}	**7.** 50_{six}	**8.** 100_{six}
9. 121_{six}	**10.** 152_{six}	**11.** 203_{six}	**12.** 111_{six}
13. 222_{six}	**14.** 333_{six}	**15.** 444_{six}	**16.** 555_{six}

1–10 B

Change from base six to base ten:

1. 1000_{six}	**2.** 1010_{six}	**3.** 1100_{six}	**4.** 1200_{six}
5. 1020_{six}	**6.** 1002_{six}	**7.** 2500_{six}	**8.** 3500_{six}
9. 4000_{six}	**10.** $12,455_{six}$	**11.** $23,004_{six}$	**12.** $34,145_{six}$

1–10 C

Change from base ten to base six:

1. 8_{ten}	**2.** 12_{ten}	**3.** 16_{ten}	**4.** 20_{ten}
5. 24_{ten}	**6.** 28_{ten}	**7.** 32_{ten}	**8.** 36_{ten}
9. 40_{ten}	**10.** 44_{ten}	**11.** 48_{ten}	**12.** 52_{ten}
13. 56_{ten}	**14.** 60_{ten}	**15.** 64_{ten}	**16.** 68_{ten}

1–10 D

Change from base ten to base six:

1. 216_{ten}	**2.** 321_{ten}	**3.** 326_{ten}	**4.** 431_{ten}
5. 536_{ten}	**6.** 1041_{ten}	**7.** 1141_{ten}	**8.** 1541_{ten}
9. 2756_{ten}	**10.** 3261_{ten}	**11.** 4857_{ten}	**12.** 9082_{ten}

1–10 E

Within each exercise the numerals are written in base six. Find the sums in base six:

1. 25 30	**2.** 34 11	**3.** 22 12	**4.** 40 13
5. 40 15	**6.** 33 21	**7.** 42 12	**8.** 31 15
9. 32 12	**10.** 22 22	**11.** 30 15	**12.** 20 22

1–10 F

Within each exercise the numerals are written in base six. Find the sums in base six:

1. 33 22	**2.** 12 13	**3.** 40 14	**4.** 33 13
5. 34 12	**6.** 22 24	**7.** 35 11	**8.** 24 25
9. 34 15	**10.** 33 15	**11.** 45 5	**12.** 35 12

1–10 G

Within each exercise the numerals are written in base six. Find the sums in base six:

1. 34	**2.** 44	**3.** 55	**4.** 45
22	14	11	21
5. 43	**6.** 55	**7.** 34	**8.** 45
34	15	25	11
9. 35	**10.** 44	**11.** 23	**12.** 55
35	32	45	55

1–10 H

Within each exercise the numerals are written in base six. Find the sums in base six:

1. 22	**2.** 14	**3.** 23	**4.** 23
11	30	22	11
20	11	10	12
5. 14	**6.** 31	**7.** 35	**8.** 34
20	13	10	21
12	12	11	22
9. 22	**10.** 45	**11.** 33	**12.** 25
22	45	24	14
12	23	15	34

■ 1–11 ROUNDING OFF WHOLE NUMBERS

In this chapter you have frequently been asked to approximate answers. In order to approximate, it was necessary to round off. Thus we say

$$38 \times 73 \approx 40 \times 70 = 2800.$$

We rounded these numerals to the nearest ten. The 38 rounded up to 40 and the 73 rounded down to 70.

We now state a formal rule for rounding whole numbers. To **round off** a whole number to a specific unit of place value, all digits that lie to the right of that place are dropped and are then replaced by zeros.

Case 1. If the part dropped begins with 0, 1, 2, 3, or 4, no change is made in the part kept.

Case 2. Increase the part kept by 1 if the part dropped

(a) begins with 5 and the rest of the digits to the right of it are not zero, or

(b) begins with 6, 7, 8, or 9.

Case 3. If the part dropped begins with 5 and the rest of the digits to the right of it are all zero, then add 1 to the part kept if it is odd, but leave it unchanged if it is even.

To illustrate the point, we round off to the nearest ten in the following ways.

Case 1. 32, 64, 73, 82, and 314
Answers: 30, 60, 70, 80, and 310

Case 2. 36, 78, 96, 316, and 527
Answers: 40, 80, 100, 320, and 530

Case 3. 15, 25, 35, 45, 55, 65, and 275
Answers: 20, 20, 40, 40, 60, 60, and 280

We round off to the nearest hundred in the following ways.

Case 1. 22, 46, 124, 131, 444, 328, 341, and 2649
Answers: 0, 0, 100, 100, 400, 300, 300, and 2600

Case 2. 51, 68, 91, 151, 175, 554, 962, and 4771
Answers: 100, 100, 100, 200, 200, 600, 1000, and 4800

Case 3. 50, 150, 250, 350, 450, 550, and 3650
Answers: 0, 200, 200, 400, 400, 600, and 3600

We use the term significant digits to describe rounded numbers. Consider the table:

Number	Number of Significant Digits		
	Three	Two	One
1,263	1,260	1,300	1,000
2,051	2,050	2,100	2,000
1,750	1,750	1,800	2,000
20,721	20,700	21,000	20,000

Note that terminal zeros, as in 20,000, are not significant digits unless we are so advised. For example, consider the last row in the table above.

$$20,721 \qquad 20,700 \qquad 21,000 \qquad 20,000$$

The digits that are underlined are significant digits. Thus in column 3 no zeros in 21,000 are significant. In column 4 no zeros in 20,000 are significant. In 20,700 note that the zero between the 2 and the 7 is significant.

Exercises for Section 1–11

1–11 A

Round off to the nearest ten:

1. 13	**2.** 15	**3.** 16	**4.** 22
5. 24	**6.** 25	**7.** 26	**8.** 27
9. 31	**10.** 34	**11.** 35	**12.** 38
13. 41	**14.** 45	**15.** 49	**16.** 52

1–11 B

Round off to the nearest ten:

1. 132	**2.** 135	**3.** 141	**4.** 145
5. 201	**6.** 208	**7.** 212	**8.** 215
9. 217	**10.** 232	**11.** 235	**12.** 239
13. 1271	**14.** 1275	**15.** 1276	**16.** 1285

1–11 C

Round off to the nearest hundred:

1. 45	**2.** 50	**3.** 52	**4.** 55
5. 60	**6.** 78	**7.** 110	**8.** 125
9. 136	**10.** 145	**11.** 150	**12.** 172
13. 205	**14.** 235	**15.** 250	**16.** 265

1–11 D

Round off to the nearest hundred and give the number of significant digits in each answer:

1. 325	**2.** 350	**3.** 375	**4.** 425
5. 450	**6.** 475	**7.** 550	**8.** 575
9. 650	**10.** 675	**11.** 1250	**12.** 1350
13. 1450	**14.** 1550	**15.** 4550	**16.** 5550

1–11 E

Perform the indicated operations and round off each answer. Give the number of significant digits in each answer.

1. $25 + 782 + 46$, nearest ten

2. $(361) \times (67)$, nearest hundred

3. $17{,}370 \div 9$, nearest ten

4. $\dfrac{684 + 737 + 97}{6}$, nearest hundred

5. $18{,}856 - 9321$, nearest thousand

6. $25{,}270 + 13{,}675 + 4060$, nearest thousand

7. $848 \div 8$, nearest ten

8. $2655 \div 15$, nearest ten

9. $(487) \times (271 + 39)$, nearest hundred

10. $78 \times (755 - 169)$, nearest thousand

1–11 F

1. The distance from San Diego to Guadalajara is 1585 miles. Give this distance to the nearest 10 miles.

2. In 1958 the total amount of mortgages owned by United States life insurance companies was $36,368,619,000. Find this amount to the nearest million dollars.

3. Give the distance from the earth to the moon to the nearest 10,000 miles if it is 238,857, to the nearest mile.

4. The diameter of the sun is estimated at 860,000 miles. Give this distance to the nearest hundred thousand miles.

5. Suppose that 39,575 copies of a pamphlet were sold. Find this number to the nearest thousand.

6. In Exercise 5 the pamphlets were sold for $1 each. Find the amount to the nearest hundred dollars.

7. In 1965 the sales for the Tractor Company were $389,190,000. Find this amount to the nearest million dollars.

8. In 1950 the population of Burleytown was 12,456. In 1965 the population had grown to 56,995. Give the increase to the nearest thousand people.

9. A tourist flew from Los Angeles to New York, a distance of 2624 miles; then from New York to London, 3504 miles. Give, to the nearest hundred, the number of miles he traveled.

10. On June 30 the total assets for a financial corporation were $580,782,442. On June 30 one year later their total assets were $687,294,812. Give the increase to the nearest hundred dollars.

Vocabulary

The section in which each word appears is indicated in parentheses.

addends (1–6)

addition (1–4, 1–5, 1–6)

associative (1–7)

associative property (1–6, 1–7)

average (Exercises 1–9 J)

axiom (1–6)

base (1–4)

base six (1–10)

braces (1–2)

closed (1–7)

closure (1–6, 1–7)

common factor (Exercises 1–5 F)

commutative (1–7)

commutative property (1–6, 1–7)

counterexample (Exercises 1–8 J)

counters (1–1)

decimal system (1–10)

difference (1–8)

digits (1–4)

disjoint sets (1–5)

distributive property (1–6, 1–7)

dividend (1–9)

divisible (1–9)

division (1–9)

divisor (1–9)

empty set (1–5)

equal (1–5)

equals symbol (1–2)

equivalent (1–5)

exponent (1–4)

Chapter Review

A

1. Write in Egyptian numerals: (a) 345   (b) 207
2. Write in Roman numerals:
   (a) 83   (b) 207   (c) 1776
3. Consider the sets $A = \{a, b, c\}$ and $B = \{r, s, x, y\}$. Find:
   (a) $n(A) + n(B)$ (b) $A \cup B$ (c) $A \cap B$ (d) Is $s \in A$?
4. Let x, y, and r represent whole numbers.
   (a) Does $x + y = y + x$? Explain.
   (b) Does $(x + y) + r = x + (y + r)$? Explain.
   (c) Does $r(x + y) = rx + ry$? Explain.
5. Does $8 - 7 = 7 - 8$? Explain.
6. We call division and multiplication *inverse* operations. Explain.
7. Find $23_{six} + 33_{six}$. Give your answer in base six and in base ten.
8. Find, to the nearest ten:
   (a) 746×29 (b) $343 + 244$ (c) $707 \div 69$
9. Express as a number of tenths:
   (a) 21   (b) 2.1   (c) 3.04
10. Does $(73 - 17) - 11 = 73 - (17 - 11)$? Explain.

B

1. Solve for n: $n = 2341 + 2009 + 3175 + 6784 + 2345$.
2. Solve for n: $n = 156,008 - 123,458$.
3. Solve for n: $n = 234,567 \div 193$. Give your answer to the nearest one.
4. If September 28 falls on Saturday, find the date of the following Friday.
5. Find the sum of the first 11 odd numbers.
6. Find the sum of the first 12 even numbers.
7. In a theatre the 24 front seats sell for $5 each; the next 36 seats, for $4 each; the next 48 seats, for $3 each; the last 60 seats, for $2 each. Find the total receipts if each seat is sold for a play.
8. A worker's annual wage was $8040. His deductions per month for taxes, insurance, and so on were $129. Find his monthly take-home pay to the nearest dollar.
9. Find the sum of 1234_{six} and 3333_{six}.
10. The product of 37 and a number is 7326. Find the number.

C

In Exercises 1–6 W is the set of whole numbers and N is the set of natural numbers.

1. Find $N \cap W$.
2. Find $N \cup W$.
3. Is $N \subseteq W$?
4. Is $3 \in W$?
5. Is $17 \in N$?
6. Is $0 \in N$?
7. If the universal set U is the set of whole numbers, is $(7 + 8) \in U$?
8. If $U = \{1, 2, 3, 4, 5, 6, 7, 8, 9, 10\}$, is $(9 - 9) \in U$?
9. Is $(8 \div 3) \in N$, with N the set of natural numbers?
10. Is $(45 \div 7) \in W$, with W the set of whole numbers?

2 The Rational Numbers, Fractions

■ **2-1 CONCEPTS OF FRACTIONS**

In this chapter we expand our scope of numbers to the set R of rational numbers, which includes the set of whole numbers and the set of fractions.

The set of whole numbers can be associated with points on a line. We mark one point on the line and call it the **origin**; we label it with the numeral 0. We choose a unit of length and mark off points on the line, as shown in Figure 2–1. With these points, we associate the natural numbers $(1, 2, 3, 4, \ldots)$. Each number is a coordinate of a point: 0 is the coordinate of the origin; 2 is the **coordinate** of A.

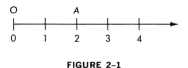

FIGURE 2-1

In the figure the arrow indicates that the line continues in this way indefinitely. Thus all whole numbers are placed in a **one-to-one correspondence** with points of this line, called the **number line** (or *number ray*, since the negatives of the natural numbers are not shown).

There are other points on the number line. For example, a point halfway between 0 and 1 is labeled $\frac{1}{2}$; a point three-fourths of the way from 1 to 2 is labeled $1\frac{3}{4}$. The numbers which we associate with these points are called **fractions.** Thus a one-to-one correspondence exists between certain points on the number line and the numbers called fractions.

In general there is a one-to-one correspondence between certain points on the number line and the rational numbers (that is, the fractions and whole numbers). There are other points on the number line which are associated with numbers that are not rational. We will study these later in Section 7–7.

Any number which can be expressed in the form a/b, where a and b are whole numbers $b \neq 0$, is called a **rational number.** For example,

$$4, \quad \tfrac{1}{2}, \quad \tfrac{3}{5}, \quad \tfrac{4}{3}, \quad 0, \quad \text{and} \quad \tfrac{4}{4}$$

are rational numbers. The rest of the set of rational numbers will be discussed in Chapter 8.

The **ratio** r of the number c to the number d is represented by the quotient of the two numbers: $r = c/d$. The ratio of the two numbers 5 and 4 can be written as 5 to 4, $\tfrac{5}{4}$, 5:4, or 1.25. When a ratio is left in fraction form, it should be reduced. Thus the ratio of 21 to 18 can be written as 7 to 6 or as $\tfrac{7}{6}$.

In $36 \div 4 = n$, or $\tfrac{36}{4} = n$, we seek a number n such that $4 \times n = 36$. Since $4 \times 9 = 36$, then $n = 9$. In $3 \div 5 = n$ we seek an n such that $5 \times n = 3$; but we cannot find such an n among the whole numbers. We use the symbol $\tfrac{3}{5}$ to represent this n.

We can think of a fraction as one or more of the equal parts of a quantity. Thus if the quantity is \$1, and 25¢ is one of the equal parts, then 75¢ is $\tfrac{3}{4}$ of \$1. Here we have taken 3 of the 4 equal parts, fourths, of the \$1. The 4 is the **denominator** of the fraction and gives the number of equal parts into which the whole is divided. The 3 is the **numerator** and gives the number of these equal parts we wish to take. The fraction $\tfrac{1}{4}$ represents the unit being used. Fractions with numerator 1 and denominator greater than 1 are called **unit fractions.**

Figure 2–2 is divided into 4 equal parts, 3 of which have been shaded. The shaded portion represents $\tfrac{3}{4}$ of the whole figure.

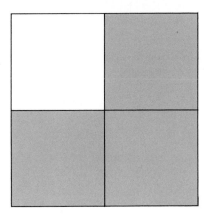

FIGURE 2–2

Figure 2–3, which is the same size as Figure 2–2, is divided into 16 equal parts, 12 of which are shaded.   Thus it appears that $\frac{12}{16} = \frac{3}{4}$ since the same portion was shaded in each figure.

This suggests that the numerator and denominator of a fraction may be multiplied by the same number (not zero) without changing the value of the fraction. For example,

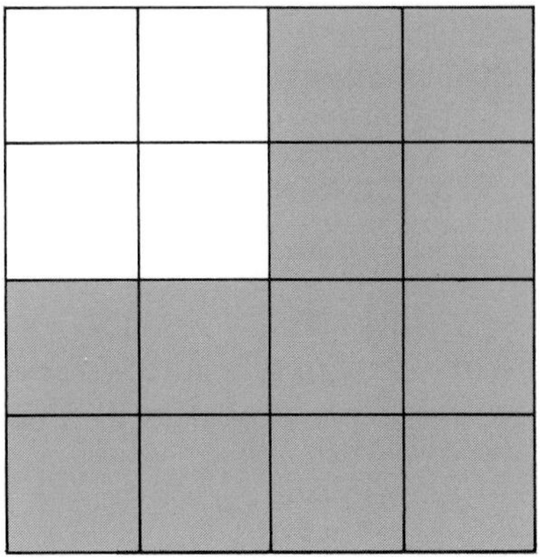

FIGURE 2–3

$$\frac{3}{4} = \frac{4 \times 3}{4 \times 4} = \frac{12}{16}, \quad \frac{3}{4} = \frac{5 \times 3}{5 \times 4} = \frac{15}{20}, \quad \frac{3}{4} = \frac{6 \times 3}{6 \times 4} = \frac{18}{24}. \tag{1}$$

Example. Write $\frac{3}{5}$ as a fraction with denominator 35.

$$\frac{3}{5} = \frac{x}{35} \,; \qquad \frac{3 \times 7}{5 \times 7} = \frac{21}{35} = \frac{x}{35} \,;$$

that is,

$$x = 3 \times 7 = 21.$$

A **mixed number** is the sum of a nonzero whole number and a fraction less than 1. Thus $1\frac{1}{2}$, $2\frac{3}{4}$, and $1\frac{4}{5}$ are mixed numbers.

A fraction a/b, $a > b$ and $b \neq 0$, can be written as a mixed number or a whole number by dividing a by b and writing the remainder, if any, over b. For example,

$$\frac{20}{3} = 3\overline{)20}^{\,6} = 6\frac{2}{3}, \tag{2}$$
$$\quad\ \underline{18}$$
$$\quad\ \ 2$$

$$\frac{15}{7} = 7\overline{)15}^{\,2} = 2\frac{1}{7}, \tag{3}$$
$$\quad\ \underline{14}$$
$$\quad\ \ 1$$

$$\frac{18}{3} = 6\frac{0}{3} = 6. \tag{4}$$

Exercises for Section 2–1

2–1 A

Figure 2–4 is divided into 8 equal parts. In each exercise tell what fraction of the big square is shaded as indicated.

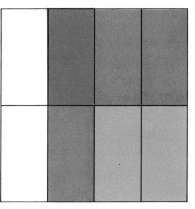

FIGURE 2–4

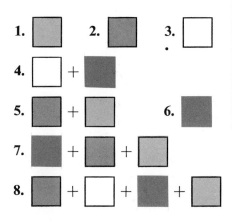

1. ▢   2. ▢   3. ▢
.

4. ▢ + ▢

5. ▢ + ▢   6. ▢

7. ▢ + ▢ + ▢

8. ▢ + ▢ + ▢ + ▢

2–1 B

Figure 2–5 is divided into 64 equal parts. In each exercise tell what fraction of the big square is shaded as indicated.

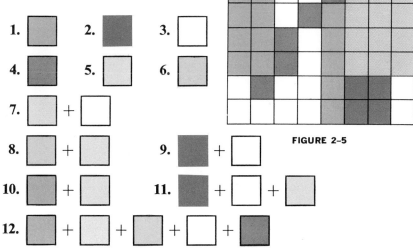

1. ▢   2. ▢   3. ▢

4. ▢   5. ▢   6. ▢

7. ▢ + ▢

8. ▢ + ▢   9. ▢ + ▢

FIGURE 2–5

10. ▢ + ▢   11. ▢ + ▢ + ▢

12. ▢ + ▢ + ▢ + ▢ + ▢

2-1 C

As in the Example, page 66, solve for x and y:

1. $\dfrac{1}{4} = \dfrac{x}{8} = \dfrac{y}{12}$ 2. $\dfrac{1}{3} = \dfrac{x}{6} = \dfrac{y}{9}$ 3. $\dfrac{1}{2} = \dfrac{x}{4} = \dfrac{y}{6}$

4. $\dfrac{1}{5} = \dfrac{x}{10} = \dfrac{y}{20}$ 5. $\dfrac{1}{8} = \dfrac{x}{16} = \dfrac{y}{24}$ 6. $\dfrac{1}{6} = \dfrac{x}{12} = \dfrac{y}{18}$

7. $\dfrac{2}{3} = \dfrac{x}{6} = \dfrac{y}{12}$ 8. $\dfrac{3}{4} = \dfrac{x}{8} = \dfrac{y}{12}$ 9. $\dfrac{2}{5} = \dfrac{x}{10} = \dfrac{y}{15}$

10. $\dfrac{3}{5} = \dfrac{x}{10} = \dfrac{y}{15}$ 11. $\dfrac{3}{8} = \dfrac{x}{16} = \dfrac{y}{24}$ 12. $\dfrac{5}{6} = \dfrac{x}{12} = \dfrac{y}{18}$

2-1 D

Solve for x and y:

1. $\dfrac{x}{3} = \dfrac{4}{6} = \dfrac{y}{12}$ 2. $\dfrac{x}{5} = \dfrac{8}{10} = \dfrac{y}{15}$ 3. $\dfrac{x}{4} = \dfrac{y}{16} = \dfrac{15}{20}$

4. $\dfrac{x}{6} = \dfrac{10}{12} = \dfrac{y}{18}$ 5. $\dfrac{x}{8} = \dfrac{14}{16} = \dfrac{y}{32}$ 6. $\dfrac{x}{3} = \dfrac{y}{9} = \dfrac{12}{18}$

7. $\dfrac{x}{7} = \dfrac{y}{14} = \dfrac{12}{28}$ 8. $\dfrac{x}{5} = \dfrac{4}{10} = \dfrac{y}{30}$ 9. $\dfrac{x}{8} = \dfrac{10}{16} = \dfrac{y}{24}$

10. $\dfrac{1}{2} = \dfrac{x}{12} = \dfrac{y}{22}$ 11. $\dfrac{5}{7} = \dfrac{10}{x} = \dfrac{35}{y}$ 12. $\dfrac{7}{9} = \dfrac{21}{x} = \dfrac{y}{18}$

2-1 E

Solve for x, y, and z:

1. $\dfrac{3}{2} = \dfrac{x}{4} = \dfrac{y}{6}$ 2. $\dfrac{5}{3} = \dfrac{x}{6} = \dfrac{y}{9}$

3. $\dfrac{4}{3} = \dfrac{x}{6} = \dfrac{y}{9}$ 4. $\dfrac{5}{2} = \dfrac{x}{8} = \dfrac{y}{12}$

5. $\dfrac{5}{4} = \dfrac{x}{8} = \dfrac{y}{12}$ 6. $\dfrac{4}{4} = \dfrac{x}{3} = \dfrac{y}{5} = \dfrac{z}{6}$

7. $\dfrac{9}{8} = \dfrac{x}{16} = \dfrac{y}{24} = \dfrac{z}{32}$ 8. $\dfrac{7}{5} = \dfrac{x}{10} = \dfrac{y}{15} = \dfrac{z}{20}$

9. $\dfrac{13}{10} = \dfrac{x}{20} = \dfrac{y}{30} = \dfrac{z}{40}$ 10. $\dfrac{7}{4} = \dfrac{x}{8} = \dfrac{y}{16} = \dfrac{z}{24}$

2-1 F

1. What fraction of a dollar is 20¢?
2. A baseball team has 9 players, 3 of whom play in the outfield. Find the fraction of the team which plays in the outfield.
3. In Exercise 2 write the fraction of the team which does not play in the outfield.
4. Joe normally works a 40-hour week. If he missed 18 hours one week, what fraction did he work?
5. A student completed 12 pages of a 20-page essay. What fraction of the essay has he completed?
6. Fred cut a yardstick in two at the 18-inch mark. What fraction of the yardstick was each part?
7. In general, out of 1000 car trips, 600 will be for less than 5 miles. What fraction will be for less than 5 miles?
8. The assignment in history was 64 pages of reading. Bill read 44 pages by noon. Find the fraction that he had left to read that afternoon.
9. In 1900, 5200 women graduated from college in the United States; in 1960, this number was 144,000; in 1966, it was 200,000.
   (a) What fraction of the number of graduates in 1960 was the number in 1900?
   (b) What fraction of the number of graduates in 1966 was the number in 1900?
10. In 1789 George Washington received 69 out of the 138 electoral votes cast. What fraction of the total vote did he receive? (*Note:* Electors voted for President and Vice-President on the same ballot. Since every elector gave Washington one of his two votes, the election was termed unanimous.)

2-1 G

1. Multiply the numerator of $\frac{3}{4}$ by 5 and the denominator by 2. Does the resulting fraction equal $\frac{3}{4}$?
2. Select the mixed numbers from $\{\frac{3}{4}, 1\frac{1}{5}, 16, 5\frac{3}{4}, 5 + 12\}$.
3. Multiply the numerator and denominator of each fraction by the number indicated:
   (a) $\frac{3}{4}$ by 3   (b) $\frac{2}{5}$ by 5   (c) $\frac{9}{10}$ by 2   (d) $\frac{4}{7}$ by 4
   (e) $\frac{7}{8}$ by 5   (f) $\frac{3}{4}$ by 6   (g) $\frac{9}{2}$ by 3   (h) $\frac{13}{5}$ by 7
   (i) In (a) through (h) is the resulting fraction equal to the given fraction?

2-1 H

Express each fraction as a mixed number:

1. $\frac{9}{4}$ **2.** $\frac{20}{7}$ **3.** $\frac{18}{5}$ **4.** $\frac{5}{4}$

5. $\frac{7}{3}$ **6.** $\frac{25}{4}$ **7.** $\frac{14}{4}$ **8.** $\frac{3}{2}$

9. $\frac{5}{4}$ **10.** $\frac{9}{8}$ **11.** $\frac{13}{8}$ **12.** $\frac{17}{8}$

2-1 I

Express each fraction as a mixed number or a whole number:

1. $\frac{8}{2}$ **2.** $\frac{6}{2}$ **3.** $\frac{18}{9}$ **4.** $\frac{3}{1}$

5. $\frac{8}{5}$ **6.** $\frac{48}{8}$ **7.** $\frac{21}{4}$ **8.** $\frac{6}{5}$

9. $\frac{16}{8}$ **10.** $\frac{16}{3}$ **11.** $\frac{21}{3}$ **12.** $\frac{19}{9}$

2-1 J

Express each number as a mixed number in simplest form:

1. $1\frac{3}{2}$ **2.** $2\frac{8}{5}$ **3.** $4\frac{9}{4}$ **4.** $\frac{33}{2}$

5. $\frac{47}{3}$ **6.** $\frac{56}{5}$ **7.** $\frac{84}{16}$ **8.** $\frac{72}{16}$

9. $\frac{60}{16}$ **10.** $1\frac{13}{8}$ **11.** $3\frac{20}{3}$ **12.** $4\frac{7}{2}$

2-1 K

In each pair of numbers find the ratio of the first to the second. Express answers in reduced fractional form.

1. (4, 5) **2.** (2, 4) **3.** (6, 8) **4.** (12, 4)

5. (15, 20) **6.** (32, 20) **7.** (34, 51) **8.** (48, 72)

9. $(\frac{1}{2}, \frac{1}{4})$ **10.** $(2\frac{1}{2}, 1\frac{1}{2})$ **11.** $(4, 1\frac{1}{2})$ **12.** (120, 84)

13. (26, 91) **14.** $(8\frac{1}{2}, 2\frac{1}{4})$ **15.** $(1\frac{13}{20}, 3\frac{3}{4})$ **16.** $(\frac{85}{100}, \frac{175}{1000})$

2-1 L

1. There are 24 women and 18 men in a class. Find the ratio of the number of women to the number of men.

2. In Exercise 1 find the ratio of the number of men to women.

3. In Exercise 1 find the ratio of the total number of people in the class to the number of women.

4. Car A traveled 124 miles on a tank of gasoline; car B, 188 miles on an equal amount of gasoline. Find the ratio of the number of miles car A traveled to the number of miles car B traveled.

5. Room 126 contains 208 chairs. Room 130 contains 180 chairs. Find the ratio of the number of chairs in room 126 to the number of chairs in room 130.

6. The Giants won 28 out of 40 games. Find the ratio of the number of wins to the number of losses.
7. Sales for one clerk amounted to $18.25; for another clerk, $24.50. Find the ratio of the sales of the first clerk to the sales of the second clerk.
8. Wrestler A weighs 285 pounds and Wrestler B weighs 295 pounds. Find the ratio of A's weight to B's weight.

■ 2-2 MULTIPLICATION OF FRACTIONS

Consider the number line (Figure 2–6). Does it seem reasonable that $\frac{1}{2}$ of 4 is 2? That $\frac{1}{4}$ of 4 is 1? You probably recognize these answers without really thinking of how you get them.

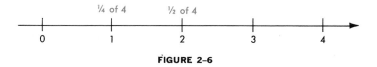

FIGURE 2–6

Now consider Figure 2–7. Does it seem reasonable that $\frac{1}{2}$ of $\frac{1}{2}$ is $\frac{1}{4}$? That $\frac{1}{4}$ of $\frac{1}{2}$ is $\frac{1}{8}$?

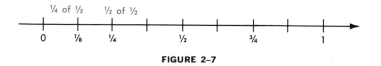

FIGURE 2–7

Note that all of the above answers may be obtained in a similar way:

$$\frac{1}{2} \text{ of } 4 = \frac{1}{2} \times \frac{4}{1} = \frac{1 \times 4}{2 \times 1} = 2;$$

$$\frac{1}{4} \text{ of } 4 = \frac{1}{4} \times \frac{4}{1} = \frac{1 \times 4}{4 \times 1} = 1;$$

$$\frac{1}{2} \text{ of } \frac{1}{2} = \frac{1}{2} \times \frac{1}{2} = \frac{1 \times 1}{2 \times 2} = \frac{1}{4};$$

$$\frac{1}{4} \text{ of } \frac{1}{2} = \frac{1}{4} \times \frac{1}{2} = \frac{1 \times 1}{4 \times 2} = \frac{1}{8}.$$

If a, b, c, and d, are whole numbers, $b \neq 0$ and $d \neq 0$, we define **multiplication** of fractions as in I.

$$\textbf{I.} \qquad \frac{a}{b} \times \frac{c}{d} = \frac{a \times c}{b \times d}$$

For example,

$$\frac{3}{4} \times \frac{1}{5} = \frac{3 \times 1}{4 \times 5}$$

$$= \frac{3}{20} \, ; \tag{1}$$

$$\frac{2}{3} \times \frac{4}{7} = \frac{2 \times 4}{3 \times 7}$$

$$= \frac{8}{21} . \tag{2}$$

Mixed numbers can be written in the form a/b, a and b integers, as follows:

$$2\tfrac{3}{4} = 2 + \tfrac{3}{4} = \tfrac{8}{4} + \tfrac{3}{4} = 8 \text{ fourths} + 3 \text{ fourths}$$
$$= (8 + 3) \text{ fourths} = \tfrac{11}{4}; \tag{3}$$

$$1\tfrac{4}{5} = \tfrac{5}{5} + \tfrac{4}{5} = 5 \text{ fifths} + 4 \text{ fifths}$$
$$= (5 + 4) \text{ fifths} = \tfrac{9}{5}. \tag{4}$$

Note that although we think the words *fourths* and *fifths*, we do not usually write them. Thus

$$1\tfrac{4}{5} = \tfrac{5}{5} + \tfrac{4}{5} = \tfrac{9}{5}.$$

We find the product of two mixed numbers as in this example:

$$2\tfrac{3}{4} \times 1\tfrac{4}{5} = \tfrac{11}{4} \times \tfrac{9}{5} = \tfrac{99}{20} = 4\tfrac{19}{20}. \tag{5}$$

To find the product of an integer a and a fraction, write a as $a/1$. For example,

$$6 \times \tfrac{3}{5} = \tfrac{6}{1} \times \tfrac{3}{5} = \tfrac{18}{5} = 3\tfrac{3}{5}; \tag{6}$$

$$2 \times 1\tfrac{1}{3} = \tfrac{2}{1} \times \tfrac{4}{3} = \tfrac{8}{3} = 2\tfrac{2}{3}. \tag{7}$$

The fraction a/b is said to be **reduced** when a and b have no common factors except 1.

Example. Reduce the fraction $\frac{16}{20}$.

$$\frac{16}{20} = \frac{4 \times 4}{4 \times 5}$$

Here a and b (16 and 20) have the common factor 4.

$$= \frac{4}{4} \times \frac{4}{5}$$

$$= 1 \times \frac{4}{5} = \frac{4}{5}.$$

Now the fraction is reduced since 4 and 5 have only the common factor 1.

If n represents a number, then II and III are true.

II. $\qquad n \times 1 = n$

III. $\qquad \frac{n}{n} = 1 \; if \; n \neq 0$

As examples of II, consider

$$3 \times 1 = 3,$$
$$5 \times 1 = 5,$$
$$\tfrac{2}{3} \times 1 = \tfrac{2}{3}.$$

Exercises for Section 2–2

2–2 A

Solve for x:

1. $2\dfrac{3}{4} = 2 + \dfrac{x}{4}$

2. $1\dfrac{5}{9} = 1 + \dfrac{x}{9}$

3. $6\dfrac{7}{8} = 6 + \dfrac{x}{8}$

4. $3\dfrac{1}{2} = 3 + x$

5. $1\dfrac{3}{4} = 1 + x$

6. $2\dfrac{5}{6} = 2 + x$

7. $4\dfrac{5}{8} = x + \dfrac{5}{8}$

8. $3\dfrac{3}{5} = 3 + \dfrac{3}{x}$

9. $9\dfrac{11}{16} = 9 + \dfrac{x}{16}$

10. $4\dfrac{7}{12} = 4 + \dfrac{7}{x}$

11. $5\dfrac{9}{10} = 5 + \dfrac{x}{10}$

12. $8\dfrac{1}{2} = 8 + x$

2-2 B

Solve for n:

1. $1\dfrac{1}{2} = \dfrac{2}{2} + \dfrac{n}{2}$ **2.** $2\dfrac{1}{2} = \dfrac{4}{2} + \dfrac{n}{2}$ **3.** $1\dfrac{1}{4} = \dfrac{n}{4} + \dfrac{1}{4}$

4. $1\dfrac{1}{5} = \dfrac{n}{5} + \dfrac{1}{5}$ **5.** $1\dfrac{1}{3} = \dfrac{3}{3} + \dfrac{n}{3}$ **6.** $2\dfrac{1}{3} = \dfrac{6}{3} + \dfrac{n}{3}$

7. $2\dfrac{1}{4} = \dfrac{n}{4} + \dfrac{1}{4}$ **8.** $2\dfrac{1}{5} = \dfrac{n}{5} + \dfrac{1}{5}$ **9.** $3\dfrac{2}{3} = \dfrac{9}{3} + \dfrac{n}{3}$

10. $4\dfrac{1}{2} = \dfrac{n}{2} + \dfrac{1}{2}$ **11.** $2\dfrac{3}{4} = \dfrac{n}{4} + \dfrac{3}{4}$ **12.** $3\dfrac{4}{5} = \dfrac{n}{5} + \dfrac{4}{5}$

2-2 C

Use the principle $n/n = 1, n \neq 0$, to solve:

1. $1 = \dfrac{n}{2}$ **2.** $1 = \dfrac{n}{3}$ **3.** $1 = \dfrac{n}{4}$ **4.** $1 = \dfrac{n}{6}$

5. $2 = \dfrac{n}{3}$ **6.** $2 = \dfrac{n}{5}$ **7.** $2 = \dfrac{n}{8}$ **8.** $2 = \dfrac{n}{12}$

9. $3 = \dfrac{n}{2}$ **10.** $3 = \dfrac{n}{4}$ **11.** $3 = \dfrac{n}{6}$ **12.** $3 = \dfrac{n}{10}$

2-2 D

Solve:

1. $2\dfrac{2}{3} = \dfrac{n}{3} + \dfrac{2}{3}$ **2.** $4\dfrac{3}{5} = \dfrac{n}{5} + \dfrac{3}{5}$

3. $3\dfrac{7}{12} = \dfrac{n}{12} + \dfrac{7}{12}$ **4.** $3\dfrac{1}{2} = \dfrac{n}{2} + \dfrac{1}{2}$

5. $3\dfrac{4}{5} = \dfrac{n}{5} + \dfrac{4}{5}$ **6.** $5\dfrac{1}{2} = \dfrac{n}{2} + \dfrac{1}{2}$

7. $4\dfrac{2}{3} = \dfrac{n}{3} + \dfrac{2}{3}$ **8.** $5\dfrac{2}{3} = \dfrac{n}{3} + \dfrac{2}{3}$

9. $1\dfrac{1}{2} = \dfrac{2}{2} + \dfrac{a}{2} = \dfrac{n}{2}$ **10.** $3\dfrac{2}{3} = \dfrac{9}{3} + \dfrac{b}{3} = \dfrac{n}{3}$

11. $4\dfrac{2}{5} = \dfrac{20}{5} + \dfrac{c}{5} = \dfrac{n}{5}$ **12.** $6\dfrac{5}{12} = \dfrac{72}{12} + \dfrac{n}{12} = \dfrac{m}{12}$

13. If $c \neq 0$, does $a = \dfrac{ac}{c}$? Explain.

14. Does $a + \dfrac{b}{c} = \dfrac{ac}{c} + \dfrac{b}{c} = \dfrac{ac + b}{c}$? Explain.

2–2 E

From 2–2 D, Exercise 14, use the fact that $a + \dfrac{b}{c} = \dfrac{ac + b}{c}$ to solve:

1. $1\dfrac{1}{2} = \dfrac{n}{2}$ **2.** $2\dfrac{1}{2} = \dfrac{n}{2}$ **3.** $4\dfrac{1}{5} = \dfrac{n}{5}$

4. $2\dfrac{2}{5} = \dfrac{n}{5}$ **5.** $1\dfrac{1}{12} = \dfrac{n}{12}$ **6.** $3\dfrac{1}{12} = \dfrac{n}{12}$

7. $2\dfrac{7}{12} = \dfrac{n}{12}$ **8.** $1\dfrac{1}{8} = \dfrac{n}{8}$ **9.** $2\dfrac{3}{8} = \dfrac{n}{8}$

10. $3\dfrac{5}{8} = \dfrac{n}{8}$ **11.** $4\dfrac{5}{8} = \dfrac{n}{8}$ **12.** $2\dfrac{7}{8} = \dfrac{n}{8}$

2–2 F

Find n:

1. $1\dfrac{1}{3} = \dfrac{n}{3}$ **2.** $1\dfrac{2}{3} = \dfrac{n}{3}$ **3.** $2\dfrac{1}{3} = \dfrac{n}{3}$

4. $2\dfrac{2}{3} = \dfrac{n}{3}$ **5.** $2\dfrac{1}{4} = \dfrac{n}{4}$ **6.** $2\dfrac{3}{4} = \dfrac{n}{4}$

7. $1\dfrac{5}{4} = \dfrac{n}{4}$ **8.** $3\dfrac{7}{4} = \dfrac{n}{4}$ **9.** $1\dfrac{1}{6} = \dfrac{n}{6}$

10. $2\dfrac{1}{6} = \dfrac{n}{6}$ **11.** $3\dfrac{5}{6} = \dfrac{n}{6}$ **12.** $3\dfrac{7}{6} = \dfrac{n}{6}$

2–2 G

Perform the following by inspection:

1. $\frac{1}{2} \times \frac{1}{3}$ **2.** $\frac{1}{2} \times \frac{1}{4}$ **3.** $\frac{1}{3} \times \frac{1}{5}$

4. $\frac{1}{4} \times \frac{1}{6}$ **5.** $\frac{1}{3} \times \frac{2}{5}$ **6.** $\frac{1}{3} \times \frac{4}{5}$

7. $\frac{1}{2} \times \frac{3}{5}$ **8.** $\frac{1}{2} \times 1$ **9.** $\frac{2}{3} \times \frac{1}{5}$

10. $\frac{4}{5} \times \frac{1}{3}$ **11.** $\frac{5}{8} \times \frac{1}{2}$ **12.** $\frac{3}{8} \times \frac{1}{2}$

2-2 H

Reduce:

1. $\frac{2}{4}$ **2.** $\frac{3}{6}$ **3.** $\frac{4}{8}$

4. $\frac{5}{10}$ **5.** $\frac{4}{12}$ **6.** $\frac{3}{9}$

7. $\frac{4}{6}$ **8.** $\frac{6}{8}$ **9.** $\frac{10}{20}$

10. $\frac{8}{12}$ **11.** $\frac{9}{12}$ **12.** $\frac{3}{12}$

2-2 I

Reduce:

1. $\frac{6}{9}$ **2.** $\frac{10}{12}$ **3.** $\frac{2}{8}$

4. $\frac{5}{15}$ **5.** $\frac{2}{6}$ **6.** $\frac{4}{16}$

7. $\frac{12}{16}$ **8.** $\frac{10}{16}$ **9.** $\frac{8}{16}$

10. $\frac{14}{16}$ **11.** $\frac{5}{20}$ **12.** $\frac{15}{20}$

2-2 J

Find the products. Write the answers as reduced fractions or reduced mixed numbers. For example,

$$1\tfrac{1}{2} \times 1\tfrac{2}{3} = \tfrac{3}{2} \times \tfrac{5}{3} = \tfrac{15}{6} = \tfrac{5}{2} = 2\tfrac{1}{2}.$$

1. $1\tfrac{1}{2} \times 1\tfrac{1}{2}$ **2.** $1\tfrac{1}{2} \times 2\tfrac{1}{2}$ **3.** $2\tfrac{1}{4} \times 1\tfrac{3}{4}$

4. $\tfrac{3}{4} \times 1\tfrac{1}{2}$ **5.** $2\tfrac{1}{4} \times \tfrac{2}{3}$ **6.** $1\tfrac{3}{4} \times \tfrac{2}{3}$

7. $2\tfrac{1}{8} \times 4$ **8.** $1\tfrac{1}{2} \times 6$ **9.** $3\tfrac{1}{2} \times \tfrac{1}{7}$

10. $1\tfrac{3}{5} \times 1\tfrac{2}{3}$ **11.** $2\tfrac{2}{3} \times \tfrac{5}{8}$ **12.** $4\tfrac{1}{2} \times 2\tfrac{1}{2}$

2-2 K

Find the products in reduced form:

1. $\tfrac{3}{4} \times \tfrac{2}{3}$ **2.** $\tfrac{1}{2} \times \tfrac{4}{9}$ **3.** $\tfrac{3}{5} \times \tfrac{5}{12}$

4. $\tfrac{1}{2} \times 6$ **5.** $\tfrac{2}{3} \times 9$ **6.** $\tfrac{2}{3} \times 12$

7. $\tfrac{4}{5} \times 10$ **8.** $\tfrac{3}{4} \times 16$ **9.** $\tfrac{3}{4} \times \tfrac{1}{6}$

10. $\tfrac{7}{8} \times \tfrac{1}{7}$ **11.** $\tfrac{5}{8} \times 8$ **12.** $\tfrac{1}{4} \times \tfrac{4}{5}$

2-2 L

Find the products in reduced form:

1. $2\tfrac{3}{4} \times 1\tfrac{7}{8}$ **2.** $3\tfrac{1}{2} \times 4\tfrac{3}{4}$ **3.** $1\tfrac{2}{5} \times \tfrac{5}{12}$

4. $3\tfrac{3}{4} \times 2\tfrac{5}{8}$ **5.** $1\tfrac{7}{8} \times 1\tfrac{3}{5}$ **6.** $2\tfrac{1}{2} \times \tfrac{1}{2}$

7. $2\tfrac{3}{8} \times 2$ **8.** $12\tfrac{1}{2} \times 2\tfrac{3}{5}$ **9.** $6\tfrac{2}{3} \times 1\tfrac{1}{2}$

10. $3\tfrac{5}{16} \times 1\tfrac{1}{3}$ **11.** $2\tfrac{4}{5} \times 2\tfrac{1}{7}$ **12.** $5\tfrac{3}{5} \times 2\tfrac{3}{4}$

2-2 M

We find a fraction of a number n by multiplying. Thus if $n = 16$ and the fraction is $\frac{3}{4}$, then $\frac{3}{4} \times \frac{16}{1} = \frac{48}{4} = 12$.

1. Find $\frac{2}{3}$ of 18.
2. A housewife started shopping with $40 and finished shopping with only $\frac{3}{8}$ of this amount. How much did she spend?
3. By April 15, the Anders family had spent $\frac{2}{3}$ of their monthly food budget. If their food budget was $174 per month, how much had they spent?
4. An electrician found that $\frac{1}{6}$ of his base monthly pay of $840 was deducted for income tax. How much tax did he pay per month?
5. Find $\frac{1}{2}$ of $\frac{1}{2}$.
6. Find $\frac{1}{2}$ of $\frac{3}{4}$.
7. A salesman received a commission of $\frac{2}{15}$ of his sales. If his sales amounted to $220, find his commission.
8. A building worth $18,275 is assessed at $\frac{4}{5}$ of its value. Find the assessed value of the building.
9. Water weighs about $62\frac{1}{2}$ pounds per cubic foot. Find the weight of $7\frac{3}{5}$ cubic feet of water.
10. The Automobile Manufacturers Association found that $\frac{3}{5}$ of the car trips in the United States are for less than 5 miles. In one community 35,750 car trips were made in 1 day. How many of these trips would you expect to be less than 5 miles?

2-2 N

1. Find:
   (a) $\frac{4}{5} \times \frac{2}{3}$ (b) $\frac{2}{3} \times \frac{4}{5}$
2. Does $1\frac{1}{2}$ times $2\frac{3}{8}$ give the same product as $2\frac{3}{8}$ times $1\frac{1}{2}$? Explain.
3. From Exercises 1–2 does it appear that $a/b \times c/d$, $b \neq 0$ and $d \neq 0$, gives the same answer as $c/d \times a/b$?
4. Do the rational numbers appear to be commutative for multiplication? Explain.
5. If p and q are rational numbers, will $p \times q$ be a rational number? For example consider that

$$8 \times 7 = 56, \quad 6 \times \frac{3}{5} = \frac{18}{5}, \quad 2\frac{1}{2} \times 5\frac{2}{3} = \frac{85}{6}.$$

Are these answers in the set of rational numbers? Name the property illustrated.

Exercises 2–2 N continued on page 78.

6. Solve for r:

(a) $\dfrac{1}{4} \times \dfrac{4}{1} = r$ (b) $2\dfrac{1}{2} \times \dfrac{2}{5} = r$ (c) $\dfrac{2}{3} \times \dfrac{3}{2} = r$

(d) $\dfrac{5}{6} \times \dfrac{6}{5} = r$ (e) $\dfrac{e}{f} \times \dfrac{f}{e} = r$ (f) $\dfrac{s}{k} \times \dfrac{k}{s} = r$

7. If a and b are rational numbers, $a \neq 0$ and $b \neq 0$, then we call a/b the reciprocal of b/a. Find the product of a/b and its reciprocal. (*Note:* b/a is the reciprocal of a/b, and a/b is the reciprocal of b/a.)

8. Find Z:

(a) $Z \times \frac{2}{3} = 1$ (b) $Z \times \frac{3}{5} = 1$

(c) $Z \times \frac{3}{2} = 1$ (d) $Z \times 1\frac{1}{5} = 1$

(e) $Z \times \frac{8}{3} = 1$ (f) $Z \times 3\frac{3}{4} = 1$

9. Solve (remember to perform operations within parentheses first):

(a) $n = (\frac{1}{2} \times \frac{2}{3}) \times \frac{5}{8}$ (b) $m = \frac{1}{2} \times (\frac{2}{3} \times \frac{5}{8})$

(c) $f = (1\frac{1}{2} \times \frac{4}{5}) \times \frac{2}{3}$ (d) $g = 1\frac{1}{2} \times (\frac{4}{5} \times \frac{2}{3})$

(e) In parts (a) and (b) does $m = n$? In parts (c) and (d) does $f = g$?

10. If a, b, c, d, e, and f are integers ($b \neq 0$, $d \neq 0$, and $f \neq 0$), does it appear that

$$\left(\frac{a}{b} \times \frac{c}{d}\right) \times \frac{e}{f} = \frac{a}{b} \times \left(\frac{c}{d} \times \frac{e}{f}\right)?$$

Name this law.

2-2 O

Solve for n:

1. $\frac{2}{3} \times \frac{7}{8} \times \frac{3}{4} = n$ **2.** $\frac{5}{6} \times \frac{2}{3} \times \frac{1}{2} = n$

3. $\frac{5}{6} \times \frac{3}{4} \times \frac{2}{5} = n$ **4.** $\frac{4}{5} \times \frac{5}{8} \times \frac{3}{2} = n$

5. $\frac{7}{9} \times \frac{3}{5} \times \frac{7}{10} = n$ **6.** $1\frac{1}{2} \times \frac{2}{3} \times \frac{7}{8} = n$

7. $2\frac{1}{2} \times 2\frac{3}{4} \times 5 = n$ **8.** $4\frac{1}{2} \times 2\frac{2}{3} \times 1\frac{1}{2} = n$

9. $4 \times 3\frac{3}{4} \times 1\frac{5}{16} = n$ **10.** $5\frac{3}{16} \times 2\frac{2}{3} \times 4\frac{7}{8} = n$

2-2 P

1. A gallon contains 8 pints. Find the number of pints in $\frac{3}{4}$ of 2 gallons.

2. A student received $\frac{3}{2}$ of the average on his test. Find his score if the average was 60.

3. Find the number of seconds in $\frac{5}{9}$ of an hour.

4. In the United States $\frac{13}{100}$ of all car drivers are between the ages of 20 and 25. Out of 5600 drivers how many are in this age bracket?

5. In 1963, $\frac{9}{25}$ of all public school students in the United States rode buses to school. If a local school district has 25,575 students, find the number of students expected to ride buses.

6. Fred has read $\frac{2}{5}$ of a history book which is 460 pages long. Jim has read $\frac{3}{4}$ of his book which is 364 pages long. Which boy has read the greater number of pages?

7. The height of the RCA building in New York is $\frac{17}{25}$ the height of the Empire State building. The Empire State building is 1250 feet high. Find the height of the RCA building.

8. How many hours are there in $13\frac{7}{8}$ days?

9. Find the number of seconds in $2\frac{4}{5}$ hours.

10. Alcohol contains, by weight, 24 parts carbon, 16 parts oxygen, and 6 parts hydrogen.

   (a) What fraction of alcohol is carbon?

   (b) Find the number of pounds of oxygen in 138 pounds of alcohol.

2-2 Q

Solve for m:

1. $1\frac{1}{2} \times \frac{2}{3} \times 4 = m$
2. $2 \times \frac{3}{4} \times \frac{1}{2} = m$
3. $4\frac{1}{2} \times 2\frac{1}{3} \times \frac{3}{4} = m$
4. $1\frac{3}{4} \times 4 \times \frac{5}{7} = m$
5. $4 \times \frac{3}{4} \times \frac{1}{2} = m$
6. $4\frac{1}{2} \times 1\frac{1}{2} \times 3 = m$
7. $16 \times \frac{3}{4} \times \frac{2}{3} = m$
8. $4\frac{1}{2} \times \frac{7}{9} \times \frac{5}{16} = m$
9. $3\frac{1}{4} \times 4 \times 1\frac{2}{3} = m$
10. $7\frac{1}{3} \times 3\frac{3}{4} \times \frac{1}{2} = m$
11. $5\frac{1}{3} \times \frac{7}{8} \times 2\frac{1}{4} = m$
12. $3\frac{6}{11} \times 1\frac{9}{13} \times 2\frac{5}{6} = m$

2-2 R

Find:

1. $\frac{2}{5}$ of $20
2. $1\frac{3}{8}$ of $10
3. $\frac{3}{4}$ of $60\frac{1}{2}$
4. $1\frac{1}{2}$ of $150
5. $\frac{2}{3}$ of $162
6. $\frac{9}{10}$ of $100
7. $\frac{5}{8}$ of $240
8. $2\frac{1}{2}$ of $8
9. $\frac{1}{4}$ of $18\frac{1}{2}$
10. $2\frac{2}{3}$ of $9
11. $5\frac{3}{8}$ of $240
12. $\frac{7}{10}$ of $750

2-2 S

Find:

1. $\frac{3}{4}$ of 16 feet   **2.** $\frac{1}{3}$ of 24 feet   **3.** $\frac{2}{5}$ of 60 feet

4. $\frac{3}{8}$ of 120 feet   **5.** $\frac{3}{5}$ of 40 yards   **6.** $\frac{1}{4}$ of 170 yards

7. $\frac{2}{5}$ of 180 yards   **8.** $\frac{9}{5}$ of 20 yards   **9.** $2\frac{1}{2}$ of 8 inches

10. $\frac{2}{7}$ of 21 inches   **11.** $1\frac{1}{2}$ of 8 inches   **12.** $5\frac{3}{4}$ of 10 inches

2-2 T

In Exercises 1–9 if a statement is true, mark it true. If it is false, write a replacement for the symbol $(<, =, >)$ to make it true.

1. $(\frac{2}{3} \times 6) < 6$ **2.** $(\frac{2}{3} \times 8) < 8$ **3.** $(\frac{3}{8} \times 8) > 8$

4. $(\frac{4}{5} \times 10) < 10$ **5.** $(\frac{1}{4} \times 16) > 16$ **6.** $(\frac{7}{16} \times 8) < 8$

7. $(\frac{3}{4} \times 12) < 12$ **8.** $(\frac{4}{7} \times 21) > 21$ **9.** $(\frac{5}{11} \times 13) > 13$

10. If $0 < \dfrac{a}{b} < 1$ and $n > 0$, does it appear that $\dfrac{a}{b} \times n < n$?

■ 2-3 DIVISION OF FRACTIONS

If e and f represent rational numbers such that $e \times f = 1$, then f is called the **reciprocal**, or multiplicative inverse, of e and e is the reciprocal of f. For example, since $\frac{3}{4} \times \frac{4}{3} = 1$, then $\frac{4}{3}$ is the reciprocal of $\frac{3}{4}$.

If a, b, c, and d represent numbers ($b \neq 0$, $c \neq 0$, and $d \neq 0$) then we establish IV as the law for division of fractions.

$$\frac{a}{b} \div \frac{c}{d} = \frac{\dfrac{a}{b}}{\dfrac{c}{d}} = \frac{\dfrac{a}{b} \times \dfrac{d}{c}}{\dfrac{c}{d} \times \dfrac{d}{c}}$$

Here we multiply by 1 in the form $\dfrac{\dfrac{d}{c}}{\dfrac{d}{c}}$.

$$= \frac{\dfrac{a}{b} \times \dfrac{d}{c}}{1}$$

Note that $\dfrac{d}{c}$ is the reciprocal of $\dfrac{c}{d}$:

$$\frac{c}{d} \times \frac{d}{c} = 1.$$

$$= \frac{ad}{bc}$$

This is true by the definition of multiplication.

Thus we have proved law IV.

$$\textbf{IV.} \qquad \frac{a}{b} \div \frac{c}{d} = \frac{ad}{bc}$$

For example,

$$2 \div \frac{3}{4} = \frac{2}{\frac{3}{4}} = \frac{2 \times \frac{4}{3}}{\frac{3}{4} \times \frac{4}{3}} = \frac{\frac{2}{1} \times \frac{4}{3}}{1} = \frac{8}{3}, \tag{1}$$

$$\frac{4}{5} \div 5 = \frac{\frac{4}{5}}{5} = \frac{\frac{4}{5} \times \frac{1}{5}}{\frac{5}{1} \times \frac{1}{5}} = \frac{\frac{4}{5} \times \frac{1}{5}}{1} = \frac{4}{25}, \tag{2}$$

$$1\frac{1}{2} \div 2\frac{3}{4} = \frac{\frac{3}{2}}{\frac{11}{4}} = \frac{\frac{3}{2} \times \frac{4}{11}}{\frac{11}{4} \times \frac{4}{11}} = \frac{\frac{3}{2} \times \frac{4}{11}}{1} = \frac{12}{22} = \frac{6}{11}. \tag{3}$$

This process can be stated in the following way: to divide a number by a fraction, we multiply the number by the reciprocal of the fraction.

$$\textbf{V.} \qquad n \div \frac{a}{b} = \frac{n}{1} \times \frac{b}{a}$$

Observe that in IV we wrote

$$\frac{\dfrac{a}{b}}{\dfrac{c}{d}}$$

This is called a complex fraction. A **complex fraction** has a fraction in its numerator, or in its denominator, or in both. For example,

$$\frac{\dfrac{3}{4}}{\dfrac{2}{5}}, \quad \frac{\dfrac{1}{2}}{\dfrac{2}{3}}, \quad \text{and} \quad \frac{5}{\dfrac{2}{3}}$$

are complex fractions.

Remember that if

$$an = b, \ a \neq 0,$$

then

$$n = b/a.$$

For example,

$$\text{if } 3n = 15, \text{ then } n = \frac{15}{3} = 5. \tag{4}$$

So, if a is a fraction, we solve in the same way. Thus

$$\text{if } \frac{2}{3}n = 10, \text{ then } n = \frac{10}{\frac{2}{3}} = 15. \tag{5}$$

Exercises for Section 2-3

2-3 A

1. What number of 5-dollar bills is equivalent to one 20-dollar bill? Is the answer $20 \div 5$?

2. What number of dimes is equivalent to 1 dollar? Is the answer $1 \div \frac{1}{10}$? Is the answer $1 \times \frac{10}{1}$?

3. What number of quarters is equivalent to 2 dollars? Is the answer $2 \div \frac{1}{4}$? Is the answer $2 \times \frac{4}{1}$?

4. What number of half-dollars is equivalent to 5 dollars? Is the answer $5 \div \frac{1}{2}$? Is the answer $5 \times \frac{2}{1}$?

5. Does $2 + 2 + 2 + 2 = 8$? Does $4 \times 2 = 8$? Does $8 \div 2 = 4$?

6. Does $\frac{1}{2} + \frac{1}{2} + \frac{1}{2} + \frac{1}{2} = 2$? Does $4 \times \frac{1}{2} = 2$? Does $2 \div \frac{1}{2} = 4$?

7. Does $\frac{2}{3} + \frac{2}{3} + \frac{2}{3} = 2$? Does $3 \times \frac{2}{3} = 2$? Does $2 \div \frac{2}{3} = 3$?

8. Does $4 \times \frac{1}{2} = 2$? Does $2 \div \frac{1}{2} = 4$?

9. Does $2 \times \frac{1}{4} = \frac{1}{2}$? Does $\frac{1}{2} \div \frac{1}{4} = 2$? Does $\frac{1}{2} \times \frac{4}{1} = 2$?

10. Does $3 \times \frac{1}{4} = \frac{3}{4}$? Does $\frac{3}{4} \div \frac{1}{4} = 3$? Does $\frac{3}{4} \times \frac{4}{1} = 3$?

11. In each exercise, 1–10, can we multiply by the reciprocal of the divisor to divide?

2-3 B

1. Does 8 ones ÷ 2 ones = 8 ÷ 2? Does $8 \div 2 = 8 \times \frac{1}{2}$?

2. Does 6 tens ÷ 3 tens = 6 ÷ 3? Does $60 \div 30 = 60 \times \frac{1}{30}$?

3. Does 8 fourths ÷ 2 fourths = 8 ÷ 2? Does $\frac{8}{4} \div \frac{2}{4} = \frac{8}{4} \times \frac{4}{2}$?

4. Does 6 tenths ÷ 3 tenths = 6 ÷ 3? Does $\frac{6}{10} \div \frac{3}{10} = \frac{6}{10} \times \frac{10}{3}$?

5. Does $\frac{6}{8} \div \frac{3}{8} = 6 \div 3$? Does $\frac{6}{8} \div \frac{3}{8} = \frac{6}{8} \times \frac{8}{3}$?

6. Does $\frac{1}{2} \div \frac{1}{4} = \frac{2}{4} \div \frac{1}{4} = 2 \div 1$? Does $\frac{1}{2} \div \frac{1}{4} = \frac{1}{2} \times \frac{4}{1}$?

7. Does $\frac{1}{3} \div \frac{1}{12} = \frac{4}{12} \div \frac{1}{12} = 4 \div 1$? Does $\frac{1}{3} \div \frac{1}{12} = \frac{1}{3} \times \frac{12}{1}$?

8. Does $\frac{4}{5} \div \frac{2}{15} = \frac{12}{15} \div \frac{2}{15} = 12 \div 2$? Does $\frac{4}{5} \div \frac{2}{15} = \frac{4}{5} \times \frac{15}{2}$?

2-3 C

In Exercises 1–6 refer to Figure 2–8. Count spaces to obtain your answers.

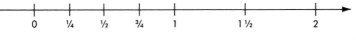

FIGURE 2–8

1. Do you see that $4 \times \frac{1}{2} = 2$? Then does $2 \div \frac{1}{2} = 4$?

2. Do you see that $2 \times \frac{1}{2} = 1$? Then does $1 \div \frac{1}{2} = 2$?

3. Do you see that $2 \times \frac{1}{4} = \frac{1}{2}$? Then does $\frac{1}{2} \div \frac{1}{4} = 2$?

4. Do you see that $3 \times \frac{1}{4} = \frac{3}{4}$? Then does $\frac{3}{4} \div \frac{1}{4} = 3$?

5. Do you see that $7 \times \frac{1}{4} = \frac{7}{4}$? Then does $\frac{7}{4} \div \frac{1}{4} = 7$?

6. Do you see that $3 \times \frac{1}{2} = \frac{3}{2}$? Then does $\frac{3}{2} \div \frac{1}{2} = 3$?

7. Check Exercises 1–6, by multiplying by the reciprocal.

    (a) Does $2 \div \frac{1}{2} = 2 \times \frac{2}{1}$?   (b) Does $1 \div \frac{1}{2} = 1 \times \frac{2}{1}$?

    (c) Does $\frac{1}{2} \div \frac{1}{4} = \frac{1}{2} \times \frac{4}{1}$?   (d) Does $\frac{3}{4} \div \frac{1}{4} = \frac{3}{4} \times \frac{4}{1}$?

    (e) Does $\frac{7}{4} \div \frac{1}{4} = \frac{7}{4} \times \frac{4}{1}$?   (f) Does $\frac{3}{2} \div \frac{1}{2} = \frac{3}{2} \times \frac{2}{1}$?

2-3 D

Write a reciprocal for each of the following:

1. $\frac{2}{5}$ **2.** $\frac{3}{8}$ **3.** $\frac{7}{9}$

4. $\frac{7}{8}$ **5.** $\frac{9}{10}$ **6.** $\frac{4}{5}$

7. 1   **8.** 2   **9.** 5

10. $1\frac{1}{2}$ **11.** $2\frac{3}{4}$ **12.** $3\frac{7}{12}$

2–3 E

Simplify each complex fraction by multiplying the numerator and denominator by the reciprocal of the denominator.

1. $\dfrac{\frac{3}{4}}{\frac{2}{3}}$ 2. $\dfrac{\frac{1}{2}}{\frac{1}{4}}$ 3. $\dfrac{\frac{1}{2}}{\frac{1}{3}}$ 4. $\dfrac{4}{\frac{2}{3}}$

5. $\dfrac{3}{\frac{1}{2}}$ 6. $\dfrac{4}{\frac{3}{8}}$ 7. $\dfrac{1}{\frac{3}{4}}$ 8. $\dfrac{2}{1\frac{1}{2}}$

9. $\dfrac{3}{1\frac{2}{3}}$ 10. $\dfrac{\frac{1}{2}}{3}$ 11. $\dfrac{\frac{3}{8}}{4}$ 12. $\dfrac{\frac{5}{6}}{6}$

2–3 F

Simplify:

1. $\dfrac{1\frac{1}{2}}{\frac{2}{3}}$ 2. $\dfrac{2\frac{3}{4}}{\frac{1}{2}}$ 3. $\dfrac{1\frac{3}{8}}{\frac{2}{3}}$ 4. $\dfrac{\frac{3}{4}}{1\frac{1}{2}}$

5. $\dfrac{2\frac{1}{2}}{\frac{7}{8}}$ 6. $\dfrac{1\frac{3}{4}}{\frac{5}{8}}$ 7. $\dfrac{1\frac{1}{4}}{1\frac{1}{2}}$ 8. $\dfrac{2\frac{3}{4}}{1\frac{1}{8}}$

9. $\dfrac{1\frac{2}{3}}{2\frac{1}{2}}$ 10. $\dfrac{2\frac{5}{8}}{1\frac{3}{4}}$ 11. $\dfrac{4\frac{2}{3}}{2\frac{1}{3}}$ 12. $\dfrac{6\frac{3}{4}}{1\frac{1}{8}}$

2–3 G

Find each quotient by inspection:

1. $\frac{4}{3} \div 2$ 2. $\frac{2}{3} \div 2$ 3. $\frac{4}{9} \div 2$

4. $\frac{5}{6} \div 5$ 5. $\frac{3}{8} \div 3$ 6. $\frac{1}{3} \div 1$

7. $1 \div \frac{1}{3}$ 8. $2 \div \frac{1}{4}$ 9. $\frac{1}{4} \div 2$

10. $3 \div \frac{2}{3}$ 11. $\frac{2}{3} \div 3$ 12. $1 \div 4$

2–3 H

Find the quotients:

1. $2 \div 1\frac{1}{2}$ 2. $4 \div 2\frac{3}{4}$ 3. $2 \div 1\frac{5}{8}$

4. $2 \div 1\frac{3}{8}$ 5. $4 \div 2\frac{1}{6}$ 6. $2 \div 1\frac{5}{6}$

7. $5 \div 2\frac{1}{4}$ 8. $3 \div 1\frac{1}{2}$ 9. $7 \div 4\frac{2}{3}$

10. $2 \div 1\frac{1}{4}$ 11. $8 \div 3\frac{5}{9}$ 12. $7 \div 8\frac{2}{5}$

2-3 I

Solve for x:

1. $\frac{2}{3} \div \frac{3}{2} = x$ 2. $\frac{3}{4} \div \frac{4}{3} = x$ 3. $\frac{3}{8} \div \frac{1}{4} = x$
4. $\frac{1}{4} \div \frac{3}{8} = x$ 5. $\frac{7}{12} \div \frac{3}{4} = x$ 6. $\frac{3}{4} \div \frac{7}{12} = x$
7. $\frac{11}{16} \div \frac{1}{2} = x$ 8. $\frac{5}{8} \div \frac{3}{4} = x$ 9. $\frac{7}{8} \div \frac{11}{16} = x$
10. $\frac{5}{8} \div \frac{3}{16} = x$ 11. $\frac{7}{12} \div \frac{5}{6} = x$ 12. $\frac{9}{10} \div \frac{3}{8} = x$

2-3 J

Find the quotients:

1. $\frac{3}{4} \div \frac{3}{8}$ 2. $\frac{5}{9} \div \frac{2}{3}$ 3. $\frac{3}{4} \div \frac{2}{3}$
4. $\frac{9}{10} \div \frac{2}{5}$ 5. $\frac{3}{5} \div \frac{9}{10}$ 6. $\frac{7}{10} \div \frac{4}{5}$
7. $\frac{7}{8} \div \frac{3}{4}$ 8. $\frac{7}{12} \div \frac{5}{6}$ 9. $\frac{11}{12} \div \frac{3}{4}$
10. $\frac{15}{16} \div \frac{5}{8}$ 11. $\frac{5}{8} \div \frac{15}{16}$ 12. $\frac{7}{16} \div \frac{7}{8}$

2-3 K

Solve for n:

1. $1\frac{1}{2} \div 2\frac{1}{4} = n$ 2. $2\frac{1}{4} \div 1\frac{1}{2} = n$ 3. $1\frac{3}{4} \div 4\frac{2}{3} = n$
4. $4\frac{1}{4} \div 1\frac{1}{4} = n$ 5. $3\frac{2}{3} \div 6\frac{5}{9} = n$ 6. $2\frac{5}{8} \div 2\frac{2}{5} = n$
7. $2\frac{5}{16} \div 2\frac{1}{2} = n$ 8. $3\frac{1}{2} \div 1\frac{3}{4} = n$ 9. $1\frac{3}{4} \div 3\frac{1}{2} = n$
10. $1\frac{1}{2} \div 3\frac{1}{2} = n$ 11. $5\frac{3}{8} \div 2\frac{11}{16} = n$ 12. $2\frac{3}{16} \div 4\frac{3}{8} = n$

2-3 L

Find the quotients:

1. $2\frac{5}{6} \div 1\frac{3}{8}$ 2. $1\frac{2}{3} \div 3\frac{5}{6}$ 3. $2\frac{3}{4} \div 5\frac{1}{2}$
4. $4\frac{1}{3} \div 1\frac{1}{2}$ 5. $6\frac{5}{6} \div 1\frac{3}{8}$ 6. $4\frac{9}{10} \div 2\frac{7}{10}$
7. $6\frac{1}{2} \div 3\frac{1}{4}$ 8. $1\frac{5}{8} \div 8\frac{1}{2}$ 9. $4\frac{5}{16} \div 7\frac{1}{2}$
10. $3\frac{11}{10} \div 2\frac{3}{8}$ 11. $5\frac{2}{5} \div 3\frac{3}{5}$ 12. $18\frac{3}{4} \div 5\frac{5}{8}$

2-3 M

Solve for n:

1. $\frac{1}{2}n = 10$ 2. $\frac{1}{3}n = 8$ 3. $\frac{3}{5}n = 12$
4. $\frac{5}{6}n = 15$ 5. $\frac{7}{10}n = 21$ 6. $\frac{5}{9}n = 25$
7. $\frac{5}{12}n = 30$ 8. $1\frac{1}{2}n = 12$ 9. $2\frac{1}{3}n = 14$
10. $3\frac{1}{5}n = 48$ 11. $7\frac{1}{2}n = 60$ 12. $12\frac{1}{2}n = 400$

2-3 N

1. A chef uses $\frac{3}{4}$ pound of coffee to make 1 urn of coffee. How many urns of coffee will he be able to make from 16 pounds of coffee?

2. To catch a plane leaving in $\frac{19}{20}$ of an hour, a man must drive $26\frac{1}{2}$ miles. Find his average speed, in miles per hour, if he wishes to arrive at the airport $\frac{1}{5}$ hour before the plane leaves.

3. If each length of pipe is $2\frac{3}{4}$ feet long, how many lengths of pipe can be cut from a pipe $25\frac{1}{2}$ feet long?

4. A cube of butter weighs $\frac{1}{4}$ pound. Find the number of cubes in $18\frac{1}{2}$ pounds of butter.

5. A bus traveled 98 miles in $1\frac{3}{4}$ hours. Find its average speed.

6. On a blueprint, $\frac{1}{4}$ inch stands for 25 feet. Find the length of a wall which is $15\frac{3}{4}$ inches long on the blueprint.

7. Find the price of butter per pound if 12 pounds cost $\$8\frac{3}{4}$. Give the answer as a fraction of a dollar.

8. A cubic foot of space holds about $7\frac{1}{2}$ gallons of water. Find the number of cubic feet of space in a container that holds 96 gallons of water.

9. The flow from a pipeline will load $\frac{2}{5}$ of a tank car in 1 hour. Find the time required to fill 1 tank car.

10. A farmer finds that he uses about $\frac{5}{8}$ bushel of seed wheat per acre of land. Find the amount of seed needed if he intends to plant 345 acres.

2-3 O

1. What whole number does not have a reciprocal? Explain.

2. Solve for n:

   (a) $n = \frac{2}{3} \div 3$ (b) $n = 3 \div \frac{2}{3}$ (c) $\frac{4}{5} \div \frac{3}{4} = n$

   (d) $\frac{3}{4} \div \frac{4}{5} = n$ (e) $1\frac{1}{2} \div 2\frac{1}{3} = n$ (f) $2\frac{1}{3} \div 1\frac{1}{2} = n$

3. If p and q are rational numbers, $q \neq 0$, then is p/q a rational number? (*Note:* Consider Exercise 2(a) with $p = \frac{2}{3}$ and $q = 3$. Study other answers in Exercise 2.)

4. From Exercises 2 and 3, does it appear that the rational numbers are closed for division? Explain.

5. Does $\frac{2}{3} \div \frac{4}{5} = \frac{4}{5} \div \frac{2}{3}$? Explain.

6. Does $2\frac{1}{2} \div 4 = 4 \div 2\frac{1}{2}$? Explain.

7. Is division of rational numbers commutative?

2-3 P

1. Find n if 16 is $\frac{3}{4}$ of n.
2. Find x if 25 is $\frac{3}{10}$ of x.
3. The number 38 is $\frac{1}{2}$ of what number?
4. In a student body election Alan received $\frac{7}{8}$ of all the votes cast. Find the total vote cast if he received 1232 votes.
5. In a certain county, property is assessed at $\frac{5}{8}$ of its value. Find the value of property assessed at \$14,720.
6. A flywheel makes 1 revolution in $\frac{3}{4}$ seconds. Find the number of revolutions per minute (rpm).
7. After a workman had installed 16 windows in an apartment building, he calculated that he had installed $\frac{2}{5}$ of the windows. Find the total number of windows.
8. If $73\frac{3}{4}$ yards of material is used to make 30 shirts, find the number of yards of material needed to make 1 shirt.
9. A man earned \$310 in 40 hours. Find his hourly wage.
10. On a map a distance of 80 miles is represented by $1\frac{3}{8}$ inch. Find the number of inches needed to represent 152 miles.

2-3 Q

1. If 6 pounds is $\frac{1}{3}$ of a load, find the weight w of the load. (*Note:* $\frac{1}{3}w = 6$.)
2. If 6 pounds is $\frac{1}{4}$ of a load, find the weight w of the load.
3. If 8 pounds is $\frac{1}{2}$ of a load, find the weight w of the load.
4. If 12 pounds is $\frac{1}{2}$ of a load, find the weight w of the load.
5. If 16 pounds is $\frac{1}{4}$ of a load, find the weight w of the load.
6. If 15 pounds is $\frac{2}{5}$ of a load, find the weight w of the load.
7. If 15 pounds is $\frac{3}{5}$ of a load, find the weight w of the load.
8. If 18 pounds is $\frac{2}{3}$ of a load, find the weight w of the load.

2-3 R

1. If 8 miles is $\frac{1}{8}$ of a trip, find the distance t for the trip. (*Note:* $\frac{1}{8}t = 8$.)
2. As in Exercise 1, let t represent the number of miles in a trip; p, the fractional part; d, the number of miles in the part. Then $pt = d$. Find t for each ordered pair (p, d):
   (a) $(\frac{1}{8}, 16)$ (b) $(\frac{3}{8}, 8)$ (c) $(\frac{5}{8}, 8)$
   (d) $(\frac{7}{8}, 8)$ (e) $(\frac{7}{10}, 14)$ (f) $(\frac{3}{10}, 12)$
   (g) $(\frac{7}{3}, 14)$ (h) $(\frac{2}{3}, 19)$ (i) $(\frac{5}{2}, 150)$

■ 2-4 PRIME NUMBERS AND THE LEAST COMMON MULTIPLE

A natural number which is greater than 1 and is divisible only by itself and 1 is called a **prime number**. For example, 2, 3, 5, 7, 11, and 13 are primes. Natural numbers not prime are called **composite numbers**; 15 is composite since it is divisible by 5 and 3. The number 1 is considered neither prime nor composite.

A whole number divisible by 2 is called an **even number**; the other whole numbers are called **odd numbers**. So, we have the set E of even numbers and the set O of odd numbers:

$$E = \{0, 2, 4, 6, \ldots\},$$
$$O = \{1, 3, 5, 7, \ldots\}.$$

All the numbers by which a number n is divisible are called the **factors** of n. For example, the set of all the factors of 24 is $\{1, 2, 3, 4, 6, 8, 12, 24\}$. Thus we can write $24 = 3 \times 8$, $24 = 4 \times 6$, and so on. When a number is written as a product of its prime factors, we call this its **prime factored form**. For example, $2 \times 2 \times 2 \times 3$ is the prime factored form of 24.

A **fundamental fact (theorem)** of arithmetic states that a given number has only one (that is, a unique) prime factored form. The order of the factors does not change the form. For example,

$$2 \times 3 \times 2 \times 2 = 2 \times 2 \times 3 \times 2 = 24.$$

The following method may be used to find the prime factors of a number.

$$
\begin{array}{r|l}
2 & 360 \\ \hline
2 & 180 \\ \hline
3 & 90 \\ \hline
2 & 30 \\ \hline
3 & 15 \\ \hline
  & 5
\end{array}
$$

We choose small prime factors and divide as shown; we continue until we reach a prime quotient. We find   (1)

$360 = 2 \times 2 \times 2 \times 3 \times 3 \times 5.$

The smallest number which is divisible by each of a set of numbers is called the **least common multiple (l.c.m.)**. For example, 12 is the l.c.m. of 2, 3, and 4, since it is the smallest natural number divisible by 2, 3, and 4.

The l.c.m. can be found in this way:

Step 1. Express each number in its prime factored form.

Step 2. The l.c.m. must contain each factor of step 1 the greatest number of times that this factor occurs in any one set of factors.

Example 1. Find the l.c.m. of 24, 18, and 20.

$$24 = 2 \times 2 \times 2 \times 3$$
$$18 = 3 \times 3 \times 2$$
$$20 = 2 \times 2 \times 5$$

The l.c.m. must contain the factors 2, 3, and 5, but it must have

$$2 \times 2 \times 2$$

since 2 occurs three times as a factor of 24. It must have

$$3 \times 3,$$

since 3 occurs twice as a factor of 18. The l.c.m. is

$$2 \times 2 \times 2 \times 3 \times 3 \times 5 = 360,$$

This statement can be shortened thus:

$$\text{l.c.m. } (24, 18, 20) = 2^3 \times 3^2 \times 5$$
$$= 360.$$

The greatest common divisor (g.c.d.) of a set of numbers is the greatest common factor of the set.

Example 2. Find the g.c.d. of 12, 30, and 24.

$$12 = 2 \times 2 \times 3$$ Common factors are 2 and 3. We write
$$30 = 5 \times 3 \times 2$$ g.c.d. (12, 30, 24) = 6.
$$24 = 2 \times 2 \times 2 \times 3$$

The symbol **l.c.m.** (*a, b, c*) means "the least common multiple of *a, b,* and *c.*" The symbol **g.c.d.** (*a, b, c*) means "the greatest common divisor of *a, b,* and *c.*"

In higher mathematics many rules for the divisibility of numbers have been developed. Listed below are some of the rules most often used.

1. Any number is divisible by 2 if its final digit is 0, 2, 4, 6, or 8.
2. Any number is divisible by 3 if the sum of its digits is divisible by 3. For example, 17,250 is divisible by 3 since

$$\frac{1 + 7 + 2 + 5 + 0}{3} = 5.$$

3. A number is divisible by 4 if the last two digits of the number express a number which is divisible by 4. For example, 17,232 is divisible by 4 since $\frac{32}{4} = 8$.
4. A number is divisible by 5 if its final digit is 0 or 5.
5. If rules 1 and 2 are true for a number, then the number is divisible by 6.
6. A number is divisible by 9 if the sum of its digits is divisible by 9. For example, 16,587 is divisible by 9 since

$$\frac{1 + 6 + 5 + 8 + 7}{9} = 3.$$

Exercises for Section 2-4

2-4 A

Express in prime factored form:

1. 10	**2.** 6	**3.** 15
4. 14	**5.** 21	**6.** 30
7. 35	**8.** 26	**9.** 39
10. 22	**11.** 65	**12.** 33

2-4 B

Express in prime factored form:

1. 4	**2.** 25	**3.** 9
4. 8	**5.** 27	**6.** 125
7. 16	**8.** 49	**9.** 81
10. 32	**11.** 100	**12.** 28

2-4 C

Express in prime factored form:

1. 30	**2.** 42	**3.** 70
4. 105	**5.** 20	**6.** 18
7. 54	**8.** 36	**9.** 50
10. 45	**11.** 180	**12.** 48

2-4 D

Express in prime factored form:

1. 60	**2.** 84	**3.** 96
4. 175	**5.** 34	**6.** 51
7. 38	**8.** 76	**9.** 120
10. 144	**11.** 205	**12.** 98

2-4 E

To find all pairs of whole numbers (a, b) such that $ab = 40$, we find this set of pairs: $\{(1, 40), (2, 20), (4, 10), (5, 8)\}$. Find all such pairs (a, b) so that ab equals:

1. 4	**2.** 8	**3.** 6
4. 12	**5.** 14	**6.** 10
7. 25	**8.** 30	**9.** 42
10. 48	**11.** 50	**12.** 38

2-4 F

Refer to the directions for 2-4 E, and find the set of pairs (a, b):

1. 32	**2.** 35	**3.** 45
4. 52	**5.** 54	**6.** 60
7. 72	**8.** 76	**9.** 80
10. 100	**11.** 110	**12.** 120

2-4 G

Refer to the directions for 2-4 E, and find the set of pairs (a, b):

1. 112	**2.** 130	**3.** 124
4. 144	**5.** 125	**6.** 150
7. 200	**8.** 204	**9.** 212
10. 220	**11.** 225	**12.** 240

2-4 H

To write a number in prime factored form, we try prime numbers as divisors. For a large number, this may mean a lot of work, particularly if the number is prime. We will develop a rule which will save time.

Consider factoring 31:

$$31 \div 2 = 15\tfrac{1}{2},$$
$$31 \div 3 = 10\tfrac{1}{3},$$
$$31 \div 5 = 6\tfrac{1}{5},$$
$$31 \div 7 = 4\tfrac{3}{7}.$$

None of these quotients is a whole number. We need not try a prime larger than 7 for the following reason. If 31 were divisible by a prime greater than 7, then the quotient would be less than 7. For example, $7 \times 7 = 49$; if $7 \times n = 31$, then $n < 7$. We have already tried prime divisors of 7 or less. Therefore we can conclude that 31 is a prime number.

Consider factoring 73. We will try these primes: 2, 3, 5, 7, and 11.

$$73 \div 2 = 36\tfrac{1}{2}$$
$$73 \div 3 = 24\tfrac{1}{3}$$
$$73 \div 5 = 14\tfrac{3}{5}$$
$$73 \div 7 = 10\tfrac{3}{7}$$
$$73 \div 11 = 6\tfrac{7}{11}$$

We need not try other divisors since $11 \times 11 = 121$. Any larger divisor would produce a quotient smaller than 11. We have tried all such smaller primes as factors. Hence 73 is prime.

Observe this property of numbers:

To factor a number n (or to determine whether it is prime), we try the primes 2, 3, 5, ..., x as divisors. We choose x as the smallest prime such that $x^2 \geq n$.

The symbol $\geq$ is read, "is greater than or equal to"; also, $\leq$ is read, "is less than or equal to." Thus for 31 above, we need try no prime larger than 7 since $7^2 > 31$. For 73, we need try no prime larger than 11 since $11^2 > 73$.

In Exercises 1–12 determine whether the number is prime or composite. If it is composite, write it in prime factored form.

1. 23	**2.** 37
3. 51	**4.** 47
5. 61	**6.** 71
7. 39	**8.** 57
9. 73	**10.** 91

2-4 I

In Exercises 1–12 determine whether the number is prime or composite. If it is composite, write it in prime factored form.

1. 43	**2.** 53	**3.** 73	**4.** 101
5. 117	**6.** 127	**7.** 211	**8.** 237
9. 251	**10.** 301	**11.** 323	**12.** 1001

2-4 J

Let $S(n)$, read "S of n," stand for the sum of all the factors of a number n. For example, $S(12) = 1 + 2 + 3 + 4 + 6 + 12 = 28$. Find $S(n)$ for the following:

1. $n = 4$	**2.** $n = 6$	**3.** $n = 8$	**4.** $n = 9$
5. $n = 7$	**6.** $n = 10$	**7.** $n = 15$	**8.** $n = 20$
9. $n = 13$	**10.** $n = 16$	**11.** $n = 22$	**12.** $n = 30$

2-4 K

Mark each statement true or false (see 2–4 J):

1. $S(2) + S(6) = S(8)$	**2.** $S(3) + S(9) = S(12)$
3. $S(6) + S(10) = S(16)$	**4.** $S(4) \times S(6) = S(24)$
5. $S(2) \times S(5) = S(14)$	**6.** $S(7) \times S(8) = S(40)$
7. $S(16) - S(8) = S(8)$	**8.** $S(20) - S(2) = S(18)$
9. $S(36) - S(11) = S(32)$	**10.** $S(12) \times S(12) = 1400$

2-4 L

Find the least common multiple (l.c.m.):

1. 4, 7	**2.** 3, 5	**3.** 4, 6	**4.** 3, 4
5. 4, 8	**6.** 2, 10	**7.** 4, 5	**8.** 10, 12
9. 6, 8	**10.** 3, 6	**11.** 3, 8	**12.** 4, 12

2-4 M

Find the l.c.m.:

1. 2, 3, 4	**2.** 2, 3, 5	**3.** 3, 4, 6	**4.** 2, 3, 8
5. 3, 4, 5	**6.** 2, 4, 5	**7.** 4, 8, 3	**8.** 3, 5, 6
9. 2, 3, 6	**10.** 4, 5, 6	**11.** 3, 6, 8	**12.** 3, 8, 12

2-4 N

Find the l.c.m.:

1. 4, 5, 10	**2.** 4, 6, 10	**3.** 3, 6, 10	**4.** 3, 4, 8
5. 4, 5, 8	**6.** 5, 6, 7	**7.** 2, 3, 4, 8	**8.** 2, 3, 4, 6
9. 2, 4, 5, 8	**10.** 2, 4, 5, 6	**11.** 4, 6, 8, 10	**12.** 4, 6, 5, 12

2-4 O

Find the l.c.m.:

1. 5, 10, 15	**2.** 2, 5, 20	**3.** 3, 5, 20	**4.** 2, 5, 15
5. 3, 6, 15	**6.** 2, 3, 16	**7.** 2, 3, 5, 12	**8.** 4, 5, 8, 10
9. 3, 5, 6, 8	**10.** 3, 6, 8, 12	**11.** 4, 5, 8, 12	**12.** 8, 15, 20, 24

2-4 P

Solve for x:

1. g.c.d. $(3, 6, 9) = x$	**2.** g.c.d. $(4, 10, 12) = x$
3. g.c.d. $(5, 10, 20) = x$	**4.** g.c.d. $(6, 9, 21) = x$
5. g.c.d. $(12, 16, 24) = x$	**6.** g.c.d. $(6, 8, 10) = x$
7. g.c.d. $(4, 8, 15) = x$	**8.** g.c.d. $(6, 10, 12, 14) = x$
9. g.c.d. $(10, 25, 35, 40) = x$	**10.** g.c.d. $(4, 17, 51) = x$

2-4 Q

If a set of numbers has g.c.d. $= 1$, the numbers are called **relatively prime.** Find the g.c.d. and tell which sets are relatively prime:

1. {2, 5, 8}	**2.** {17, 51}	**3.** {7, 17, 21}
4. {8, 40, 64}	**5.** {3, 6, 9}	**6.** {10, 12, 13}
7. {10, 12, 21}	**8.** {4, 6, 8, 9}	**9.** {23, 24, 25, 26}
10. {12, 18, 21}	**11.** {12, 15, 24, 32}	**12.** {6, 18, 42}

13. Let A be the set of factors of 10; B, the set of factors of 15. Then $A = \{1, 2, 5, 10\}$ and $B = \{1, 3, 5, 15\}$. Also, g.c.d. $(10, 15)$ is the largest element of $A \cap B$. Find this element.

14. As in Exercise 13, find g.c.d. $(14, 28, 56)$.

■ 2–5 ADDITION OF FRACTIONS

Consider Figure 2–9.

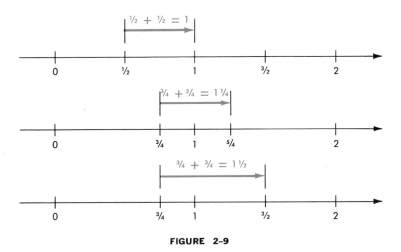

FIGURE 2–9

By counting spaces, do you see that:

$$\frac{1}{2} + \frac{1}{2} = \frac{1+1}{2} = \frac{2}{2} = 1?$$

$$\frac{3}{4} + \frac{2}{4} = \frac{3+2}{4} = \frac{5}{4} = 1\frac{1}{4}?$$

$$\frac{3}{4} + \frac{3}{4} = \frac{3+3}{4} = \frac{6}{4} = 1\frac{1}{2}?$$

If a, b, and c represent numbers, $b \neq 0$, then VI is true.

$$\textbf{VI.} \qquad \frac{a}{b} + \frac{c}{b} = \frac{a+c}{b}$$

For example, we have

$$\tfrac{5}{8} + \tfrac{7}{8} = \tfrac{12}{8}, \tag{1}$$

that is, 5 eighths + 7 eighths = 12 eighths. As another example,

$$5\tfrac{1}{3} + 1\tfrac{2}{3} = \tfrac{16}{3} + \tfrac{5}{3} = \tfrac{21}{3}. \tag{2}$$

If a, b, c, and d represent numbers, $b \neq 0$ and $d \neq 0$, then VII follows.

VII. $$\frac{a}{b} + \frac{c}{d} = \frac{ad}{bd} + \frac{cb}{db} = \frac{ad + cb}{bd}$$

For example, we have

$$\frac{3}{4} + \frac{2}{5} = \frac{3 \times 5}{4 \times 5} + \frac{2 \times 4}{5 \times 4} = \frac{15}{20} + \frac{8}{20} = \frac{23}{20}. \tag{3}$$

Also,

$$2\frac{3}{5} + 1\frac{3}{8} = \frac{13}{5} + \frac{11}{8} = \frac{13 \times 8}{5 \times 8} + \frac{11 \times 5}{8 \times 5} = \frac{159}{40}. \tag{4}$$

In VII, bd is called the **common denominator.** To add a set of fractions, we can use the product of all the denominators as a common denominator.

Example 1. Find $\frac{3}{4} + \frac{7}{8} + \frac{1}{2}$.

$$\frac{3}{4} + \frac{7}{8} + \frac{1}{2} = \frac{3 \times 8 \times 2}{4 \times 8 \times 2} + \frac{7 \times 4 \times 2}{8 \times 4 \times 2} + \frac{1 \times 4 \times 8}{2 \times 4 \times 8}$$

$$= \frac{48}{64} + \frac{56}{64} + \frac{32}{64}$$

$$= \frac{136}{64} = \frac{17}{8}$$

This same problem can be worked more quickly by using 8 as the common denominator:

$$\frac{3}{4} + \frac{7}{8} + \frac{1}{2} = \frac{3 \times 2}{4 \times 2} + \frac{7}{8} + \frac{1 \times 4}{2 \times 4} = \frac{6 + 7 + 4}{8} = \frac{17}{8}.$$

Here 8 is the **least common denominator.**

The **least common denominator** (l.c.d.) of a set of fractions is the least common multiple of the denominators of the fractions. For example, the l.c.d. of $\frac{3}{4}$, $\frac{5}{6}$, and $\frac{7}{12}$ is 12 since

$$\text{l.c.m. } (4, 6, 12) = 12.$$

In addition of fractions we use the principle $n \times 1 = n$ and the lowest common denominator as shown in Examples 2 and 3.

Example 2. Find $\frac{3}{4} + \frac{5}{6} + \frac{7}{12}$.

$$\frac{3}{4} = \frac{3 \times 3}{4 \times 3} = \frac{9}{12} \qquad \text{Note, } \frac{3}{4} \times \frac{3}{3} = \frac{3}{4} \times 1.$$

$$\frac{5}{6} = \frac{5 \times 2}{6 \times 2} = \frac{10}{12} \qquad \text{Note, } \frac{5}{6} \times \frac{2}{2} = \frac{5}{6} \times 1.$$

$$\frac{7}{12} = \qquad\qquad \frac{7}{12}$$

$$\frac{26}{12} = 2\frac{2}{12} = 2\frac{1}{6}$$

Example 3. Find $1\frac{2}{3} + 3\frac{4}{5} + 2\frac{3}{8} + 3\frac{7}{12}$.

$$1\frac{2}{3} = 1\frac{80}{120}$$
$$3\frac{4}{5} = 3\frac{96}{120}$$
$$2\frac{3}{8} = 2\frac{45}{120}$$
$$3\frac{7}{12} = 3\frac{70}{120}$$

Here we first find the sum of the whole numbers; we then write each fraction in terms of the l.c.d. and add.

$$9\frac{291}{120} = 9 + 2\frac{51}{120} = 11\frac{51}{120}, \text{ that is, } 11\frac{17}{40}$$

Exercises for Section 2-5

2-5 A

Find s by inspection:

1. $s = \frac{1}{4} + \frac{3}{4}$ **2.** $s = \frac{3}{8} + \frac{7}{8}$ **3.** $s = \frac{1}{3} + \frac{2}{3}$

4. $s = \frac{1}{2} + \frac{1}{2}$ **5.** $s = \frac{2}{3} + \frac{2}{3}$ **6.** $s = \frac{5}{6} + \frac{5}{6}$

7. $s = \frac{7}{8} + \frac{5}{8}$ **8.** $s = \frac{1}{8} + \frac{5}{8}$ **9.** $s = \frac{7}{12} + \frac{5}{12}$

10. $s = \frac{4}{5} + \frac{3}{5}$ **11.** $s = \frac{1}{5} + \frac{3}{5}$ **12.** $s = \frac{7}{16} + \frac{11}{16}$

2-5 B

Solve for x, y, and s:

1. $\dfrac{1}{2} + \dfrac{2}{3} = \dfrac{x}{6} + \dfrac{y}{6} = s$ **2.** $\dfrac{3}{4} + \dfrac{5}{8} = \dfrac{x}{8} + \dfrac{y}{8} = s$

3. $\dfrac{3}{2} + \dfrac{3}{7} = \dfrac{x}{14} + \dfrac{y}{14} = s$ **4.** $\dfrac{5}{6} + \dfrac{3}{4} = \dfrac{x}{12} + \dfrac{y}{12} = s$

5. $3 + \dfrac{2}{3} = \dfrac{x}{3} + \dfrac{y}{3} = s$ **6.** $\dfrac{2}{5} + \dfrac{7}{4} = \dfrac{x}{20} + \dfrac{y}{20} = s$

Exercises 2–5 B continued on page 98.

7. $\dfrac{5}{9} + \dfrac{7}{12} = \dfrac{x}{36} + \dfrac{y}{36} = s$ **8.** $\dfrac{7}{8} + \dfrac{5}{12} = \dfrac{x}{24} + \dfrac{y}{24} = s$

9. $\dfrac{5}{6} + \dfrac{7}{8} = \dfrac{x}{24} + \dfrac{y}{24} = s$ **10.** $\dfrac{2}{3} + \dfrac{5}{4} = \dfrac{x}{12} + \dfrac{y}{12} = s$

11. $\dfrac{5}{7} + \dfrac{7}{5} = \dfrac{x}{35} + \dfrac{y}{35} = s$ **12.** $\dfrac{3}{4} + \dfrac{13}{30} = \dfrac{x}{60} + \dfrac{26}{y} = s$

2-5 C

Solve for m:

1. $m = \frac{1}{2} + \frac{1}{3}$ **2.** $m = \frac{1}{2} + \frac{1}{5}$ **3.** $m = \frac{1}{2} + \frac{3}{10}$

4. $m = \frac{1}{2} + \frac{2}{3}$ **5.** $m = \frac{1}{2} + \frac{5}{7}$ **6.** $m = \frac{1}{2} + \frac{3}{5}$

7. $m = \frac{1}{4} + \frac{1}{3}$ **8.** $m = \frac{3}{4} + \frac{3}{5}$ **9.** $m = \frac{2}{3} + \frac{1}{8}$

10. $m = \frac{1}{2} + \frac{4}{5}$ **11.** $m = \frac{2}{3} + \frac{3}{5}$ **12.** $m = \frac{5}{7} + \frac{1}{2}$

2-5 D

Find each sum:

1. $\frac{1}{2} + \frac{1}{3} + \frac{1}{4}$ **2.** $\frac{1}{2} + \frac{2}{3} + \frac{3}{4}$ **3.** $\frac{2}{3} + \frac{1}{4} + \frac{1}{2}$

4. $\frac{2}{3} + \frac{3}{4} + \frac{5}{8}$ **5.** $\frac{1}{3} + \frac{3}{4} + \frac{7}{8}$ **6.** $\frac{2}{3} + \frac{1}{4} + \frac{3}{8}$

7. $\frac{5}{8} + \frac{1}{2} + \frac{1}{3}$ **8.** $\frac{7}{8} + \frac{2}{3} + \frac{3}{4}$ **9.** $\frac{3}{4} + \frac{2}{3} + \frac{1}{6}$

10. $\frac{3}{4} + \frac{5}{8} + \frac{15}{16}$ **11.** $\frac{1}{2} + \frac{7}{8} + \frac{7}{12}$ **12.** $\frac{2}{5} + \frac{3}{10} + \frac{3}{4}$

2-5 E

Solve for x:

1. $1\frac{1}{2} + \frac{3}{4} = x$ **2.** $2\frac{1}{2} + \frac{5}{8} = x$ **3.** $3\frac{1}{2} + \frac{11}{12} = x$

4. $\frac{1}{2} + 2\frac{2}{3} = x$ **5.** $1\frac{1}{3} + \frac{7}{9} = x$ **6.** $2\frac{3}{8} + \frac{3}{4} = x$

7. $1\frac{1}{4} + 1\frac{1}{2} = x$ **8.** $1\frac{1}{3} + 1\frac{1}{2} = x$ **9.** $2\frac{1}{2} + 3\frac{3}{4} = x$

10. $3\frac{2}{3} + 1\frac{5}{12} = x$ **11.** $1\frac{5}{6} + 2\frac{1}{2} = x$ **12.** $2\frac{2}{3} + 1\frac{7}{9} = x$

2-5 F

Add:

1. $2\frac{1}{2}$ **2.** $3\frac{2}{3}$ **3.** $1\frac{3}{4}$ **4.** $2\frac{4}{9}$
$\quad 1\frac{3}{4}$ $\quad 5\frac{5}{6}$ $\quad 2\frac{5}{8}$ $\quad 3\frac{3}{4}$
$\quad 3\frac{5}{8}$ $\quad 1\frac{1}{3}$ $\quad 1\frac{5}{16}$ $\quad 2\frac{5}{12}$

5. $2\frac{7}{8}$ **6.** $2\frac{2}{3}$ **7.** $3\frac{3}{4}$ **8.** $5\frac{5}{8}$
$\quad 4\frac{1}{3}$ $\quad 4\frac{1}{2}$ $\quad 2\frac{2}{5}$ $\quad 2\frac{7}{9}$
$\quad 5\frac{1}{2}$ $\quad 3\frac{5}{8}$ $\quad 5\frac{3}{10}$ $\quad 4\frac{3}{4}$

2-5 G

Add:

1. $5\frac{1}{2}$	**2.** $4\frac{1}{2}$	**3.** $12\frac{1}{4}$	**4.** $7\frac{1}{2}$
$2\frac{5}{12}$	$2\frac{3}{4}$	$2\frac{5}{8}$	$3\frac{4}{5}$
$3\frac{2}{3}$	$5\frac{7}{9}$	$5\frac{1}{3}$	$2\frac{3}{10}$
	$2\frac{1}{2}$		$5\frac{3}{3}$

5. $3\frac{7}{8}$	**6.** $2\frac{1}{2}$	**7.** $1\frac{3}{4}$	**8.** $13\frac{1}{2}$
$2\frac{3}{4}$	$12\frac{3}{4}$	$2\frac{5}{16}$	$24\frac{2}{3}$
$3\frac{2}{3}$	$32\frac{5}{16}$	$1\frac{5}{8}$	$13\frac{7}{12}$
	$19\frac{5}{8}$		$21\frac{5}{9}$

2-5 H

Solve for n:

1. $n = 1\frac{3}{4} + 2\frac{2}{3} + \frac{5}{8}$ **2.** $n = 20\frac{1}{2} + 15\frac{1}{3} + 2\frac{7}{8}$

3. $n = 3\frac{4}{5} + 5\frac{7}{10} + 4\frac{1}{2}$ **4.** $n = 5\frac{3}{5} + 2\frac{3}{4} + 7\frac{5}{6}$

5. $n = \frac{2}{3} + \frac{3}{4} + 1\frac{1}{2} + \frac{7}{8}$ **6.** $n = 1\frac{1}{2} + 1\frac{3}{4} + 1\frac{7}{8} + 1\frac{11}{16}$

7. $n = 5\frac{2}{3} + 9\frac{3}{4} + 8\frac{1}{2} + 4\frac{3}{5}$ **8.** $n = 16\frac{5}{8} + 12\frac{3}{8} + 11\frac{13}{16} + 20\frac{3}{4}$

2-5 I

1. In the hop, skip, and jump event an athlete hopped $5\frac{1}{3}$ feet, skipped $5\frac{1}{4}$ feet, and jumped $5\frac{7}{8}$ feet. Find his total distance.
2. A contractor needed the total length of the side of a building. The plans give the lengths as shown. Find the total length.

FIGURE 2-10

3. An investment group bought 35 shares of Polex at $22\frac{1}{2}$ per share, 40 shares of Iron Works at $56\frac{3}{4}$ per share, and 32 shares of E.B.M. at $18\frac{7}{8}$ per share. Find the total cost of this investment. Write your answer as a mixed number of dollars.
4. Four heirs to an estate received $\frac{1}{4}$, $\frac{1}{8}$, $\frac{1}{3}$, and $\frac{2}{9}$ of the estate. The rest was left to charity. If the estate was valued at $14,400, what amount went to charity?

Exercises 2-5 I continued on page 100.

5. A machine part consists of 5 pieces with these measurements: $6\frac{5}{16}$ inches, $7\frac{1}{2}$ inches, $4\frac{3}{4}$ inches, 3 inches, and $\frac{11}{16}$ inch. Find the over-all length.

6. The loin from half a beef was cut into several different parts. Find the weight of the loin if its parts and corresponding weights were as follows: fat, $5\frac{3}{4}$ pounds; bones, $6\frac{1}{2}$ pounds; flank, $10\frac{1}{4}$ pounds; waste, $3\frac{1}{4}$ pounds; tenderloin, $6\frac{1}{2}$ pounds; sirloin, $13\frac{3}{4}$ pounds.

7. Six men worked the following hours on a job: 27 hours, 25 minutes; 18 hours, 35 minutes; 16 hours, 20 minutes; 16 hours, 45 minutes; 17 hours, 55 minutes; 24 hours, 24 minutes. Find the average time worked per man. Give your answer as a mixed number of hours.

8. A city playfield has 4 sides with lengths of $25\frac{3}{4}$ feet, $28\frac{1}{2}$ feet, $30\frac{5}{16}$ feet, and $24\frac{15}{16}$ feet. Find the cost to enclose the playfield if the fencing costs $\frac{3}{4}$ dollar per foot.

9. A carpenter needs these pieces of framing lumber: 12, each $14\frac{1}{2}$ feet long; 4, each $18\frac{3}{4}$ feet long; 18, each $8\frac{7}{8}$ feet long. Find the total length of the pieces.

10. The sides of a field are straight lines with these dimensions: $16\frac{2}{3}$ feet, $20\frac{1}{2}$ feet, $19\frac{3}{4}$ feet, and $24\frac{7}{8}$ feet. Find the distance around the field.

2-5 J

Find the total of these lengths:

1. $4\frac{5}{8}$ ft and $3\frac{1}{2}$ ft

2. $2\frac{9}{10}$ ft and $7\frac{3}{5}$ ft

3. $16\frac{2}{3}$ ft and $10\frac{5}{8}$ ft

4. $12\frac{3}{4}$ ft and $9\frac{7}{12}$ ft

5. $3\frac{15}{16}$ ft and $3\frac{7}{8}$ ft

6. $2\frac{1}{2}$ ft, $4\frac{3}{8}$ ft, and $2\frac{5}{12}$ ft

7. $1\frac{1}{12}$ ft, $3\frac{5}{6}$ ft, and $4\frac{1}{2}$ ft

8. $9\frac{3}{8}$ ft, $4\frac{1}{4}$ ft, and $12\frac{1}{2}$ ft

9. $3\frac{3}{4}$ ft, $2\frac{5}{8}$ ft, and $\frac{11}{16}$ ft

10. $9\frac{3}{4}$ ft, $\frac{9}{16}$ ft, 5 ft, and $\frac{2}{3}$ ft

2-5 K

Find the total number of dollars:

1. \$3 and \$4$\frac{1}{2}$

2. \$2$\frac{2}{3}$ and \$$\frac{5}{6}$

3. \$1$\frac{1}{2}$ and \$2$\frac{1}{2}$

4. \$12$\frac{3}{4}$ and \$17$\frac{7}{8}$

5. \$4$\frac{5}{8}$ and \$3$\frac{5}{12}$

6. \$2$\frac{1}{2}$, \$3$\frac{1}{4}$, and \$5$\frac{3}{4}$

7. \$2$\frac{1}{4}$, \$5$\frac{1}{3}$, and \$12$\frac{3}{4}$

8. \$4$\frac{1}{2}$, \$$\frac{7}{8}$, and \$16$\frac{3}{4}$

9. \$18$\frac{1}{4}$, \$31$\frac{2}{5}$, and \$19$\frac{9}{10}$

10. \$8$\frac{3}{10}$, \$17$\frac{4}{5}$, \$3$\frac{1}{2}$, and \$1$\frac{17}{20}$

2–5 L

We can simplify a complex fraction such as

$$\frac{\frac{1}{2} + \frac{3}{4}}{\frac{2}{3} + \frac{5}{8}}$$

by multiplying the numerator and denominator by the l.c.d. of all the fractions. Hence

$$\frac{24(\frac{1}{2} + \frac{3}{4})}{24(\frac{2}{3} + \frac{5}{8})} = \frac{12 + 18}{16 + 15}$$

$$= \frac{30}{31}.$$

Simplify:

1. $\dfrac{\frac{1}{2} + \frac{2}{3}}{\frac{3}{4}}$

2. $\dfrac{\frac{1}{4} + \frac{1}{4}}{\frac{2}{3}}$

3. $\dfrac{\frac{7}{8} + \frac{3}{4}}{\frac{1}{2}}$

4. $\dfrac{\frac{3}{2} + \frac{3}{4}}{\frac{5}{8}}$

5. $\dfrac{\frac{3}{4} + \frac{1}{2}}{\frac{5}{8} + \frac{1}{4}}$

6. $\dfrac{\frac{2}{3} + \frac{5}{12}}{\frac{3}{8} + \frac{1}{2}}$

7. $\dfrac{\frac{3}{8} + \frac{1}{2}}{\frac{5}{9} + \frac{1}{3}}$

8. $\dfrac{\frac{1}{3} + \frac{11}{12}}{\frac{1}{2} + \frac{3}{4}}$

9. $\dfrac{\frac{2}{3} + \frac{3}{4} + \frac{1}{8}}{\frac{1}{2} + \frac{2}{3}}$

10. $\dfrac{\frac{1}{2} + 2 + \frac{3}{4}}{\frac{1}{5} + \frac{3}{10}}$

11. $\dfrac{4 + \frac{7}{8} + 1\frac{1}{2}}{\frac{3}{4} + \frac{5}{8}}$

12. $\dfrac{\frac{1}{2} + 2\frac{3}{4} + \frac{5}{8}}{\frac{1}{2} + \frac{11}{8}}$

2–5 M

Simplify:

1. $\dfrac{\frac{3}{4} + \frac{5}{8}}{2 + \frac{1}{2}}$

2. $\dfrac{1 + \frac{3}{7}}{\frac{3}{10} + \frac{1}{5}}$

3. $\dfrac{\frac{4}{5} + \frac{3}{10} + 1}{\frac{4}{5} + \frac{1}{2}}$

4. $\dfrac{1 + \frac{2}{5} + \frac{1}{3}}{\frac{7}{15} + \frac{2}{5}}$

5. $\dfrac{1\frac{1}{3} + \frac{5}{12}}{\frac{3}{4} + \frac{5}{16}}$

6. $\dfrac{\frac{4}{9} + \frac{2}{3} + \frac{1}{2}}{\frac{1}{3} + \frac{1}{4}}$

7. $\dfrac{\frac{3}{4} + \frac{3}{5} + 2}{\frac{4}{9} + \frac{1}{2}}$

8. $\dfrac{\frac{3}{8} + 1 + \frac{7}{5}}{\frac{13}{20} + \frac{1}{2}}$

9. $\dfrac{\frac{1}{2} + \frac{3}{4} + 1\frac{1}{2}}{\frac{1}{4} + \frac{1}{8} + \frac{5}{12}}$

10. $\dfrac{\frac{2}{3} + \frac{3}{4} + \frac{3}{8}}{\frac{1}{2} + \frac{1}{4} + \frac{1}{3}}$

11. $\dfrac{4 + \frac{2}{3} + \frac{1}{2}}{\frac{1}{4} + \frac{5}{12} + \frac{1}{2}}$

12. $\dfrac{\frac{3}{5} + \frac{2}{3} + \frac{1}{2}}{\frac{17}{30} + \frac{11}{15} + \frac{3}{5}}$

2-5 N

Solve:

1. $m = \dfrac{3}{\frac{3}{4}} + \dfrac{\frac{1}{2}}{\frac{3}{4}}$

2. $n = (3 + \frac{1}{2}) \div \frac{3}{4}$

3. $x = \frac{6}{2} + \frac{8}{2}$

4. $y = \dfrac{6 + 8}{2}$

5. $p = \dfrac{\frac{2}{3}}{1\frac{1}{2}} + \dfrac{\frac{5}{8}}{1\frac{1}{2}}$

6. $q = (\frac{2}{3} + \frac{5}{8}) \div 1\frac{1}{2}$

7. $s = (2\frac{2}{3} + 1\frac{11}{15}) \div 1\frac{4}{11}$

8. $t = \dfrac{2\frac{2}{3}}{1\frac{4}{11}} + \dfrac{1\frac{11}{15}}{1\frac{4}{11}}$

2-5 O

Solve the equations in Exercises 1–8:

1. $m = \frac{2}{3} + (\frac{1}{2} + 2)$

2. $n = (\frac{2}{3} + \frac{1}{2}) + 2$

3. $x = 1\frac{2}{3} + (3\frac{1}{2} + \frac{3}{4})$

4. $y = (1\frac{2}{3} + 3\frac{1}{2}) + \frac{3}{4}$

5. $p = (2\frac{5}{8} + \frac{1}{2}) + 3$

6. $q = 2\frac{5}{8} + (\frac{1}{2} + 3)$

7. $r = 1\frac{5}{8} + (2 + 5)$

8. $s = (1\frac{5}{8} + 2) + 5$

9. If p, q, and r are rational numbers, does it appear to you that $(p + q) + r = p + (q + r)$? What is this law called?

2-5 P

Solve the equations in Exercises 1–8:

1. $l = \frac{5}{8} \times (\frac{1}{2} + \frac{1}{4})$

2. $m = (\frac{5}{8} \times \frac{1}{2}) + (\frac{5}{8} \times \frac{1}{4})$

3. $n = (2 \times 1\frac{1}{2}) + (2 \times \frac{3}{4})$

4. $z = 2 \times (1\frac{1}{2} + \frac{3}{4})$

5. $p = \frac{2}{3} \times (\frac{3}{8} + 2)$

6. $q = (\frac{2}{3} \times \frac{3}{8}) + (\frac{2}{3} \times 2)$

7. $r = (\frac{7}{16} \times \frac{3}{4}) + (\frac{7}{16} + \frac{7}{8})$

8. $s = \frac{7}{16} (\frac{3}{4} + \frac{7}{8})$

9. If p, q, and r are rational numbers, does it appear to you that $p \times (q + r) = (p \times q) + (p \times r)$? What is this law called?

2-5 Q

Solve for x:

1. $x + \frac{1}{2} = \frac{5}{8}$

2. $x + \frac{2}{3} = \frac{11}{12}$

3. $x + \frac{3}{4} = \frac{13}{16}$

4. $x + \frac{5}{6} = 1$

5. $x + \frac{7}{8} = 2\frac{1}{4}$

6. $x + \frac{5}{6} = 2\frac{1}{3}$

7. $x + \frac{1}{8} = \frac{1}{6}$

8. $x + \frac{7}{8} = 1\frac{5}{6}$

9. $x + 3\frac{1}{4} = 4\frac{1}{2}$

10. $x + 7\frac{1}{8} = 9$

11. $x + 12\frac{1}{4} = 13\frac{1}{3}$

12. $x + 25\frac{1}{6} = 30\frac{1}{8}$

2–5 R

Solve for x:

1. $x - \frac{1}{2} = \frac{7}{8}$ **2.** $x - \frac{1}{3} = \frac{3}{4}$ **3.** $x - \frac{5}{8} = \frac{1}{4}$

4. $x - \frac{3}{4} = \frac{5}{6}$ **5.** $x - 3\frac{1}{3} = 3\frac{1}{3}$ **6.** $x - 2\frac{1}{2} = 2\frac{1}{2}$

7. $x - 5\frac{1}{8} = 5\frac{1}{8}$ **8.** $x - 12\frac{1}{2} = 12\frac{1}{2}$ **9.** $x - 3\frac{5}{6} = 2\frac{1}{3}$

10. $x - 7\frac{3}{5} = 2\frac{1}{10}$ **11.** $x - 4\frac{1}{2} = 3\frac{1}{10}$ **12.** $x - 7\frac{1}{3} = 4\frac{7}{10}$

■ 2–6 SUBTRACTION OF FRACTIONS

Consider Figure 2–11.

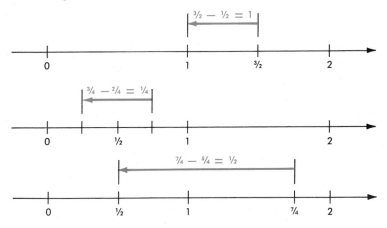

FIGURE 2–11

By counting spaces, do you see that

$$\frac{3}{2} - \frac{1}{2} = \frac{3-1}{2} = \frac{2}{2} = 1?$$

$$\frac{3}{4} - \frac{2}{4} = \frac{3-2}{4} = \frac{1}{4}?$$

$$\frac{7}{4} - \frac{5}{4} = \frac{7-5}{4} = \frac{2}{4} = \frac{1}{2}?$$

When a, b, and c represent numbers, $b \neq 0$, we find that VIII is true.

$$\text{VIII.} \qquad \frac{a}{b} - \frac{c}{b} = \frac{a-c}{b}$$

When a, b, c, and d are numbers, $b \neq 0$ and $d \neq 0$, then we find that IX is true.

$$\text{IX.} \qquad \frac{a}{b} - \frac{c}{d} = \frac{ad}{bd} - \frac{cb}{bd} = \frac{ad - cb}{bd}$$

Example 1. Find $\frac{3}{4} - \frac{2}{5}$.

$$\frac{3}{4} - \frac{2}{5} = \frac{3 \times 5}{4 \times 5} - \frac{2 \times 4}{5 \times 4}$$

$$= \frac{15 - 8}{20} = \frac{7}{20}$$

Although IX will apply to the subtraction of any two rational numbers, it is sometimes easier to write the fractional parts in terms of their l.c.d. and then apply VIII.

Example 2. Find $3\frac{3}{4} - 1\frac{1}{3}$.

$$3\frac{3}{4} - 1\frac{1}{3} = 3\frac{9}{12} - 1\frac{4}{12}$$

$$= 2\frac{5}{12}.$$

Consider this example with "borrowing":

Example 3. Solve: $n = 4\frac{1}{3} - 1\frac{2}{3}$.

$n = 4\frac{1}{3} - 1\frac{2}{3}$ Since $\frac{2}{3} > \frac{1}{3}$, we write $4\frac{1}{3} = 3 + \frac{3}{3} + \frac{1}{3} = 3\frac{4}{3}$.

$n = 3\frac{4}{3} - 1\frac{2}{3}$

$n = 2\frac{2}{3}$

Exercises for Section 2-6

2-6 A

Find the differences by inspection:

1. $\frac{3}{4} - \frac{1}{4}$ **2.** $\frac{7}{8} - \frac{3}{8}$ **3.** $\frac{1}{2} - \frac{1}{2}$ **4.** $\frac{7}{12} - \frac{1}{2}$

5. $\frac{11}{12} - \frac{5}{12}$ **6.** $\frac{7}{16} - \frac{3}{16}$ **7.** $\frac{1}{2} - \frac{1}{4}$ **8.** $\frac{3}{4} - \frac{1}{2}$

9. $1 - \frac{1}{4}$ **10.** $1 - \frac{2}{3}$ **11.** $2 - \frac{3}{4}$ **12.** $\frac{1}{2} - \frac{1}{3}$

2–6 B

Solve for y:

1. $y = \frac{3}{4} - \frac{1}{2}$
2. $y = \frac{7}{8} - \frac{1}{2}$
3. $y = \frac{3}{4} - \frac{3}{8}$
4. $y = \frac{11}{16} - \frac{1}{2}$
5. $y = \frac{2}{3} - \frac{1}{5}$
6. $y = \frac{4}{5} - \frac{3}{10}$
7. $y = \frac{7}{8} - \frac{2}{3}$
8. $y = \frac{7}{12} - \frac{2}{5}$
9. $y = \frac{2}{3} - \frac{4}{9}$
10. $y = \frac{5}{8} - \frac{1}{3}$
11. $y = \frac{1}{2} - \frac{3}{16}$
12. $y = \frac{2}{3} - \frac{7}{12}$

2–6 C

Solve for n:

1. $\frac{11}{16} - \frac{3}{8} = n$
2. $\frac{7}{8} - \frac{2}{3} = n$
3. $\frac{1}{2} - \frac{1}{5} = n$
4. $\frac{7}{12} - \frac{1}{3} = n$
5. $\frac{1}{2} - \frac{3}{10} = n$
6. $\frac{5}{8} - \frac{1}{5} = n$
7. $\frac{3}{4} - \frac{2}{5} = n$
8. $\frac{11}{15} - \frac{2}{3} = n$
9. $\frac{2}{3} - \frac{4}{15} = n$
10. $\frac{13}{16} - \frac{1}{3} = n$
11. $\frac{7}{8} - \frac{11}{24} = n$
12. $\frac{17}{24} - \frac{5}{16} = n$

2–6 D

Find the differences:

1. $1\frac{3}{4} - \frac{1}{2}$
2. $1\frac{1}{2} - \frac{1}{3}$
3. $1\frac{1}{2} - \frac{3}{8}$
4. $2\frac{2}{3} - 1\frac{1}{6}$
5. $4\frac{7}{8} - 1\frac{1}{3}$
6. $3\frac{1}{2} - 1\frac{1}{4}$
7. $4\frac{1}{2} - 1\frac{1}{3}$
8. $3\frac{7}{8} - 1\frac{1}{4}$
9. $2\frac{1}{2} - 1\frac{1}{3}$
10. $6\frac{3}{4} - 3\frac{3}{8}$
11. $13\frac{3}{4} - 5\frac{2}{3}$
12. $15\frac{13}{16} - 9\frac{2}{3}$

2–6 E

Find the differences:

1. $2\frac{1}{2} - 1\frac{3}{4}$
2. $4\frac{1}{3} - 1\frac{2}{3}$
3. $5\frac{1}{4} - 2\frac{3}{4}$
4. $4\frac{3}{8} - 1\frac{7}{8}$
5. $3\frac{7}{12} - 1\frac{11}{12}$
6. $4 - 1\frac{1}{2}$
7. $5 - 3\frac{2}{3}$
8. $4 - 3\frac{7}{12}$
9. $6 - 2\frac{4}{5}$
10. $4\frac{1}{2} - 1\frac{5}{8}$
11. $5\frac{3}{8} - 2\frac{7}{12}$
12. $6\frac{1}{3} - 2\frac{1}{2}$

2–6 F

Subtract:

1. $4\frac{11}{16}$
   $1\frac{1}{2}$

2. $3\frac{1}{3}$
   $1\frac{4}{5}$

3. $4\frac{1}{4}$
   $2\frac{3}{5}$

4. $5\frac{1}{3}$
   $2\frac{3}{5}$

5. $6\frac{3}{8}$
   $2\frac{2}{3}$

6. $8\frac{1}{2}$
   $5\frac{23}{32}$

7. $4\frac{7}{16}$
   $1\frac{25}{32}$

8. $9\frac{5}{8}$
   $4\frac{13}{16}$

9. $7\frac{3}{4}$
   $5\frac{15}{16}$

10. $4\frac{1}{8}$
    $2\frac{2}{3}$

11. $7\frac{1}{2}$
    $2\frac{11}{15}$

12. $14\frac{1}{4}$
    $9\frac{11}{15}$

2-6 G

Find the differences:

1. $4 - 2\frac{11}{16}$ **2.** $7 - 3\frac{31}{32}$ **3.** $8 - 4\frac{15}{16}$

4. $7\frac{1}{2} - 2\frac{3}{4}$ **5.** $6\frac{5}{8} - 1\frac{5}{8}$ **6.** $7\frac{1}{4} - 2\frac{5}{6}$

7. $8\frac{1}{6} - 2\frac{1}{2}$ **8.** $9\frac{5}{6} - 2\frac{15}{16}$ **9.** $8\frac{3}{4} - 2\frac{5}{6}$

10. $10\frac{3}{10} - 3\frac{5}{6}$ **11.** $8\frac{1}{2} - 3\frac{13}{15}$ **12.** $5\frac{2}{3} - 1\frac{14}{15}$

2-6 H

Subtract:

1. $11\frac{1}{4} - 9\frac{4}{5}$ **2.** $15\frac{1}{3} - 9\frac{1}{12}$ **3.** $14\frac{1}{3} - 5\frac{3}{5}$

4. $13\frac{2}{15} - 9\frac{7}{12}$ **5.** $24\frac{1}{5} - 19\frac{5}{6}$ **6.** $20\frac{3}{10} - 15\frac{23}{60}$

7. $14\frac{11}{16} - 9\frac{7}{9}$ **8.** $24\frac{7}{8} - 13\frac{11}{12}$ **9.** $48\frac{5}{9} - 39\frac{23}{24}$

10. $29\frac{3}{16} - 19\frac{7}{10}$ **11.** $48\frac{3}{8} - 27\frac{9}{10}$ **12.** $51\frac{17}{24} - 44\frac{19}{20}$

2-6 I

1. Mr. Gregory bought some electronics stock for $35\frac{5}{8}$ dollars per share. Find the amount of increase in the value of the stock if he sold it 31 days later for $41\frac{1}{2}$ dollars per share.

2. In Exercise 1 assume that the value of the stock increased steadily. Find the average daily increase per share for the 31 days.

3. A piece of metal $3\frac{11}{16}$ inches long is cut from a piece which is $17\frac{1}{2}$ inches long. If $\frac{1}{16}$ inch is lost in waste, find the length of the piece remaining.

4. Find the thickness of the tubing in Figure 2–12.

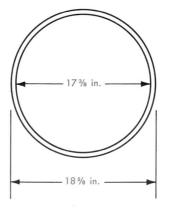

17 3/8 in.

18 5/8 in.

FIGURE 2–12

5. A prize bull lost weight while on display at the county fair. If his weight changed from $1327\frac{1}{4}$ pounds to $1298\frac{1}{2}$ pounds, find the number of pounds lost.

6. Two cars leave the same city and drive steadily in the same direction. At the end of $4\frac{1}{2}$ hours, car A has traveled $295\frac{1}{2}$ miles and car B has traveled $248\frac{7}{10}$ miles. How much farther has car A traveled than car B?

7. In 1942 Ernie Lombardi won the National League batting championship with an average of $\frac{33}{100}$. Twenty years later Tommy Davis won that honor with an average of $\frac{173}{500}$. Which player had the better average? By how much?

8. In 1800 Thomas Jefferson received $\frac{1}{2}$ of the electoral votes cast and was elected President. In 1832 Andrew Jackson received $\frac{219}{268}$ of the electoral votes and was elected President. How much larger was the fraction of votes received by Jackson than the fraction of votes received by Jefferson?

9. One bookcase has 4 shelves, each $2\frac{3}{4}$ feet long. A second bookcase has 3 shelves, each $3\frac{3}{8}$ feet long. Which bookcase has the greater amount of shelving? By how much?

10. A $22\frac{7}{8}$-pound live turkey weighed $19\frac{1}{3}$ pounds when dressed. The price of the turkey was $30\frac{1}{2}$¢ a pound, live weight, and 36¢ a pound dressed. Which is the better buy?

2-6 J

Find the difference between each pair of weights:

1. $16\frac{2}{3}$ lb and $9\frac{7}{8}$ lb
2. $14\frac{3}{4}$ lb and $11\frac{2}{3}$ lb
3. $10\frac{9}{10}$ lb and $8\frac{14}{15}$ lb
4. $48\frac{11}{16}$ lb and $37\frac{5}{8}$ lb
5. $107\frac{1}{2}$ lb and $95\frac{15}{16}$ lb
6. $36\frac{3}{4}$ lb and $19\frac{5}{8}$ lb
7. 27 lb and $17\frac{13}{48}$ lb
8. $271\frac{1}{3}$ lb and $195\frac{25}{48}$ lb
9. $75\frac{3}{16}$ lb and $\frac{173}{16}$ lb
10. $87\frac{1}{2}$ lb and 19 lb

2-6 K

Find the difference between each pair of lengths:

1. $7\frac{1}{3}$ yd and $4\frac{1}{2}$ yd
2. $18\frac{1}{2}$ yd and $9\frac{7}{10}$ yd
3. $21\frac{1}{2}$ yd and $19\frac{5}{6}$ yd
4. 100 yd and $37\frac{1}{2}$ yd
5. $16\frac{1}{6}$ yd and $11\frac{2}{3}$ yd
6. $28\frac{1}{5}$ yd and $19\frac{1}{2}$ yd
7. $13\frac{2}{3}$ yd and $10\frac{5}{6}$ yd
8. $24\frac{3}{4}$ yd and $19\frac{3}{8}$ yd
9. $47\frac{25}{48}$ yd and $29\frac{1}{2}$ yd
10. 31 yd and $24\frac{11}{16}$ yd

■ 2-7 RELATIVE SIZE OF RATIONAL NUMBERS

We can compare the members of a set of rational numbers by writing them in terms of their l.c.d. and then comparing the numerators.

Example. Compare the fractions $\frac{3}{4}$, $\frac{15}{16}$, $\frac{7}{8}$, and $\frac{11}{12}$.

$$\frac{3}{4} = \frac{36}{48}, \quad \frac{15}{16} = \frac{45}{48}, \quad \frac{7}{8} = \frac{42}{48}, \quad \frac{11}{12} = \frac{44}{48}$$

Since $45 > 44 > 42 > 36$, we know that

$$\frac{15}{16} > \frac{11}{12} > \frac{7}{8} > \frac{3}{4}.$$

We can also compare two positive rational numbers by using properties X, XI, and XII.

$$\textbf{X.} \qquad \frac{a}{b} = \frac{c}{d} \text{ if } ad = bc$$

For example,

$$\frac{3}{4} = \frac{15}{20} \text{ since } 3 \times 20 = 4 \times 15. \tag{1}$$

$$\textbf{XI.} \qquad \frac{a}{b} > \frac{c}{d} \text{ if } ad > bc$$

For example,

$$\frac{15}{16} > \frac{3}{4} \text{ since } (4 \times 15) > (3 \times 16). \tag{2}$$

$$\textbf{XII.} \qquad \frac{a}{b} < \frac{c}{d} \text{ if } ad < bc$$

For example,

$$\frac{4}{9} < \frac{13}{27} \text{ since } (4 \times 27) < (9 \times 13). \tag{3}$$

Exercises for Section 2-7

2-7 A

If a statement is true, mark it true. If it is false, write a replacement for the symbol ($<$, $=$, $>$) to make it true.

1. $\frac{3}{4} = \frac{4}{5}$
2. $\frac{5}{8} = \frac{11}{16}$
3. $\frac{12}{15} = \frac{20}{25}$
4. $\frac{7}{8} > \frac{15}{16}$
5. $\frac{7}{8} > \frac{20}{24}$
6. $\frac{1}{3} > \frac{1}{4}$
7. $\frac{15}{16} < \frac{7}{8}$
8. $\frac{21}{22} < \frac{19}{20}$
9. $\frac{35}{48} < \frac{19}{24}$
10. $\frac{11}{12} > \frac{4}{5}$
11. $\frac{13}{16} < \frac{7}{9}$
12. $\frac{2}{3} = \frac{14}{15}$

2-7 B

If a statement is true, mark it true. If it is false, write a replacement for the symbol $(<, =, >)$ to make it true.

1. $\frac{5}{8} < \frac{11}{13}$ 2. $\frac{3}{8} = \frac{1}{3}$ 3. $\frac{7}{12} = \frac{1}{2}$ 4. $\frac{5}{9} > \frac{15}{19}$

5. $\frac{2}{3} = \frac{22}{33}$ 6. $\frac{14}{15} = \frac{25}{27}$ 7. $\frac{9}{10} > \frac{10}{9}$ 8. $\frac{3}{4} < \frac{4}{3}$

9. $\frac{7}{8} = \frac{8}{7}$ 10. $\frac{13}{15} = \frac{14}{17}$ 11. $\frac{1}{6} < \frac{1}{7}$ 12. $\frac{1}{10} > \frac{1}{12}$

2-7 C

If a statement is true, mark it true. If it is false, write a replacement for the symbol $(<, =, >)$ to make it true.

1. $\frac{11}{9} < \frac{10}{7}$ 2. $\frac{3}{2} = \frac{7}{4}$ 3. $\frac{6}{5} = \frac{11}{9}$ 4. $2\frac{2}{3} < 2\frac{3}{8}$

5. $4\frac{1}{2} > 3\frac{11}{10}$ 6. $6\frac{1}{3} > 5\frac{12}{7}$ 7. $1\frac{5}{8} = \frac{26}{16}$ 8. $2\frac{7}{8} = \frac{46}{15}$

9. $5\frac{1}{2} < 4\frac{19}{12}$ 10. $7\frac{2}{3} = 6\frac{5}{4}$ 11. $11\frac{1}{2} = 9\frac{14}{5}$ 12. $4\frac{3}{5} < 3\frac{17}{10}$

2-7 D

Arrange in order of size:

1. $\frac{1}{2}, \frac{1}{4}, \frac{3}{4}$ 2. $\frac{5}{8}, \frac{1}{2}, \frac{7}{12}$ 3. $\frac{1}{4}, \frac{1}{3}, \frac{1}{5}$ 4. $\frac{3}{10}, \frac{1}{5}, \frac{1}{4}$

5. $\frac{1}{3}, \frac{2}{9}, \frac{3}{7}$ 6. $\frac{11}{16}, \frac{13}{24}, \frac{13}{18}$ 7. $\frac{5}{7}, \frac{9}{14}, \frac{13}{21}$ 8. $\frac{4}{5}, \frac{9}{10}, \frac{5}{8}$

9. $\frac{7}{10}, \frac{69}{100}, \frac{19}{25}$ 10. $\frac{3}{5}, \frac{7}{10}, \frac{17}{25}$ 11. $\frac{11}{16}, \frac{5}{8}, \frac{7}{12}$ 12. $\frac{31}{100}, \frac{3}{10}, \frac{7}{25}$

2-7 E

Arrange in order of size:

1. $\frac{1}{2}, \frac{3}{4}, \frac{5}{8}, \frac{7}{12}$ 2. $\frac{2}{3}, \frac{7}{12}, \frac{5}{9}, \frac{11}{18}$ 3. $1\frac{1}{2}, \frac{7}{5}, \frac{11}{10}, 2\frac{1}{10}$

4. $2\frac{3}{8}, 1\frac{15}{12}, 2\frac{1}{2}, 2\frac{4}{5}$ 5. $1\frac{11}{12}, 2, 1\frac{13}{12}, 1\frac{7}{6}$ 6. $\frac{15}{8}, \frac{16}{7}, \frac{15}{7}, \frac{14}{6}$

7. $3\frac{3}{8}, 3\frac{5}{12}, 3\frac{2}{3}, 2\frac{19}{12}$ 8. $1\frac{31}{48}, 1\frac{19}{24}, 1\frac{11}{12}, 1\frac{1}{2}$ 9. $\frac{3}{4}, \frac{3}{8}, \frac{3}{5}, \frac{3}{10}, \frac{3}{2}$

2-7 F

To round off the mixed number $a + b/c$, we use the following rules: (1) if $b/c < 1/2$, we round off to a; (2) if $b/c > 1/2$, we round off to $a + 1$; (3) if $b/c = 1/2$ and a is even, we round off to a, but if a is odd, we round off to $a + 1$. For example, $2\frac{1}{3} \approx 2$, $3\frac{2}{3} \approx 4$, $2\frac{1}{2} \approx 2$, and $5\frac{1}{2} \approx 6$.

Round off to the nearest number:

1. $3\frac{4}{5}$ 2. $6\frac{1}{2}$ 3. $7\frac{1}{2}$ 4. $1\frac{15}{21}$

5. $2\frac{1}{3}$ 6. $7\frac{13}{25}$ 7. $9\frac{3}{8}$ 8. $7\frac{3}{5}$

9. $4\frac{2}{5}$ 10. $6\frac{6}{11}$ 11. $7\frac{3}{4}$ 12. $19\frac{4}{11}$

2-7 G

Round off to the nearest number:

1. $17\frac{7}{12}$
2. $24\frac{4}{9}$
3. $18\frac{3}{10}$
4. $19\frac{1}{2}$
5. $22\frac{6}{12}$
6. $18\frac{9}{16}$
7. $24\frac{13}{20}$
8. $18\frac{7}{15}$
9. $6\frac{9}{17}$
10. $24\frac{3}{7}$
11. $24\frac{4}{7}$
12. $165\frac{5}{11}$

2-7 H

In each case, give the greatest length:

1. $2\frac{1}{3}$ ft, $1\frac{5}{4}$ ft, $2\frac{1}{6}$ ft
2. $4\frac{2}{5}$ ft, $4\frac{7}{15}$ ft, $4\frac{2}{3}$ ft
3. $19\frac{1}{10}$ ft, $19\frac{2}{21}$ ft, $19\frac{1}{5}$ ft
4. $8\frac{3}{8}$ ft, $8\frac{7}{16}$ ft, $8\frac{15}{32}$ ft
5. $4\frac{2}{7}$ ft, $4\frac{5}{16}$ ft, $4\frac{3}{8}$ ft
6. $\frac{7}{8}$ ft, $\frac{9}{10}$ ft, $\frac{4}{5}$ ft
7. $\frac{15}{16}$ ft, $\frac{7}{8}$ ft, $\frac{2}{3}$ ft
8. $\frac{5}{8}$ ft, $\frac{2}{3}$ ft, $\frac{17}{24}$ ft
9. $\frac{15}{8}$ ft, $\frac{17}{9}$ ft, $\frac{35}{24}$ ft
10. $\frac{30}{7}$ ft, $\frac{93}{21}$ ft, $4\frac{1}{3}$ ft

2-7 I

If a statement is true, mark it true. If it is false, write a replacement for the symbol ($<$, $=$, $>$) to make it true.

1. $(\frac{1}{2} + \frac{2}{3}) < 1$
2. $(2\frac{1}{2} - \frac{3}{4}) > 1\frac{1}{5}$
3. $(2\frac{1}{2} \times \frac{2}{5}) = \frac{5}{5}$
4. $(4 \div \frac{1}{3}) < 12\frac{7}{8}$
5. $(4\frac{5}{8} - \frac{3}{4}) < 3\frac{1}{4}$
6. $(6\frac{1}{2} + 1\frac{4}{5}) < 8\frac{1}{10}$
7. $(2\frac{3}{4} \times \frac{5}{8}) < 2$
8. $(\frac{9}{10}$ of $20) = 18$
9. $(\frac{7}{5} - 1\frac{1}{8}) > \frac{7}{40}$
10. $\frac{17}{32} < (\frac{1}{8} + \frac{9}{32})$
11. $(4\frac{1}{2} + \frac{2}{3} + \frac{1}{4}) < 5$
12. $(\frac{4}{5}$ of $\$15) < \$13$

2-7 J

If a statement is true, mark it true. If it is false, write a replacement for the symbol ($<$, $=$, $>$) to make it true.

1. $(\frac{3}{5}$ of $40) < 25$
2. $(\frac{4}{5}$ of $20) = 16$
3. $(\frac{7}{8}$ of $16\frac{1}{2}) < 14\frac{2}{5}$
4. $(\frac{3}{4}$ of $21\frac{2}{3}) = 18\frac{2}{7}$
5. $(\frac{9}{10}$ of $120\frac{1}{2}) < 108\frac{3}{8}$
6. $(\frac{5}{6}$ of $60\frac{5}{6}) > 51\frac{1}{2}$
7. $(2\frac{1}{2}$ of $13\frac{3}{4}) = 34\frac{7}{22}$
8. $(\frac{3}{2}$ of $16\frac{1}{4}) < 24\frac{2}{5}$
9. $(\frac{15}{16}$ of $27) > 25$
10. $(\frac{19}{32}$ of $40\frac{1}{2}) = 24\frac{3}{64}$

Vocabulary

The section in which each word appears is indicated in parentheses.

common denominator (2–5)
complex fraction (2–3)
composite numbers (2–4)
coordinate (2–1)
denominator (2–1)
even number (2–4)
factors (2–4)
fractions (2–1)
fundamental fact (theorem)
  (2–4)
greatest common divisor (g.c.d.)
  (2–4)
least common denominator
  (l.c.d.) (2–5)
least common multiple (l.c.m.)
  (2–4)

mixed number (2–1)
multiplication (2–2)
number line (2–1)
numerator (2–1)
odd number (2–4)
one-to-one correspondence (2–1)
origin (2–1)
prime factored form (2–4)
prime number (2–4)
ratio (2–1)
rational number (2–1)
reciprocal (2–2, 2–3)
reduced (2–2)
relatively prime (Exercises
  2–4 Q)
unit fractions (2–1)

Chapter Review

A

In Exercises 1–6 perform the indicated operations:

1. $\frac{2}{3} + \frac{3}{5} + \frac{1}{2}$

2. $\frac{3}{4} + \frac{5}{6} - \frac{3}{8}$

3. $\frac{5}{12} + \frac{1}{8} - \frac{1}{6}$

4. $\frac{2}{3} \times \frac{3}{5} \times \frac{5}{8}$

5. $(\frac{5}{7} \times \frac{3}{10}) \div \frac{2}{3}$

6. $2\frac{3}{4} \div 1\frac{2}{3}$

7. If $\frac{2}{3}$ of a number n is 64, find the number.

8. If a number n is divided by $\frac{2}{3}$, the quotient is 27. Find the number.

9. Given $S = \{\frac{2}{3}, \frac{3}{5}, \frac{11}{15}\}$, find the largest member.

10. Consider the inequality $x - \frac{5}{8} > \frac{11}{15}$.

    (a) May $x = 4$?   (b) May $x = 5$?   (c) May $x = 6$?

    (d) May $x = \frac{163}{120}$?   (e) May x be any value greater than $\frac{163}{120}$?

B

1. Which elements of $\{3, \frac{1}{4}, \frac{1}{2}, 0, 2, 2\frac{2}{5}\}$ are rational numbers?
2. In Exercise 1 which elements of the set are unit fractions?
3. Does $\dfrac{2}{3} = \dfrac{2}{3} \times \dfrac{3\frac{1}{2}}{3\frac{1}{2}}$? Explain.
4. Find the product of the fraction a/b and its reciprocal.
5. If a/b and c/d are rational numbers, is $a/b \times c/d$ a member of the set of rational numbers?
6. Two fractions have denominators x and y. Is xy a common denominator of the two fractions? Give an example.
7. May two fractions have several common denominators? Give examples to explain.
8. Is 20 a common multiple of 2 and 5? Does l.c.m. $(2, 5) = 20$? If not, explain.
9. Consider two fractions, a/b and r/b, where a, b, and r are natural numbers and $a > r$. Which is the larger fraction? Explain.
10. Does $\dfrac{a}{b} = \dfrac{\frac{1}{2}}{\frac{1}{2}} \times \dfrac{a}{b}$? Explain.

REVIEW OF CHAPTERS 1–2

A

If a statement is true, mark it true. If it is false, write a replacement for the part underlined to make it true.

1. The fundamental operations of arithmetic are <u>addition, subtraction, multiplication, and division</u>.

2. Where W is the set of whole numbers and N is the set of natural numbers, <u>$N \subseteq W$</u>.

3. In Exercise 2, <u>$N \cap W = N$</u>.

4. The Roman numeral XXXIV means <u>$10 + 10 + 10 + 5 - 1$</u>.

5. If s and t represent two natural numbers, then <u>$s \times t$ is a member of set N; also, $s + t$ is a member</u> of set N.

6. If $n = 342_{\text{six}}$, then <u>$n = 124_{\text{ten}}$</u>.

7. The lengths of two steel bars are 4 feet and 60 inches. The ratio of these lengths is $\frac{4}{60}$.

8. The reciprocal of $1\frac{2}{3}$ is $\frac{5}{3}$.

9. l.c.m. $(4, 6, 10) = \underline{120}$.

10. If $n = \dfrac{a}{k} + \dfrac{b}{k}$, $k \neq 0$, then $n = \underline{\dfrac{a+b}{k}}$.

11. If $\dfrac{a}{b} \neq \dfrac{c}{d}$, then $\underline{ad \neq bc}$.

12. We use the principle $n \times 1 = n$ to show that

$$\frac{\frac{1}{2} + \frac{1}{4}}{\frac{1}{2}} = \frac{\frac{1}{2} + \frac{1}{4}}{\frac{1}{2}} \times \frac{4}{4}.$$

B

1. Write 3458 as a sum in powers of 10.

2. Solve for n: $n = 238 + 4091 + 6782 + 4563$.

3. Solve for n: $n = \frac{1}{5} + \frac{1}{8} + \frac{1}{3} + \frac{1}{10}$.

4. If $p = 2a + 2b$, find p when $a = 507$ and $b = 4193$.

5. Solve for n: $n = 17 \times (310 + 9)$.

6. If $n = \frac{3}{4} \times 608$, is $n < 608$?

7. If 7 pounds of coffee costs $6.86, find the cost of 1 pound of coffee.

8. If $\frac{3}{4}$ pound of coffee costs 60¢, find the cost of 1 pound of coffee.

9. Simplify

$$\frac{\frac{3}{5} + \frac{5}{6}}{\frac{5}{12}}.$$

10. Solve for n: $\frac{12}{13} \times n = 48$.

11. The cost of an article is $\frac{12}{13}$ of the selling price. If the cost is $60.00, find the selling price. (*Note*: $\frac{12}{13} \times S = C$.)

12. Simplify

$$\frac{(\frac{1}{2} \times 4084) + (\frac{1}{4} \times 3164)}{\frac{2}{3} \times 12}.$$

3 Decimal Fractions and Percent

Any fraction with an integral power of ten as its denominator is called a **decimal fraction.** Decimal fractions are normally expressed in positional notation, and are then called decimals. Consider these examples:

$$\tfrac{7}{10}, \text{ or } 0.7; \quad \tfrac{13}{100}, \text{ or } 0.13; \quad \tfrac{217}{1000}, \text{ or } 0.217 \tag{1}$$

The concepts of positional notation and addition are used to express decimals. Thus

$$0.675 = \tfrac{6}{10} + \tfrac{7}{100} + \tfrac{5}{1000} = \tfrac{675}{1000}. \tag{2}$$

Notice this array.

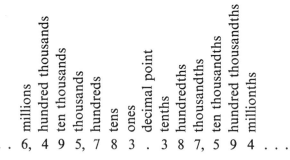

In the array we see that each position has a place value ten times the place value of the position to its right. We read 0.387594 as

114

three hundred eighty-seven thousand, five hundred ninety-four millionths. The name *millionths* is used since the numeral ends in the millionths position.

The sum of a whole number and a decimal fraction is called a mixed decimal. In reading and writing mixed decimals we use the word *and* to indicate the decimal point.

$$2.5 = \text{two and five tenths} = 2\tfrac{5}{10}, \tag{3}$$

$$13.06 = \text{thirteen and six hundredths} = 13\tfrac{6}{100}, \tag{4}$$

$$5.307 = \text{five and three hundred seven thousandths},$$

$$= 5\tfrac{307}{1000}. \tag{5}$$

A decimal can be expressed as a common fraction or a mixed number as follows:

$$0.5 = \tfrac{5}{10} = \tfrac{1}{2}; \quad 0.37 = \tfrac{37}{100}; \quad 2.73 = 2\tfrac{73}{100} = \tfrac{273}{100}. \tag{6}$$

Exercises for Section 3-1

3-1 A

Refer to Equation (2) on page 114 and express each number as a sum of common fractions with denominators which are powers of 10:

1. 0.23	**2.** 0.47	**3.** 0.625	**4.** 0.078
5. 0.1234	**6.** 0.0057	**7.** 0.0712	**8.** 0.165
9. 0.473	**10.** 0.061	**11.** 0.2025	**12.** 0.14007

3-1 B

Express in positional notation:

1. $\tfrac{7}{10}$	**2.** $\tfrac{17}{100}$	**3.** $\tfrac{97}{100}$	**4.** $\tfrac{6}{10}$
5. $\tfrac{75}{100}$	**6.** $\tfrac{48}{100}$	**7.** $\tfrac{615}{1000}$	**8.** $\tfrac{737}{1000}$
9. $\tfrac{88}{1000}$	**10.** $\tfrac{9}{1000}$	**11.** $\tfrac{13}{1000}$	**12.** $\tfrac{995}{1000}$

3-1 C

Express in positional notation:

1. $\tfrac{18}{10}$	**2.** $\tfrac{13}{10}$	**3.** $\tfrac{37}{10}$	**4.** $\tfrac{175}{100}$
5. $\tfrac{273}{100}$	**6.** $\tfrac{195}{100}$	**7.** $\tfrac{875}{100}$	**8.** $\tfrac{85}{10}$
9. $\tfrac{175}{10}$	**10.** $\tfrac{965}{100}$	**11.** $\tfrac{1365}{1000}$	**12.** $\tfrac{2080}{1000}$

3–1 D

Express in positional notation:

1. $\dfrac{16}{10}$ 2. $\dfrac{16}{100}$ 3. $\dfrac{16}{1000}$ 4. $\dfrac{16}{10,000}$

5. $\dfrac{16}{100,000}$ 6. $\dfrac{16}{1,000,000}$ 7. $\dfrac{375}{10}$ 8. $\dfrac{375}{100}$

9. $\dfrac{375}{1000}$ 10. $\dfrac{375}{10,000}$ 11. $\dfrac{375}{100,000}$ 12. $\dfrac{375}{1,000,000}$

3–1 E

Express in words:

1. 0.3   **2.** 0.03   **3.** 0.003   **4.** 0.0003
5. 0.00003   **6.** 0.000003   **7.** 2.6   **8.** 2.06
9. 2.006   **10.** 45.93   **11.** 45.093   **12.** 45.0093

3–1 F

Express in words:

1. 12.7   **2.** 4.09   **3.** 46.005   **4.** 109.3
5. 220.06   **6.** 47.47   **7.** 1.0375   **8.** 2.202
9. 4.0605   **10.** 12.75   **11.** 244.05   **12.** 19.0705

3–1 G

Solve and express answers in positional notation:

1. $n = \frac{3}{10} + \frac{7}{100}$ **2.** $n = \frac{147}{100} + \frac{19}{100}$

3. $n = \frac{27}{100} + \frac{27}{1000}$ **4.** $n = \frac{76}{100} + \frac{195}{1000}$

5. $n = \frac{16}{10} - \frac{13}{100}$ **6.** $n = \frac{9}{10} - \frac{3}{1000}$

7. $n = 1\frac{7}{10} - \frac{109}{100}$ **8.** $n = 4\frac{3}{10} - \frac{275}{100}$

9. $n = \frac{6}{10} + \frac{5}{100} + \frac{173}{1000}$ **10.** $n = \frac{87}{100} + \frac{587}{1000}$

11. $n = \frac{1}{10} + \frac{1}{100} + \frac{1}{10,000}$ **12.** $n = \frac{3}{10} + \frac{3}{100} + \frac{575}{1000}$

3–1 H

Express in positional notation:

1. three tenths
2. seventeen tenths
3. six hundredths
4. six thousandths

5. one hundredth
6. seventy-five hundredths
7. two hundred six thousandths
8. thirty-eight thousandths
9. ninety-one ten thousandths
10. nine thousand eight ten thousandths

3-1 I

Express in positional notation:

1. one and three tenths
2. fourteen and two hundredths
3. seven thousand and one tenth
4. four hundred fifty and six hundredths
5. seven and eighty-one hundredths
6. eight and seven thousandths
7. nineteen and nineteen hundredths
8. eighty-five and five hundredths
9. four hundred three and one tenth
10. eighteen thousand five and six hundredths

3-1 J

Express as a common fraction in reduced form:

1. 0.8	**2.** 0.7	**3.** 0.4	**4.** 0.06
5. 0.25	**6.** 0.5	**7.** 0.35	**8.** 0.48
9. 0.1	**10.** 0.15	**11.** 0.20	**12.** 0.85

3-1 K

Express as a common fraction in reduced form:

1. 0.36	**2.** 0.64	**3.** 0.75	**4.** 0.35
5. 0.125	**6.** 0.275	**7.** 0.095	**8.** 0.065
9. 0.072	**10.** 0.094	**11.** 0.185	**12.** 0.575

3-1 L

Express as a mixed number or a common fraction in reduced form:

1. 1.6	**2.** 19.50	**3.** 0.755	**4.** 14.48
5. 25.25	**6.** 10.2	**7.** 15.4	**8.** 24.8
9. 8.125	**10.** 7.625	**11.** 4.725	**12.** 5.875

3–1 M

A number may be expressed in many ways. Consider these examples:

3 tenths is 30 hundredths,
or 3 tenths is 300 thousandths.

Determine x in each statement:
1. 9 tenths is x hundredths.
2. 13 tenths is x hundredths.
3. 125 tenths is x hundredths.
4. 4 hundredths is x thousandths.
5. 13 hundredths is x thousandths.
6. 9 tenths is x thousandths.
7. 25 tenths is x thousandths.
8. 125 tenths is x hundredths.
9. 31 hundredths is x thousandths.
10. 9 tenths is x ten thousandths.

3–1 N

Express as decimal fractions in positional notation:

1. $\frac{3}{5}$	2. $\frac{7}{20}$	3. $\frac{11}{25}$	4. $\frac{23}{25}$
5. $\frac{19}{20}$	6. $\frac{1}{4}$	7. $\frac{1}{2}$	8. $\frac{3}{4}$
9. $\frac{17}{50}$	10. $\frac{7}{25}$	11. $\frac{13}{50}$	12. $\frac{33}{20}$

■ 3–2   ADDITION OF DECIMAL FRACTIONS

We can find the sum S of 4.12 and 24.36 in the following way:

$$
\begin{aligned}
S &= 4.12 + 24.36 \\
&= (4 + \tfrac{1}{10} + \tfrac{2}{100}) + (24 + \tfrac{3}{10} + \tfrac{6}{100}) \\
&= (4 + 24) + (\tfrac{1}{10} + \tfrac{3}{10}) + (\tfrac{2}{100} + \tfrac{6}{100}) \qquad (1) \\
&= 28 + \tfrac{4}{10} + \tfrac{8}{100} \\
&= 28.48.
\end{aligned}
$$

In (1) we use the associative and commutative properties to group like units: ones, tenths, and hundredths. Usually in a problem like this we write the numerals in a column with the decimal points in the same vertical line.

4.12	Step 1. (2 + 6) hundredths = 8 hundredths
24.36	Step 2. (1 + 3) tenths = 4 tenths, and so on
28.48	

A **complex decimal** is composed of a decimal and a common fraction. For example,

$$0.07\tfrac{1}{2} = \text{seven and one-half hundredths,} \tag{2}$$

$$0.33\tfrac{1}{3} = \text{thirty-three and one-third hundredths,} \tag{3}$$

$$4.205\tfrac{3}{4} = \text{four and two hundred five and three-fourths thousandths.} \tag{4}$$

Exercises for Section 3-2

3-2 A

Find the sums by inspection:

1. $2.1 + 0.7$	**2.** $4.4 + 4.6$
3. $1.25 + 0.03$	**4.** $2.5 + 1.5$
5. $1.8 + 4.2$	**6.** $10.5 + 0.6$
7. $10.8 + 1.5$	**8.** $0.6 + 0.8$
9. $0.7 + 0.7$	**10.** $0.8 + 0.2$
11. $6.4 + 0.6$	**12.** $0.02 + 0.24$
13. $0.05 + 0.55$	**14.** $5.11 + 0.05$
15. $5.0 + 1.5$	**16.** $5.00 + 0.51 + 0.05$
17. $1.000 + 0.001$	**18.** $0.101 + 0.102$
19. $0.4 + 0.2 + 0.4$	**20.** $0.8 + 0.02 + 0.08$

3-2 B

Solve for x:

1. $0.3 + 0.8 + 0.7 = x$	**2.** $0.25 + 0.36 + 0.09 = x$
3. $0.37 + 0.91 + 0.07 = x$	**4.** $0.75 + 0.86 + 0.91 = x$
5. $0.63 + 0.07 + 0.42 = x$	**6.** $0.125 + 0.1681 + 0.175 = x$

7. $0.265 + 0.089 + 0.707 = x$

8. $0.183 + 0.195 + 0.728 + 0.009 = x$

9. $0.2074 + 0.0125 + 0.0652 + 0.9791 = x$

10. $0.2500 + 0.7056 + 0.8813 = x$

3-2 C

Add:

1. 12.65	**2.** 19.27	**3.** 25.57	**4.** 39.87
1.08	32.08	18.36	45.65
5. 44.08	**6.** 72.64	**7.** 88.752	**8.** 9.009
93.08	35.91	94.060	38.754
9. 16.109	**10.** 128.256	**11.** 375.008	**12.** 605.713
87.552	256.095	105.992	617.824

3-2 D

Solve for m:

1. $m = 3.8 + 9.9 + 7.5$
2. $m = 16.2 + 37.8 + 9.5$
3. $m = 0.05 + 19.25 + 48.09$
4. $m = 16.00 + 9.05 + 7.75$
5. $m = 75.25 + 15.50 + 38.45$
6. $m = 105.37 + 200.01 + 93.48$
7. $m = 65.30 + 19.45 + 105.72$
8. $m = 18.008 + 9.145 + 1000.009$
9. $m = 75.487 + 0.095 + 19.714$
10. $m = 100.25 + 95.25 + 120.75$
11. $m = 36.591 + 1.063 + 0.346$
12. $m = 201.500 + 1543.101 + 7.834$

3-2 E

Add:

1. 16.07	**2.** 70.53	**3.** 422.43	**4.** 8.065
195.38	88.42	96.00	9.321
42.09	109.75	80.75	7.059
5. 16.013	**6.** 21.207	**7.** 45.286	**8.** 197.251
9.147	88.945	64.097	246.371
18.724	33.757	138.389	87.022
9. 202.475	**10.** 1675.38	**11.** 2750.075	**12.** 8068.145
105.375	972.42	1064.025	7220.036
246.825	808.03	4073.375	6046.029

3-2 F

Solve for t:

1. $t = 0.005 + 0.125 + 0.755$
2. $t = 2.006 + 0.994 + 0.755$
3. $t = 1.723 + 0.680 + 0.932$
4. $t = 4.072 + 1.016 + 4.912$
5. $t = 8.324 + 8.423 + 7.000$
6. $t = 65.3 + 19.8 + 17.6 + 45.7$
7. $t = 18.7 + 36.4 + 17.8 + 24.3$
8. $t = 72.8 + 48.9 + 93.7 + 88.0$
9. $t = 20.48 + 30.72 + 60.18 + 17.35$
10. $t = 95.375 + 87.465 + 148.379$

3-2 G

1. Pieces of steel rod with lengths 14.5 feet, 20.7 feet, 19.6 feet, and 38.5 feet were needed for wall braces. Find the total length needed.
2. A clerk sold a lamp for $14.75, a set of dishes for $68.95, a stool for $7.25, and a wastebasket for $2.45. Find his total sales.
3. The weather bureau recorded the following daily rainfall measurements: Monday, 1.45 inches; Tuesday, 1.08 inches; Wednesday, 0.48 inches; Thursday, 0.75 inches; Friday, 1.19 inches; Saturday, 1.23 inches; and Sunday, 1.03 inches. Find the total rainfall for the week.
4. Table salt is composed of sodium, atomic weight 22.991, and chlorine, atomic weight 35.457. Find the sum of the atomic weights of the elements in table salt.
5. Water is composed of one part hydrogen, atomic weight 1.0080, and two parts oxygen, atomic weight 16.0000. Find the sum of the atomic weights in one molecule of water.
6. The four National Seashores in the United States and their areas in acres are: Cape Cod, 10,460.85; Cape Hatteras, 24,705.23; Padre Island, 39,000.00; Point Reyes, 5262.24. Find the total area set aside for National Seashores.
7. A buyer for a clothing store spent $150.25 on shirts, $652.75 on sport coats, $65.72 on ties, and $120.85 on socks. Find his total bill.

Exercises 3-2 G continued on page 122.

8. On a trip a family bought gasoline in the following amounts: 13.6 gallons, 10.9 gallons, 11.7 gallons, 14.4 gallons, 8.9 gallons, 9.4 gallons, and 13.7 gallons. Find the total amount of gasoline used.

9. A student must pay $75.50 for tuition. He needs four books which cost $6.50, $4.75, $3.75, and $8.56. Find the amount of money he needs for tuition and books.

10. Find the distance around a field whose sides are 217.3 feet, 88.7 feet, 210.9 feet, and 86.4 feet.

3-2 H

In the formula $P = a + b + c$ determine P for each ordered triple (a, b, c):

1. (1.7, 2.8, 0.9)
2. (21.2, 6.8, 19.7)
3. (35.0, 19.4, 21.5)
4. (68.6, 95.4, 72.3)
5. (0.019, 0.913, 0.016)
6. (1.001, 2.156, 3.187)
7. (9.751, 0.755, 6.009)
8. (1.452, 7.095, 6.824)
9. (95.27, 88.00, 17.65)
10. (100.95, 13.72, 64.74)
11. (88.07, 95.45, 62.48)
12. (124.07, 364.32, 186.27)

3-2 I

Solve for z:

1. $z - 1.82 = 4.07$
2. $z - 9.0 = 0.7$
3. $z - 11.09 = 17.36$
4. $z - 3.875 = 0.995$
5. $z - 9.808 = 1.292$
6. $z - 45.752 = 9.685$
7. $z - 73.06 = 19.94$
8. $z - 105.0 = 91.6$
9. $z - 14.14 = 85.76$
10. $z - 136.75 = 202.98$
11. $z - 88.752 = 9.807$
12. $z - 1065.35 = 8722.76$

3-2 J

In each exercise find the total weight:

1. 7.4 lb and 13.6 lb
2. 18.7 lb and 41.3 lb
3. 19.92 lb and 17.47 lb
4. 0.062 lb and 0.138 lb
5. 0.1027 lb and 0.8863 lb
6. 1.75 lb, 1.85 lb, and 1.32 lb
7. 4.08 lb, 4.13 lb, and 4.21 lb
8. 15.25 lb, 16.48 lb, and 13.72 lb
9. 21.37 lb, 7.00 lb, and 19.98 lb
10. 68.075 lb, 71.144 lb, and 8.066 lb

■ 3-3 SUBTRACTION WITH DECIMAL FRACTIONS

Consider this example of subtraction. (Note that like units—hundredths, tenths, and ones—are aligned.)

Example 1. Find $9.37 - 6.25$.

$$\begin{array}{r} 9.37 \\ 6.25 \\ \hline 3.12 \end{array}$$

The concept of *borrowing*, or *regrouping*, was not used in Example 1. However, we can *borrow* with decimal fractions in the same manner as we do with whole numbers.

Example 2. Find $8.762 - 5.278$.

Since

$$\begin{aligned} 8.762 &= 8.75 + 0.012 \\ &= 8.6 + 0.15 + 0.012, \end{aligned}$$

we have:

ones	tenths	hundredths	thousandths
8 .	6	15	12
5 .	2	7	8
3 .	4	8	4

The regrouping, or "borrowing," in Example 2 can be shown another way:

$$\begin{aligned} 8.762 &= 8 + 0.6 + 0.15 + 0.012 \\ 5.278 &= 5 + 0.2 + 0.07 + 0.008 \\ \hline &\ 3 + 0.4 + 0.08 + 0.004, \end{aligned}$$

that is, 3.484. The problem is usually done in this manner:

$$\begin{array}{r} 8.762 \\ 5.278 \\ \hline 3.484 \end{array}$$

Exercises for Section 3-3

3-3 A

Find by inspection:

1. $2.5 - 0.5$	**2.** $3.6 - 0.4$	**3.** $4.7 - 0.3$
4. $18.9 - 0.7$	**5.** $25.6 - 0.3$	**6.** $4.8 - 1.6$
7. $9.7 - 7.7$	**8.** $11.2 - 0.9$	**9.** $12.3 - 0.9$
10. $14.6 - 0.8$	**11.** $5.23 - 0.09$	**12.** $6.27 - 0.08$
13. $4.32 - 0.08$	**14.** $17.21 - 0.19$	**15.** $18.31 - 0.28$

3-3 B

Solve for x:

1. $x = 16 - 0.5$	**2.** $x = 23 - 0.8$
3. $x = 48 - 0.9$	**4.** $x = 32 - 0.8$
5. $x = 27 - 0.5$	**6.** $x = 16.2 - 0.5$
7. $x = 23.4 - 0.8$	**8.** $x = 48.1 - 0.9$
9. $x = 32.7 - 0.8$	**10.** $x = 27.6 - 0.5$
11. $x = 9.71 - 8.65$	**12.** $x = 8.32 - 4.93$
13. $x = 7.77 - 4.65$	**14.** $x = 18.32 - 9.38$
15. $x = 17.65 - 9.49$	**16.** $x = 3.0007 - 1.2579$

3-3 C

Solve for m:

1. $m = 42.5 - 29.4$	**2.** $m = 1.75 - 1.43$
3. $m = 18.57 - 12.39$	**4.** $m = 12.94 - 4.83$
5. $m = 17.39 - 14.87$	**6.** $m = 23.25 - 12.91$
7. $m = 17.16 - 9.24$	**8.** $m = 112.34 - 97.75$
9. $m = 87.20 - 79.14$	**10.** $m = 108.64 - 97.48$

3-3 D

Solve for c:

1. $c = 4.000 - 3.285$	**2.** $c = 2.000 - 0.307$
3. $c = 3.000 - 1.902$	**4.** $c = 5.000 - 2.817$
5. $c = 10.000 - 5.362$	**6.** $c = 81.700 - 41.852$
7. $c = 42.500 - 11.344$	**8.** $c = 79.600 - 18.752$
9. $c = 47.800 - 29.940$	**10.** $c = 12.700 - 0.909$

3-3 E

Solve for y:

1. $8.25 - 3.69 = y$ 2. $4.91 - 2.87 = y$
3. $3.37 - 1.09 = y$ 4. $7.79 - 4.77 = y$
5. $9.13 - 6.48 = y$ 6. $75.24 - 69.87 = y$
7. $89.13 - 48.21 = y$ 8. $104.18 - 97.32 = y$
9. $2164.31 - 975.82 = y$ 10. $632.756 - 495.758 = y$

3-3 F

Subtract:

1. 16.29   2. 27.38   3. 91.13
    9.75   14.92   77.22
   ----   -----   -----

4. 42.37   5. 57.62   6. 84.37
   19.26   49.48   69.25
   -----   -----   -----

7. 10.065   8. 27.021   9. 19.208
    7.234   8.029   14.666
   ------   ------   ------

10. 112.031   11. 256.0325   12. 486.2751
     97.028   132.2524   295.4769
    -------   --------   --------

3-3 G

Solve for n:

1. $n + 11.3 = 34.9$ 2. $n + 7.3 = 11.0$
3. $n + 9.0 = 17.26$ 4. $n + 9.0 = 10.75$
5. $n + 8.75 = 11.32$ 6. $n + 28.45 = 31.62$
7. $n + 13.43 = 19.27$ 8. $n + 25.48 = 75.33$
9. $n + 82.375 = 90.084$ 10. $n + 100.751 = 175.751$
11. $n + 246.955 = 298.991$ 12. $n + 736.375 = 1028.424$

3-3 H

1. One clerk sold 114.7 yards of material and a second clerk sold 194.3 yards. Find the difference in the sales.
2. A student purchased shoes for $13.75, a sport coat for $32.45, and a pair of slacks for $11.65. If his clothing allowance was $75.00, find how much he had left.

Exercises 3–3 H continued on page 126.

3. The airmail rate from the United States to Chile is $1.85 for the first pound and $0.55 for each additional pound. The same service from the United States to Hong Kong is $1.68 for the first pound and $0.79 for each additional pound. Find the difference in cost if a 3-pound package is sent by airmail from the United States to each place.

4. In North America the population density is about 28.5 people per square mile. If the same statistic for South America is 21.9, find the difference in population densities.

5. A man owed a repair bill of $450.75 on his car. He paid $72.00 on June 1, $109.50 on July 1, $97.75 on August 1, and $87.25 on September 1. Find the amount he had left to pay.

6. The Suez Canal is 100.62 miles long and the Panama Canal is 50.04 miles long. Which is longer? By how many miles?

7. One year, a family spent $1875.85 for food and $375.75 for clothing. The next year, they spent $1972.95 for food and $401.25 for clothing. Find the family's increase in expenditure for each of the two items.

8. Mrs. Anders bought a blouse for $4.95, a skirt for $8.35, and a handkerchief for $1.15. She gave the clerk a $20 bill and received $5.15 in change. Was this the correct change? Explain.

9. A student purchased supplies for $7.48 at the bookstore. As change from a $10 bill, he was given 2 one-dollar bills, a quarter, and 2 dimes. Was this the correct change? Explain.

10. At the beginning of track season a college athlete ran the 100-yard dash in 11.1 seconds. By the end of the season he ran it in 10.3 seconds. By how much did he reduce his time?

3-3 I

The measurements of certain steel fittings are given, in inches, as $a \pm b$ (read "a plus or minus b"). For example, $a \pm b = 6.00 \pm 0.25$ indicates that the range goes from 5.75 inches to 6.25 inches. Find the range for each ordered pair (a, b):

1. (5.00, 0.15)		**2.** (7.00, 0.45)	
3. (19.00, 0.75)		**4.** (21.00, 0.35)	
5. (8.500, 0.025)		**6.** (7.250, 0.015)	
7. (8.750, 0.005)		**8.** (10.105, 0.012)	
9. (27.335, 0.025)		**10.** (45.815, 0.105)	
11. (97.000, 0.125)		**12.** (756.000, 0.225)	

3-3 J

In the formula $P = S - C$ determine P for each ordered pair (S, C):

1. (10.0, 2.7)
2. (27.5, 18.6)
3. (48.3, 29.9)
4. (175.32, 97.08)
5. (97.4, 83.9)
6. (69.35, 49.95)
7. (82.37, 74.61)
8. (108.73, 99.09)
9. (75.8, 62.4)
10. (418.37, 375.85)
11. (675.75, 500.37)
12. (2675.389, 1987.75)

3-3 K

Find the difference between each pair of lengths:

1. 0.178 ft and 0.099 ft
2. 0.953 ft and 0.812 ft
3. 1.0020 ft and 1.0018 ft
4. 7.0701 ft and 7.0695 ft
5. 5.00 ft and 3.55 ft
6. 20.081 ft and 20.079 ft
7. 125.6 ft and 75.8 ft
8. 30.69 ft and 19.48 ft
9. 756.35 ft and 648.98 ft
10. 1872.64 ft and 975.09 ft

■ 3-4 MULTIPLICATION OF DECIMAL FRACTIONS

The product of two decimal fractions can be found by using common fractions, as in (1) and (2):

$$2.7 \times 3.6 = \tfrac{27}{10} \times \tfrac{36}{10} = \tfrac{972}{100} = 9.72 \tag{1}$$
$$0.15 \times 3.9 = \tfrac{15}{100} \times \tfrac{39}{10} = \tfrac{585}{1000} = 0.585 \tag{2}$$

These problems are usually solved as shown below.

```
  2.7        We find the product 36 × 27 = 972.
  3.6
─────
 16 2
 81
─────
 9.72        We "point off" two places, 9.72.


 0.15        We find the product 39 × 15 = 585.
 3.9
─────
13 5
 45
─────
0.585        We "point off" three places to obtain 0.585.
```

From examples like the ones on the previous page, we can make the following generalization.

I.   Where $a \times b = c$, **the product** c **has as many places to the right of the decimal point as the sum of the numbers of such places in the factors** a **and** b.

The procedure for *rounding off*, described in Section 1–11, applies to rounding decimals. Thus if

$$n = 13.47615, \tag{3}$$

then

$n \approx 13.4762$ to the nearest ten thousandth,

$n \approx 13.476$ to the nearest thousandth,

$n \approx 13.48$ to the nearest hundredth,

$n \approx 13.5$ to the nearest tenth.

Approximation is useful in locating the decimal point in a product. Consider the example.

Example. Solve for p: $p = 2.8 \times 17.9$.

We find $28 \times 179 = 5012$. We know that

$$2.8 \approx 3 \quad \text{and} \quad 17.9 \approx 20.$$

Hence

$$p \approx 3 \times 20, \quad \text{or } 60.$$

Thus

$$p = 50.12.$$

Note that our estimate is 60. An answer of 5.012, 501.2, or 5012 would be unreasonably far from 60. The only reasonable answer would therefore be 50.12.

The system for counting significant digits in rounding decimals is similar to the system already discussed for rounding off whole numbers (Section 1–11).

Number	Number of Significant Digits		
	Three	Two	One
42.63	42.6	43	40
2.034	2.03	2.0	2
0.4756	0.476	0.48	0.5
0.05196	0.0520	0.052	0.05

Note that terminal zeros to the right of the decimal point are significant digits. For example, all the digits underlined in the following numbers are significant:

$$\underline{2.0}, \quad \underline{5.00}, \quad \underline{39.000}, \quad \underline{110.70}.$$

The initial zeros underlined in these numbers are not significant:

$$0.6, \quad 0.06, \quad 0.0061.$$

Exercises for Section 3–4

3–4 A

In Exercises 1–4 note that $12 \times 16 = 192$.

1. (a) Does $1.2 \times 1.6 = \frac{12}{10} \times \frac{16}{10} = \frac{192}{100}$?
   (b) Does $\frac{192}{100} = 1.92$?

2. (a) Does $12 \times 1.6 = \frac{12}{1} \times \frac{16}{10} = \frac{192}{10}$?
   (b) Does $\frac{192}{10} = 19.2$?

3. (a) Does $0.12 \times 1.6 = \frac{12}{100} \times \frac{16}{10} = \frac{192}{1000}$?
   (b) Does $\frac{192}{1000} = 0.192$?

4. (a) Does $0.12 \times 0.16 = \dfrac{12}{100} \times \dfrac{16}{100} = \dfrac{192}{10,000}$?

   (b) Does $\dfrac{192}{10,000} = 0.0192$?

To answer the questions in Exercises 5–8, refer to I, page 128:

5. In Exercise 1 do we "point off" 2 places?
6. In Exercise 2 do we "point off" 1 place?
7. In Exercise 3 do we "point off" 3 places?
8. In Exercise 4 do we "point off" 4 places?

3-4 B

In Exercises 1–10 note that $314 \times 126 = 39{,}564$. Use approximation to find an estimate of p and the product p, as in this example:

$$p = 3.14 \times 1.26,$$

$$p \approx 3 \times 1, \text{ or } 3;$$

hence

$$p = 3.9564.$$

This answer is reasonable since $p \approx 3$.

1. $p = 31.4 \times 126$ **2.** $p = 31.4 \times 1.26$
3. $p = 3.14 \times 12.6$ **4.** $p = 0.314 \times 126$
5. $p = 0.0314 \times 1260$ **6.** $p = 314 \times 0.126$
7. $p = 31.4 \times 12.6$ **8.** $p = 3.14 \times 1260$
9. $p = 0.0314 \times 12.6$ **10.** $p = 0.314 \times 0.126$

11. In Exercises 1–10 use I, page 128, to locate the decimal point in p. Are your answers the same as those you found by using approximation?

3-4 C

Find each product by inspection:

1. 0.1×5 **2.** 0.1×15 **3.** 0.1×126
4. 0.1×2572 **5.** $0.1 \times 21{,}305$ **6.** 0.01×7
7. 0.01×18 **8.** 0.01×212 **9.** 0.01×1000
10. $0.01 \times 10{,}300$ **11.** 0.3×7 **12.** 0.4×12
13. 0.5×64 **14.** 0.5×120 **15.** 0.6×14
16. 0.6×10 **17.** 0.7×8 **18.** 0.6×20
19. 0.5×200 **20.** 0.05×200 **21.** 0.03×300

3-4 D

Find each product:

1. 0.75×0.06 **2.** 0.16×0.25 **3.** 0.32×0.32
4. 0.75×0.08 **5.** 1.5×2.5 **6.** 4.8×1.2
7. 3.6×2.5 **8.** 7.5×4.8 **9.** 6.4×0.64
10. 2.5×0.25 **11.** 5.2×0.52 **12.** 4.8×0.48

3-4 E

Place the decimal point in each answer:

1. $0.06 \times 181 = 1086$
2. $4.5 \times 70.1 = 31545$
3. $8.25 \times 25 = 20625$
4. $0.125 \times 84.8 = 106$
5. $0.065 \times 70.4 = 45760$
6. $9.452 \times 24.1 = 2277932$
7. $0.035 \times 3.5 = 1225$
8. $84.2 \times 0.002 = 1684$
9. $197.48 \times 0.022 = 434456$
10. $10,028 \times 0.002 = 20056$

3-4 F

In each exercise, (a) approximate; (b) multiply to find the exact product.

1. 27.5	2. 68.7	3. 100.8	4. 29.9
0.68	4.9	22.6	14.5

5. 26.87	6. 48.36	7. 8.7	8. 16
0.25	9.9	13.42	0.75

9. 908	10. 225.6	11. 12.75	12. 80.6
4.7	14.3	0.375	0.81

3-4 G

Solve for p:

1. $p = 7.05 \times 8$
2. $p = 18.3 \times 5$
3. $p = 62.7 \times 8$
4. $p = 84.5 \times 9$
5. $p = 12.8 \times 2.5$
6. $p = 16.5 \times 4.4$
7. $p = 84.5 \times 1.9$
8. $p = 72.4 \times 3.3$
9. $p = 128.2 \times 4.5$
10. $p = 0.075 \times 22.4$
11. $p = 62.4 \times 18.5$
12. $p = 16.5 \times 204.72$

3-4 H

In each exercise, (a) approximate; (b) multiply to find the exact product.

1. 0.13×6.709
2. 2.4×17.55
3. 50.1×8.732
4. 18.1×92.04
5. 7.523×18.9
6. 225.1×7.55
7. 88.75×12.2
8. 64.82×0.0065
9. 17.523×2.02
10. 87.75×0.146
11. 19.903×4.5
12. 16.725×8.84

3-4 I

In Exercises 1–9, find the products:

1. 10×23.7 **2.** 10×0.4628 **3.** 10×5.713

4. 100×17.075 **5.** $10^2 \times 2.5133$ **6.** $10^2 \times 2.336$

7. 81.0752×10^3 **8.** 8.10752×10^4 **9.** 0.810752×10^5

10. Write a pattern for multiplying a decimal by 10^p, where p is a positive whole number. Compare your pattern with the one developed in Exercises 1–9 above.

3-4 J

1. An I-beam weighs 14.3 pounds per foot of length. Find the total weight of 48.5 feet of this I-beam.

2. A cube-shaped tank 1 foot by 1 foot by 1 foot contains 7.48 gallons of water when filled. Find the number of gallons in 5 such tanks.

3. Find the number of gallons of water needed to fill a cube-shaped tank 2 feet by 2 feet by 2 feet.

4. Find the number of gallons of water needed to fill a box-shaped vat 4 feet by 4 feet by 2 feet.

5. Find the weekly wage earned by a student who works 28 hours a week at $1.75 per hour.

6. A farmer sold his chickens for 20.5¢ per pound. If raising them cost 11.7¢ per pound, find the profit he made from selling 1075 pounds of chickens.

7. For a term of college, a student found that he needed a mathematics book which cost $8.75, a chemistry book which cost $7.50, and 6 notebooks which cost $1.25 each. Find the total cost of the books.

8. A farmer raised 9 tons of sugar beets which tested 132.5 pounds of sugar per 1000 pounds of beets. Find the number of pounds of sugar he should get from his total crop. (*Note:* 1 ton = 2000 pounds)

9. In a certain community the tax rate on a home is $5.245 per hundred dollars of assessed valuation. Find the taxes on a home assessed at $10,500.

10. A salesman was to receive 0.035 of his sales as a bonus. Find his bonus on sales of $1240.50.

3-4 K

In each exercise a unit of measurement and a number of units n are given. Find the total. (For example, if the unit of measurement is 7 feet and the number of units is 4, then the total is (4 × 7) feet, or 28 feet.)

1. 1600 lb, $n = 1.7$
2. 250 lb, $n = 0.075$
3. 1800 lb, $n = 12.32$
4. 48.5 lb, $n = 2.255$
5. 8640 lb, $n = 0.75$
6. 1200 ft, $n = 2025$
7. 500 ft, $n = 3.65$
8. 1400 ft, $n = 0.25$
9. 1400 ft, $n = 0.025$
10. 1400 ft, $n = 0.0025$

3-4 L

1. A shipyard estimator knows that steel plate work requires about 0.375 man-hour per hundred pounds of net structure completed. How many man-hours are needed to complete 16,800 pounds of such steel plate structure?
2. An I-beam weighs about 14.7 pounds per running foot. Find the weight of 3 such I-beams, each 20.5 feet long.
3. Find the total cost for 5 water pumps at $7.87 each and 7 gaskets at $0.24 each.
4. A kilogram is a metric unit of weight. It is approximately equal to 2.2046 pounds. Find the number of pounds in 120 kilograms.
5. A traveler was allowed to take 20 kilograms of luggage on the plane. Find the number of pounds of luggage allowed. (*Note:* 1 kilogram = 2.2046 pounds)
6. One meter is equal to 39.37 inches. Find the number of inches in 200 meters.
7. Find the difference, in inches, between 100 meters and 100 yards. (*Note:* 1 yard = 36 inches)
8. If water weighs about 8.34 pounds per gallon, find the weight of the water in a tank which contains 87.5 gallons.
9. One cubic foot of air weighs about 0.0806 pounds. Find the weight of the air in a room which contains 962.5 cubic feet.
10. In one city electric power costs $0.032 per kilowatt hour. Find the cost to operate a motor rated at 1050 watts if the motor runs continuously from 8:00 A.M. Tuesday until 8:00 P.M. the next Thursday. (*Note:* 1 kilowatt = 1000 watts)

3-4 M

Round off to the nearest tenth and give the number of significant digits in each answer:

1. 0.05	**2.** 0.25	**3.** 0.75	**4.** 0.08
5. 0.18	**6.** 0.78	**7.** 0.02	**8.** 4.649
9. 5.147	**10.** 18.961	**11.** 17.036	**12.** 18.475
13. 90.051	**14.** 187.223	**15.** 24.956	**16.** 28.0501

3-4 N

In the formula $p = rb$ determine p for each of the ordered pairs (r, b):

1. (0.05, 12)	**2.** (0.02, 24)	**3.** (0.125, 48)
4. (0.065, 80)	**5.** (0.075, 92)	**6.** (0.042, 75)
7. (0.035, 600)	**8.** (0.09, 708)	**9.** (0.141, 700)
10. (0.242, 648)	**11.** (1.455, 2640)	**12.** (2.075, 3420)

3-4 O

Solve for x:

1. $\dfrac{x}{2.5} = 17.5$ **2.** $\dfrac{x}{1.06} = 9$

3. $\dfrac{x}{0.06} = 7.5$ **4.** $\dfrac{x}{2.75} = 16$

5. $\dfrac{x}{20.9} = 4.4$ **6.** $\dfrac{x}{10.09} = 6.21$

7. $\dfrac{x}{19.3} = 24.7$ **8.** $\dfrac{x}{18} = 0.065$

9. $\dfrac{x}{95.25} = 4.065$ **10.** $\dfrac{x}{70.318} = 9.43$

11. $\dfrac{x}{98.8} = 10.7$ **12.** $\dfrac{x}{965.2} = 1058.2$

3-4 P

Find to the nearest cent and give the number of significant digits in each answer:

1. 0.75 of $180   **2.** 0.25 of $24.80

3. 0.6 of $995.35   **4.** 0.86 of $1000

5. 0.035 of $460.80

6. 0.125 of $1264.48

7. 0.0625 of $64.18

8. 0.005 of $4640.45

9. 1.25 of $700

10. 1.075 of $105.50

11. 3.33 of $60.45

12. 2.75 of $3640.12

13. 6.67 of $29.95

14. 1.05 of $158.98

15. 1.0125 of $460

16. 2.103 of $6790.50

■ **3-5 DIVISION WITH DECIMAL FRACTIONS**

To divide by a decimal fraction, we usually write an equivalent problem with divisor a whole number.

Example 1. Solve $n = 48.3 \div 2.1$.

$$n = \frac{48.3}{2.1} \times \frac{10}{10} = \frac{483}{21}$$ Thus $n = 483 \div 21$, a whole number.

$$n = 23$$

Example 1 is usually written in the following manner.

```
      2 3.
2.1 )48.3
  ∧  42  ∧
      6 3
      6 3
```

The symbol ∧ is used to show that the divisor and the dividend are multiplied by 10.

Example 2. Solve $n = 18.5 \div 0.04$.

```
          462.5
0.04 )18.500
   ∧  16  ∧
       25
       24
       10
        8
       20
       20
```

Note that $\dfrac{18.5 \times 100}{0.04 \times 100} = \dfrac{1850}{4}$.

Thus $18.5 \div 0.04 = 1850 \div 4$.

We affix as many zeros to the right of the decimal point in the dividend as needed to complete the division.

Example 3. Solve $n = 0.012 \div 3.3$.

```
        .003636
3.3 )0.0120000
  ^      ^
         99
        ___
        210
        198
        ___
        120
         99
        ___
        210
        198
        ___
         12
```

This quotient is a repeating decimal. We round off to an appropriate accuracy. Thus $0.003636 = 0.004$, to the nearest thousandth; or $0.00363 = 0.0036$, to the nearest ten thousandth; and so on.

In general, the following steps are involved in solving $n = a \div b$, where b represents a decimal number not zero.

1. Multiply a and b by the power of 10 necessary to make the divisor a whole number.

2. Divide in the manner used in the division of whole numbers.

3. After the division in Step 2 is completed, place the decimal point in n directly above its position in the dividend.

Exercises for Section 3-5

3-5 A

Find the quotients by inspection:

1. $6.2 \div 2$	**2.** $4.5 \div 5$	**3.** $8.1 \div 9$
4. $4.8 \div 6$	**5.** $1.6 \div 4$	**6.** $8 \div 0.5$
7. $18 \div 0.5$	**8.** $9 \div 0.5$	**9.** $12 \div 0.5$
10. $20 \div 0.5$	**11.** $10 \div 0.1$	**12.** $8 \div 0.1$
13. $5 \div 0.1$	**14.** $4 \div 0.2$	**15.** $7 \div 0.2$

3-5 B

Solve for n:

1. $n = 16.8 \div 0.4$	**2.** $n = 248 \div 0.4$	**3.** $n = 64 \div 0.04$
4. $n = 28 \div 0.04$	**5.** $n = 16.5 \div 5$	**6.** $n = 87.3 \div 9$
7. $n = 10.55 \div 5$	**8.** $n = 28.7 \div 7$	**9.** $n = 100 \div 2.5$
10. $n = 14.4 \div 1.2$	**11.** $n = 5.76 \div 2.4$	**12.** $n = 3.24 \div 1.8$

3–5 C

In each exercise, (a) approximate n; (b) find the exact quotient:

1. $n = 810 \div 0.09$
2. $n = 36.1 \div 1.9$
3. $n = 35.15 \div 1.9$
4. $n = 67.84 \div 21.2$
5. $n = 25.6 \div 0.8$
6. $n = 16.9 \div 0.13$
7. $n = 55.35 \div 4.5$
8. $n = 3.627 \div 0.09$
9. $n = 27 \div 0.25$
10. $n = 688.84 \div 6.8$
11. $n = 213.75 \div 28.5$
12. $n = 60.84 \div 0.12$

3–5 D

In each exercise, (a) approximate; (b) find the exact quotient:

1. $10.24 \div 3.2$
2. $24.3 \div 2.7$
3. $19.6 \div 4.9$
4. $59.5 \div 17.5$
5. $239.2 \div 11.5$
6. $110.11 \div 18.2$
7. $114.27 \div 29.3$
8. $33.66 \div 0.17$
9. $48.804 \div 174.3$
10. $432.63 \div 43.7$
11. $284.28 \div 20.6$
12. $6.11249 \div 6.07$

3–5 E

1. A canned ham weighs 5 pounds and costs $4.05. Find the price per pound.
2. An airplane flew 661.5 miles in 2.75 hours. Find the average speed to the nearest tenth of a mile per hour.
3. A clerk earns $96.52 in a 40-hour week. What does he earn per hour?
4. A family paid $80.00 as a down payment on a refrigerator which cost $309.92. Find the amount of each payment if the family paid the balance in 12 equal payments.
5. A clerk made the following sales: Monday, $43.75; Tuesday, $28.75; Wednesday, $19.80; Thursday, $29.35; Friday, $31.49; Saturday, $72.75. Find the clerk's average daily sales. Give your answer to the nearest cent.
6. Water weighs about 62.43 pounds per cubic foot. Find the number of cubic feet in 717.945 pounds of water.
7. A gallon of water weighs approximately 8.34 pounds. Find the number of gallons in 128.86 pounds of water. Give your answer to the nearest tenth.
8. In 1962 the estimated population of North America was 269,000 thousand; the area is about 9362 thousand square miles. Find

Exercises 3–5 E continued on page 138.

the population density in thousands of people per thousand square miles. Give your answer to the nearest tenth.

9. A building has an assessed value of $8775. This represents 0.9 of the market value. Find the market value.

10. As an average, the center on a basketball team makes 0.48 of his shots. How many shots must he attempt to make 120 baskets?

3-5 F

In the formula $I = \dfrac{E}{R}$, determine I to the nearest tenth for each of the ordered pairs (E, R):

1. (2.75, 0.5)   2. (15.2, 0.12)   3. (80, 4.35)
4. (26, 9.5)   5. (16.75, 4.25)   6. (80.5, 17.1)
7. (93.62, 18.71)   8. (43.91, 12.64)   9. (106.5, 24.4)
10. (136.09, 36.7)   11. (18.75, 24.82)   12. (24.19, 49.85)

3-5 G

In each exercise, (a) approximate; (b) find the answers to the nearest hundredth:

1. $6.5\overline{)13.08}$ 2. $13.08\overline{)6.5}$ 3. $750\overline{)89.95}$
4. $190.3\overline{)390.9}$ 5. $18.72\overline{)48}$ 6. $75\overline{)2.5}$
7. $700\overline{)40}$ 8. $21.65\overline{)12.375}$ 9. $48.57\overline{)21.62}$
10. $437.6\overline{)2675.08}$ 11. $609\overline{)225.74}$ 12. $4372.8\overline{)19,360.48}$

3-5 H

Solve for y in Exercises 1–9:

1. $1.65 \div 10 = y$ 2. $42.78 \div 10 = y$
3. $0.625 \div 10 = y$ 4. $8.0756 \div 100 = y$
5. $291.073 \div 10^2 = y$ 6. $0.42075 \div 10^2 = y$
7. $180.07 \div 1000 = y$ 8. $97.64 \div 10^3 = y$
9. $5.507 \div 10^3 = y$ 10. $6.034 \div 10^2 = y$

11. Write a rule for dividing a decimal by 10^p, where p is a positive whole number.

3-5 I

Solve, giving each answer to the nearest thousandth:

1. $13x = 1.69$ 2. $6.6x = 57.75$
3. $24.01x = 77.529$ 4. $1.8x = 25.92$

5. $0.012x = 0.00144$ **6.** $0.64x = 1.024$
7. $9.87x = 100$ **8.** $0.035x = 200.75$
9. $121.8x = 8.95$ **10.** $1.725x = 34.5$
11. $98x = 21.732$ **12.** $756.8x = 14,275.9$

■ 3-6 DECIMAL EQUIVALENTS AND ORDER

In both applied and theoretical mathematics it is often convenient to express a common fraction in decimal form. The following example illustrates two methods.

Example 1. Find the equivalent, in decimal form, of the following fractions: (a) $\frac{1}{2}$ (b) $\frac{7}{8}$ (c) $\frac{2}{3}$.

(a) Method 1. $\frac{1}{2} \times \frac{5}{5} = \frac{5}{10}$, or 0.5.

$$\text{Method 2.} \quad \frac{1}{2} = 2\overline{)1.0} \quad \overset{0.5}{}$$

(b) Method 1. $\frac{7}{8} \times \frac{125}{125} = \frac{875}{1000}$, or 0.875

$$\text{Method 2.} \quad \frac{7}{8} = 8\overline{)7.000} \quad \overset{0.875}{}$$

(c) Method 1. $\dfrac{2}{3} \times \dfrac{33\frac{1}{3}}{33\frac{1}{3}} = \dfrac{66\frac{2}{3}}{100}$, or $0.66\dfrac{2}{3}$

$$\text{Method 2.} \quad \frac{2}{3} = 3\overline{)2.000\ldots} \quad \overset{0.666\ldots}{}$$

Thus

$$\tfrac{2}{3} = 0.66\ldots, \text{ or } 0.66\tfrac{2}{3}.$$

Also,

$$\tfrac{2}{3} \approx 0.67.$$

In Method 1 we use the principle $n \times 1 = n$. In Method 2 we use the fact that $a/b = a \div b$ if $b \neq 0$.

In Example 1(a) we say that 0.5 is a **terminating decimal** since $\frac{1}{2}$ is exactly 0.5. In Example 1(c) 0.666 . . . is called a **nonterminating,** or unending, **decimal,** as indicated by the three dots, . . .

The concept of positional notation can be used to write a decimal as a common fraction.

Example 2. Write as a common fraction: (a) 0.25 (b) 0.325 (c) 2.075.

(a) $0.25 = 25$ hundredths $= \frac{25}{100}$, or $\frac{1}{4}$

(b) $0.325 = 325$ thousandths $= \frac{325}{1000}$, or $\frac{13}{40}$

(c) $2.075 = 2$ and 75 thousandths $= 2\frac{75}{1000}$, or $2\frac{3}{40}$

To show the **order relation,** or relative size, of two numbers, we first express each in terms of a common unit. For example, $\frac{3}{4} = 9$ *twelfths* and $\frac{5}{6} = 10$ *twelfths*; since 10 twelfths is greater than 9 twelfths, then $\frac{5}{6} > \frac{3}{4}$. Decimal units are convenient for many such problems.

Example 3. Arrange in order of size: 0.49, 0.487, and 0.5.
We use one thousandth as the common unit. Since

$$0.500 > 0.490 > 0.487,$$

then

$$0.5 > 0.49 > 0.487.$$

Example 4. Now we arrange 1.23, $1\frac{1}{4}$, 1.209, and $1\frac{1}{5}$ in order of size. We use one thousandth as the common unit. Since

$$1.250 > 1.230 > 1.209 > 1.200,$$

then

$$1\frac{1}{4} > 1.23 > 1.209 > 1\frac{1}{5}.$$

Example 5. Express as a pure decimal: (a) $0.25\frac{1}{2}$ (b) $0.006\frac{1}{4}$.

(a) $0.25\frac{1}{2} = 25\frac{1}{2}$ hundredths

$= 25.5$ hundredths $= \dfrac{25.5}{100} \times \dfrac{10}{10} = \dfrac{255}{1000}$

$= 0.255$

(b) $0.006\frac{1}{4} = 6\frac{1}{4}$ thousandths

$= 6.25$ thousandths

$= \dfrac{6.25}{1000} \times \dfrac{100}{100} = \dfrac{62,500}{100,000}$

$= 0.00625$

Exercises for Section 3–6

3–6 A

Solve for x:

1. $\dfrac{1}{5} \times \dfrac{x}{x} = \dfrac{2}{10} = 0.2$

2. $\dfrac{3}{4} \times \dfrac{x}{x} = \dfrac{75}{100} = 0.75$

3. $\dfrac{5}{8} \times \dfrac{x}{x} = \dfrac{625}{1000} = 0.625$

4. $\dfrac{7}{20} \times \dfrac{x}{x} = \dfrac{35}{100} = 0.35$

5. $\dfrac{7}{40} \times \dfrac{x}{x} = \dfrac{175}{1000} = 0.175$

6. $\dfrac{3}{80} \times \dfrac{x}{x} = \dfrac{375}{10,000} = 0.0375$

7. $\dfrac{9}{16} \times \dfrac{x}{x} = \dfrac{5625}{10,000} = 0.5625$

8. $\dfrac{1}{32} \times \dfrac{x}{x} = \dfrac{3125}{100,000} = 0.03125$

3–6 B

Express as decimals:

1. $\frac{1}{4}$ 2. $\frac{1}{5}$ 3. $\frac{2}{5}$ 4. $\frac{3}{4}$

5. $\frac{1}{2}$ 6. $\frac{3}{5}$ 7. $\frac{1}{8}$ 8. $\frac{4}{5}$

9. $\frac{5}{8}$ 10. $\frac{1}{16}$ 11. $\frac{7}{16}$ 12. $\frac{7}{8}$

13. $\frac{7}{10}$ 14. $\frac{3}{8}$ 15. $\frac{11}{16}$ 16. $\frac{5}{32}$

3–6 C

Express as common fractions in reduced form:

1. 0.4   2. 0.35   3. 0.5   4. 0.75

5. 0.8   6. 0.72   7. 0.08   8. 0.05

9. 0.24   10. 0.36   11. 0.85   12. 0.95

13. 0.02   14. 0.01   15. 0.99   16. 0.16

3–6 D

Express as decimals to the nearest thousandth:

1. $\frac{1}{3}$ 2. $\frac{1}{7}$ 3. $\frac{2}{3}$ 4. $\frac{4}{7}$

5. $\frac{5}{17}$ 6. $\frac{2}{9}$ 7. $\frac{3}{7}$ 8. $\frac{1}{6}$

9. $\frac{11}{17}$ 10. $\frac{5}{6}$ 11. $\frac{5}{9}$ 12. $\frac{5}{11}$

13. $\frac{7}{9}$ 14. $\frac{9}{11}$ 15. $\frac{5}{7}$ 16. $\frac{13}{21}$

3-6 E

Express as common fractions or mixed numbers:

1. 1.5	**2.** 3.48	**3.** 11.65	**4.** 1.008
5. 2.075	**6.** 4.055	**7.** 10.010	**8.** 13.605
9. 9.125	**10.** 1.0625	**11.** 5.875	**12.** 10.1875
13. 4.0375	**14.** 20.925	**15.** 12.625	**16.** 18.9375

3-6 F

Arrange in order of size:

1. 0.28, 0.279	**2.** 0.012, 0.01188	**3.** 0.64, 0.650
4. 0.401, 0.4011	**5.** 0.04, 0.004	**6.** 0.012, 0.009
7. 0.143, 0.1399	**8.** 1.101, 1.1009	**9.** 1.21, 1.2075
10. 13.0610, 13.0609	**11.** 9.011, 9.002	**12.** 3.141, 3.1401

3-6 G

If a statement is true, mark it true. If it is false, write a replacement for the symbol ($>$, $=$, $<$) to make it true.

1. $1.05 < 1.1$	**2.** $1.75 = 1\frac{3}{4}$	**3.** $1.65 < 1.599$
4. $0.019 > 0.0189$	**5.** $2\frac{3}{8} > 2.401$	**6.** $4 < 3.999$
7. $2\frac{1}{3} < 2.334$	**8.** $1.24 > 1\frac{1}{5}$	**9.** $7.495 = 7\frac{99}{200}$
10. $0.35 < \frac{7}{20}$	**11.** $1.85 > \frac{37}{20}$	**12.** $4.05 = 3\frac{21}{20}$

3-6 H

Find the difference in each pair of lengths. Express answers in decimal form.

1. 3.75 ft and $1\frac{1}{4}$ ft	**2.** 5.08 ft and $2\frac{4}{5}$ ft
3. 16.381 ft and $9\frac{3}{8}$ ft	**4.** 40.00 ft and $30\frac{1}{2}$ ft
5. $7\frac{7}{8}$ ft and 7.625 ft	**6.** $2\frac{1}{4}$ ft and 0.75 ft
7. 0.082 ft and $\frac{3}{5}$ ft	**8.** 1.0075 ft and $\frac{3}{50}$ ft
9. 3.0125 ft and 6.0050 ft	**10.** 75.85 ft and $71\frac{13}{25}$ ft

3-6 I

Express as pure decimals:

1. $0.12\frac{1}{2}$	**2.** $0.75\frac{1}{2}$	**3.** $0.25\frac{1}{4}$	**4.** $0.05\frac{1}{4}$
5. $0.16\frac{1}{4}$	**6.** $0.70\frac{1}{2}$	**7.** $0.62\frac{1}{2}$	**8.** $0.15\frac{3}{8}$
9. $2.132\frac{3}{4}$	**10.** $1.07\frac{3}{8}$	**11.** $0.007\frac{1}{2}$	**12.** $0.012\frac{1}{4}$
13. $0.125\frac{3}{5}$	**14.** $0.225\frac{1}{5}$	**15.** $0.0175\frac{7}{8}$	**16.** $0.045\frac{3}{16}$

3-6 J

A nonterminating decimal in which digits repeat can be expressed as a fraction. Consider $n = 0.1212\ldots$ Note that

$$100 \times 0.1212\ldots = 12.1212\ldots$$

Now we write these equations and subtract:

$$100n = 12.1212\ldots$$
$$n = 0.1212\ldots$$
$$\overline{99n = 12}$$
$$n = \tfrac{12}{99}.$$

Thus

$$0.1212\ldots = \tfrac{12}{99}.$$

In each exercise express n as a common fraction.

1. $n = 0.111\ldots$
To do this, solve

$$10n = 1.111\ldots,$$
$$n = 0.111\ldots$$

2. $n = 0.555\ldots$
To do this, solve

$$10n = 5.555\ldots,$$
$$n = 0.555\ldots$$

3. $n = 0.123123\ldots$
To do this, solve

$$1000n = 123.123\ldots,$$
$$n = 0.123\ldots$$

4. $n = 0.0909\ldots$
To do this, solve

$$100n = 9.09\ldots,$$
$$n = 0.09\ldots$$

5. $n = 0.1717\ldots$

6. $n = 0.243243\ldots$

■ 3-7 PERCENT

The Latin term *per centum* means *by the hundred* and was used by the Romans to designate fractions which were easily changed to hundredths. The term **percent** (symbol, %), now part of our everyday language, means *hundredths*. Thus

$$r\% \text{ means } \frac{r}{100}.$$

In (1) and (2) notice how the statements on the left are expressed in terms of percent.

$10 is $\frac{1}{2}$ of $20. Thus $10 is 50% of $20, since $50\% = \frac{50}{100} = \frac{1}{2}$.   (1)

60 is $1\frac{1}{2}$ of 40. Thus 60 is 150% of 40, since $150\% = \frac{150}{100} = 1\frac{1}{2}$.   (2)

We use the definition of percent to express a decimal as a number of percent.

Example 1. Express as a number of percent: (a) 0.25   (b) 0.465 (c) 1.23.

(a) $0.25 = \frac{25}{100} = 25\%$

(b) $0.465 = \dfrac{46.5}{100} = 46.5\%$

(c) $1.23 = \frac{123}{100} = 123\%$

Also, we use the definition of percent to express a number of percent as a decimal.

Example 2. Express as a decimal: (a) 34% (b) 6% (c) 254%.

(a) $34\% = \frac{34}{100} = 0.34$

(b) $6\% = \frac{6}{100} = 0.06$

(c) $254\% = \frac{254}{100} = 2.54$

To express a common fraction or a mixed number n as a number of percent, we first express n as a decimal; then express the decimal as a number of percent.

Example 3. Express as a number of percent: (a) $\frac{3}{4}$ (b) $1\frac{1}{8}$.

(a) By division we find

$$\tfrac{3}{4} = 0.75.$$

Then

$$n = \tfrac{3}{4} = 0.75 = \tfrac{75}{100} = 75\%.$$

(b) By division we find

$$\tfrac{1}{8} = 0.125.$$

Then

$$n = 1\frac{1}{8} = 1.125 = \frac{112.5}{100} = 112.5\%.$$

To express a number of percent in terms of a fraction, we also use the definition, $r\% = r/100$.

Example 4. Express as fractions: (a) 72% (b) $8\frac{3}{4}\%$.

(a) $72\% = \frac{72}{100} = \frac{18}{25}$

(b) $8\frac{3}{4}\% = \frac{8\frac{3}{4}}{100} = \frac{\frac{35}{4}}{100} \times \frac{4}{4} = \frac{35}{400}$ or $\frac{7}{80}$

The following general statements can be made.

II.   **If n represents a number, then $n = 100n\%$.**

III.   **If r represents a number, then $r\% = \dfrac{r}{100}$.**

The student will improve his understanding of the topic if he keeps in mind that *percent means hundredths.*

Exercises for Section 3-7

3-7 A

Express in percent:

1. 0.05	**2.** 0.15	**3.** 0.23	**4.** 0.36
5. 0.75	**6.** 0.86	**7.** 0.93	**8.** 1.05
9. 1.25	**10.** 1.95	**11.** 1.50	**12.** 1.75
13. 0.625	**14.** 0.0725	**15.** 0.125	**16.** 0.0175

3-7 B

Express in percent, to the nearest 0.1%:

1. $\frac{1}{8}$	**2.** $\frac{1}{5}$	**3.** $\frac{1}{2}$	**4.** $\frac{1}{4}$
5. $\frac{3}{8}$	**6.** $\frac{2}{5}$	**7.** $\frac{7}{8}$	**8.** $\frac{3}{4}$
9. 1	**10.** $\frac{3}{5}$	**11.** $\frac{7}{25}$	**12.** 2
13. $\frac{13}{10}$	**14.** $\frac{23}{16}$	**15.** $\frac{17}{12}$	**16.** $\frac{3}{2}$

3-7 C

Express in percent, to the nearest 0.1%:

1. $\frac{1}{3}$	**2.** $\frac{3}{5}$	**3.** $\frac{1}{9}$	**4.** $\frac{11}{10}$
5. $\frac{1}{16}$	**6.** $\frac{2}{7}$	**7.** $5\frac{4}{9}$	**8.** $\frac{237}{100}$
9. $\frac{2}{3}$	**10.** $2\frac{1}{5}$	**11.** $\frac{5}{9}$	**12.** $\frac{927}{1000}$
13. $1\frac{2}{3}$	**14.** $\frac{9}{16}$	**15.** $\frac{3}{7}$	**16.** $\frac{9}{5}$

3-7 D

Express as: (a) a decimal; (b) a reduced fraction or mixed number:

1. 1%	**2.** 2%	**3.** 5%	**4.** 25%
5. 35%	**6.** 50%	**7.** 75%	**8.** 80%
9. 10%	**10.** 100%	**11.** 115%	**12.** 160%
13. $12\frac{1}{2}\%$	**14.** 10.5%	**15.** 200%	**16.** $10\frac{1}{5}\%$

3-7 E

Express as: (a) a decimal (or complex decimal); (b) a reduced fraction or mixed number:

1. $\frac{1}{2}\%$	**2.** $1\frac{1}{2}\%$	**3.** $37\frac{1}{2}\%$	**4.** 40%
5. $\frac{1}{4}\%$	**6.** $\frac{7}{8}\%$	**7.** $87\frac{1}{2}\%$	**8.** 22%
9. $22\frac{1}{2}\%$	**10.** 32.5%	**11.** $66\frac{2}{3}\%$	**12.** $6\frac{1}{4}\%$
13. $16\frac{2}{3}\%$	**14.** $2\frac{1}{8}\%$	**15.** $72\frac{1}{4}\%$	**16.** $33\frac{1}{3}\%$

3-7 F

Rewrite the statements, using percent in place of the number(s).

1. He allots $\frac{1}{5}$ of his pay check to recreation.
2. They have completed 0.72 of their work.
3. Our team got $\frac{3}{4}$ of the rebounds.
4. Five out of every 100 people voted against the issue.
5. Mays' batting average was $\frac{33}{100}$.
6. The shortstop successfully completed 0.755 of his attempts.
7. The material is 0.52 cotton and 0.48 wool.
8. We have completed 648 of the 1000 pages in the book.
9. A student received 150 out of 200 possible points on his midterm examination.
10. This medicine is $0.32\frac{1}{2}$ filler.

■ 3-8 PERCENTAGE, RATE, AND BASE

The most common uses of percent can be described with the simple pattern $p = r \times b$, where p, r, and b represent numbers. In this pattern, p represents the **percentage**; r, the **rate**; b, the **base**.

$$\text{IV.} \qquad p = r \times b$$

If we know the values of two of the variables in the ordered triple (p, r, b), we can easily find the third by using formula IV.

Example 1. Find 15% of 70.

$$p = r \times b$$
$$p = 0.15 \times 70 = 10.5$$

Example 2. If 25% of a number is 80, find the number.

$$p = r \times b$$
$$80 = 0.25 \times b$$
$$b = 80 \div 0.25 = 320$$

Example 3. What percent of 200 is 40?

$$p = r \times b$$
$$40 = r \times 200$$
$$r = 40 \div 200 = 0.20, \text{ or } 20\%$$

Example 4. Find the amount of money which must be invested at 4% for 1 year to produce $14.00 in interest.

$$p = r \times b$$
$$14 = 0.04 \times b$$
$$b = 14 \div 0.04 = 350$$

The amount is $350.00.

In each example note that we have a rate r times a base b; the product is the percentage p. The rate is expressed in percent.

Exercises for Section 3-8

3-8 A

For each ordered pair (r, b), use the formula $p = rb$ to find p:

1. $(5\%, 110)$
2. $(12\%, 40)$
3. $(24\%, 160)$
4. $(35\%, 200)$
5. $(4\frac{1}{2}\%, 120)$
6. $(3\frac{1}{2}\%, 16.4)$
7. $(9\frac{1}{4}\%, 200)$
8. $(3\frac{3}{4}\%, 500)$
9. $(120\%, 18)$
10. $(130\%, 5.6)$
11. $(115\%, 740)$
12. $(104\frac{1}{2}\%, 190.8)$

3-8 B

1. Find $13\frac{1}{2}\%$ of $648.
2. On a loan of $1000, a borrower must pay $7\frac{1}{2}\%$ interest each year. Find his interest on a loan of $1000 for 6 years.
3. Find 127% of 3680 pounds.
4. Sales tax is 4% of the amount of the purchase. Find the sales tax on a load of firewood which costs $18.75.
5. The original enrollment in a class was 48. After 6 weeks, $12\frac{1}{2}\%$ of the students had dropped. Find the number left.
6. Find $\frac{1}{2}\%$ of 8424 tons.
7. Find 50% of 8424 people.
8. In a western city 30% of the days in September were cloudy and the rest clear. Find the number of clear days.
9. Ten years ago a man paid $27.25 for a tool. Today he must pay 115% of that price for the same tool. Find the cost today.
10. In 1804 Thomas Jefferson received 92% of the 176 electoral votes cast. Find the number of votes he received. Round off your answer to the nearest vote.

3-8 C

In the formula $p = rb$ determine b for each ordered pair (r, p):

1. $(5\%, 20)$
2. $(10\%, 10)$
3. $(4\frac{1}{2}\%, 4.5)$
4. $(20\%, 36)$
5. $(12\frac{1}{2}\%, 13)$
6. $(42\%, 8.4)$
7. $(60\%, 120)$
8. $(110\%, 22)$
9. $(75\%, 21)$
10. $(82\%, 87.74)$
11. $(4\frac{1}{4}\%, 114.75)$
12. $(24\%, 0.0576)$

3-8 D

1. Find the base if the rate is 15% and the percentage is 60.
2. During a storm, 6% of the houses in one block were destroyed. If 12 houses were destroyed, find the original number in the block.
3. A man paid $34.00 for sales tax on a purchase of some furniture. If the rate of tax was 4%, find the total amount he paid.
4. A student has saved $87.50, which is 35% of the amount she needs to begin the next quarter of school. Find the amount she still needs to save.
5. Find the base if the rate is $4\frac{1}{2}$% and the percentage is $56.26.
6. For one worker, a 15% increase in salary results in a new salary of $7360 a year. Find the old salary. (*Note:* The new salary is 115% of the old.)
7. A used-car dealer bought a convertible and marked the price up $22\frac{1}{2}$% to $1249.50. What did he pay for the car?
8. In 1903 Pittsburgh won the National League Pennant with 91 wins. This was 65% of the games they played. Find the number of games they lost that year.
9. For one dealer, the markup on a suit of clothes is $23.05. Find the cost to the dealer if he uses a 35% rate of markup.
10. How much money must be invested at 4.85% in order to earn $121.25 in one year?

3-8 E

In the formula $p = rb$ determine r for each ordered pair (p, b):

1. (5, 20)   2. (3, 20)   3. (15, 40)
4. (17, 100)   5. (7.5, 200)   6. (35, 200)
7. (19, 380)   8. (82.6, 99.2)   9. (6, 240)
10. (47.7, 9.54)   11. (1677.5, 13.75) 12. (40.365, 1242)

3-8 F

1. Find what percent 105 is of 875.
2. What percent of $125.75 is $45.27?
3. A local philanthropist contributed $3500 toward the $10,000 needed to start a boys' club. What percent of the total amount needed did he contribute?

Exercises 3–8 F continued on page 150.

4. A college honor society had 321 members. If the total student body had 5350 members, find the percent of the student body in the honor society.

5. The catcher on a baseball team got 24 hits in 60 times at bat. Find his batting average as a number of percent.

6. On the first day of a psychology class, the enrollment was 140. Only 105 of the students finished the course. What percent finished the course?

7. Pure gold is called 24 carat. Find the percent of gold in a 20-carat gold ring.

8. A dealer bought suits at $52.50 each and sold them for $67.50 each. Find the percent of markup.

9. A student has completed 75 of the 120 semester units she needs for her degree. What percent of the total remains to be completed?

10. For some banking purposes, 360 is considered to be a year.

    (a) What fraction of such a year is 225 days?

    (b) What percent of such a year is 225 days?

3-8 G

1. Does $\frac{1}{2}\% \times 200 = \frac{1}{2} \times (1\% \times 200)$?
2. Does $\frac{1}{4}\% \times 200 = \frac{1}{4} \times (1\% \times 200)$?
3. Does $\frac{1}{8}\% \times 1600 = \frac{1}{8} \times (1\% \times 1600)$?
4. Does $2\frac{1}{4}\% \times 1600 = (2\% \times 1600) + [\frac{1}{4} \times (1\% \times 1600)]$?
5. Find the following.

    (a) $\frac{1}{2}\% \times 200$ (b) $\frac{1}{4}\% \times 400$

    (c) $\frac{1}{8}\% \times 1600$ (d) $2\frac{1}{4}\% \times 1600$

6. A buyer paid $4000 for some stock. He paid a stockbroker $\frac{1}{2}\%$ of this amount as commission. Find his total cost.

7. A salesman sold a house for $22,500. He was paid $3\frac{1}{2}\%$ of this amount as a commission. Find his commission.

8. During the trip from ranch to market, a load of cattle lost $1\frac{1}{2}\%$ of their weight. Find the weight of the cattle at the ranch if they weighed 19,700 pounds at the market. (*Note:* The weight at the market was $98\frac{1}{2}\%$ of the weight at the ranch.)

9. A body falling from rest reaches a speed of 32 feet per second at the end of 1 second. At the end of $2\frac{1}{2}$ seconds, the speed is 250% of the speed at the end of 1 second. Find the speed after $2\frac{1}{2}$ seconds.

10. If $r \times b = 7$ and $r = 2\frac{1}{3}\%$, find b.

■ 3-9 SCIENTIFIC NOTATION

In Section 1–4 note that exponents and powers provide a concise form for expressing large numbers. For example,

$$100 = 1 \times 10^2, 1000 = 1 \times 10^3, 100{,}000 = 1 \times 10^5, \quad (1)$$

$$200 = 2 \times 10^2, 7000 = 7 \times 10^3, 400{,}000 = 4 \times 10^5. \quad (2)$$

A number is expressed in **scientific notation** if it is stated as a product of a number n, $1 \le n < 10$, and a power of 10.

Example 1. Write the following numbers in scientific notation: (a) 1200 (b) 8,970,000.

(a) $1200 = 1.2 \times 1000$　　(b) $8{,}970{,}000 = 8.97 \times 1{,}000{,}000$
$ = 1.2 \times 10^3$　　　　$\phantom{(b) 8{,}970{,}000} = 8.97 \times 10^6$

Numbers between 0 and 1 (or their approximations) can be expressed in scientific notation. First, however, we must make some definitions. You know that $10^1 = 10$, $10^2 = 100$, $10^3 = 1000$, and so on. Now we extend this notation in a manner useful in scientific notation. We define: $10^0 = 1$; $10^{-1} = \frac{1}{10}$ (read, "10 to the negative 1 power equals $\frac{1}{10}$"); $10^{-2} = \frac{1}{10^2} = \frac{1}{100}$ (read, "10 to the negative 2 power equals $\frac{1}{10^2}$ equals $\frac{1}{100}$"); and so on. Hence we have

$$\vdots$$
$$10^3 = 1000,$$
$$10^2 = 100,$$
$$10^1 = 10,$$
$$10^0 = 1,$$
$$10^{-1} = \frac{1}{10} = 0.1,$$
$$10^{-2} = \frac{1}{10^2} = 0.01,$$
$$10^{-3} = \frac{1}{10^3} = 0.001,$$
$$\vdots$$

In Example 2 we express some numbers n, where

$$0 < n < 1,$$

in scientific notation.

Example 2. Express the following in scientific notation: (a) 0.023
(b) 0.0023 (c) 0.00023.

(a) $0.023 = \dfrac{2.3}{100} = \dfrac{2.3}{10^2} = 2.3 \times 10^{-2}$

(b) $0.0023 = \dfrac{2.3}{1000} = \dfrac{2.3}{10^3} = 2.3 \times 10^{-3}$

(c) $0.00023 = \dfrac{2.3}{10,000} = \dfrac{2.3}{10^4} = 2.3 \times 10^{-4}$

In mathematics we use scientific notation to show the number of significant digits in a number in the following way. A number expressed in scientific notation is written in the form

$$a \times 10^n,$$

where $1 \le a < 10$. We follow this rule: the number of significant digits in a shows the number of significant digits in the number. Consider (3), (4), (5), and (6). Significant digits are underlined.

$$2100 = 2.1 \times 10^3, \tag{3}$$

$$2000 = 2.00 \times 10^3, \tag{4}$$

$$17,000 = 1.7000 \times 10^4, \tag{5}$$

$$0.170 = 1.70 \times 10^{-1}. \tag{6}$$

Exercises for Section 3-9

3-9 A

Express in scientific notation:

1. 1000	**2.** 10,000	**3.** 70	**4.** 500
5. 900	**6.** 3000	**7.** 7000	**8.** 14
9. 805	**10.** 120	**11.** 1900	**12.** 27,200
13. 3500	**14.** 29,500	**15.** 1,600,000	**16.** 19,700,000

3-9 B

Express in scientific notation:

1. 0.01	**2.** 0.05	**3.** 0.0001	**4.** 0.0005
5. 0.065	**6.** 0.0072	**7.** 0.0101	**8.** 0.000065
9. 0.00044	**10.** 0.00298	**11.** 0.000374	**12.** 0.06008
13. 0.0000172	**14.** 0.000709	**15.** 0.0000113	**16.** 0.000000653

3-9 C

Express each number in ordinary decimal notation, and underline the significant digits in each answer:

1. 1.7×10^2	**2.** 4.8×10^3	**3.** 7×10^6
4. 1.3×10^5	**5.** 4.57×10^3	**6.** 2.09×10^5
7. 3.62×10^2	**8.** 9.09×10^3	**9.** 1.83×10^2
10. 7.05×10^6	**11.** 8.12×10^4	**12.** 9.33×10^5

3-9 D

Express in ordinary decimal notation:

1. 3×10^{-2}	**2.** 7×10^{-3}	**3.** 1.6×10^{-2}
4. 4.5×10^{-3}	**5.** 6.06×10^{-4}	**6.** 1.12×10^{-3}
7. 4.75×10^{-4}	**8.** 1.07×10^{-4}	**9.** 1.39×10^{-6}
10. 6.102×10^{-8}	**11.** 4.713×10^{-4}	**12.** 8.008×10^{-7}

3-9 E

Express in scientific notation:

1. 186,000 (the speed of light in miles per second)
2. 86,400 (the number of seconds in a day)
3. 1083 (the melting point of copper, in degrees centigrade)
4. 0.005611 (the weight, in pounds, of a cubic foot of hydrogen)
5. $43,000 (the annual salary of the Vice-President of the United States)
6. 3049 (the number of miles, by road, between San Francisco and New York)
7. 0.7457 (the number of kilowatts in 1 horsepower)
8. 0.00397 (the number of British thermal units in 1 calorie)
9. 0.014 (the number of seconds required for light to travel from San Francisco to New York)
10. 0.3937 (the number of inches in 1 centimeter)

■ 3–10 FRACTIONS IN BASE SIX

In Section 1–10 we studied a system of whole numbers in base six. The fundamental concepts in base six are the same as in base ten or in any other base. Consider the following two arrays in which each number has a fraction part.

In base ten we define place value in powers of ten. In base six we define place value in powers of six. Thus

$$67.58_{\text{ten}} = [(6 \times 10) + (7 \times 1) + (5 \times \tfrac{1}{10}) + (8 \times \tfrac{1}{100})]_{\text{ten}}, \qquad (1)$$

$$34.52_{\text{six}} = [(3 \times 6) + (4 \times 1) + (5 \times \tfrac{1}{6}) + (2 \times \tfrac{1}{36})]_{\text{ten}}. \qquad (2)$$

From (2) note that the units of place value to the right of the point are

$$\tfrac{1}{6}, \quad \tfrac{1}{36}, \quad \tfrac{1}{216}, \quad \tfrac{1}{1296}, \cdots,$$

when expressed in base ten. That is,

$$\frac{1}{6^1}, \quad \frac{1}{6^2}, \quad \frac{1}{6^3}, \quad \frac{1}{6^4}, \cdots$$

To add, subtract, multiply, and divide in base six, we can apply the principles used in base ten. For example, we add in base six in the following way.

Example 1. Find the sum: $1.23_{\text{six}} + 2.44_{\text{six}} + 4.35_{\text{six}}$.

$$
\begin{array}{ll}
1.23 & 3 + 4 + 5 = 12_{\text{ten}} = 20_{\text{six}}; \text{ we "carry" 2.} \\
2.44 & 2 + 2 + 4 + 3 = 11_{\text{ten}} = 15_{\text{six}}; \text{ we "carry" 1.} \\
\underline{4.35} & 1 + 1 + 2 + 4 = 8_{\text{ten}} = 12_{\text{six}} \\
12.50_{\text{six}} &
\end{array}
$$

Example 2. Find the difference: $24.50_{six} - 2.34_{six}$.

24.50	$10_{six} - 4_{six} = 2_{six}$
2.34	$4_{six} - 3_{six} = 1_{six}$
22.12_{six}	$24_{six} - 2_{six} = 22_{six}$

Multiplication and division are somewhat more complicated than addition and subtraction. We have shown only addition and subtraction because the purpose of this section is to show that a system in base six can readily be developed in the manner of our base ten system.

Exercises for Section 3-10

3-10 A

If $n = 2 + (3 \times \frac{1}{6}) + (4 \times \frac{1}{36})$, then $n = 2.34_{six}$. Express n in base six:

1. $n = 3 + (2 \times \frac{1}{6}) + (5 \times \frac{1}{36})$
2. $n = (4 \times 6) + (3 \times 1) + (5 \times \frac{1}{6}) + (2 \times \frac{1}{36})$
3. $n = (2 \times 6) + (5 \times 1) + (1 \times \frac{1}{6}) + (3 \times \frac{1}{36})$
4. $n = (4 \times 6) + (0 \times 1) + (0 \times \frac{1}{6}) + (5 \times \frac{1}{36})$
5. $n = (2 \times 6) + (2 \times \frac{1}{6}) + (3 \times \frac{1}{36})$
6. $n = (4 \times 6) + (3 \times \frac{1}{36})$
7. $n = (2 \times 6^2) + (3 \times 6) + (2 \times 1) + (5 \times \frac{1}{6})$
8. $n = (3 \times 6^3) + (2 \times 6) + (3 \times 1) + (4 \times \frac{1}{6})$
9. $n = (3 \times 6^3) + (3 \times 1) + (2 \times \frac{1}{6}) + (5 \times \frac{1}{36})$
10. $n = (4 \times 6^3) + (5 \times \frac{1}{6}) + (2 \times \frac{1}{36})$

3-10 B

In each exercise a number is expressed in base six. As in (2), page 154, express each number in base ten.

1. 0.4	**2.** 0.24
3. 0.32	**4.** 0.43
5. 0.204	**6.** 0.124
7. 0.232	**8.** 0.451
9. 3.502	**10.** 2.423
11. 4.153	**12.** 3.244

3–10 C

If $n = 0.2_{six} + 0.5_{six}$, then $n = 1.1_{six}$. Within each exercise all numbers are expressed in base six. Solve for n in base six:

1. $n = 0.2 + 0.1$ **2.** $n = 0.3 + 0.2$
3. $n = 0.3 + 0.3$ **4.** $n = 0.4 + 0.4$
5. $n = 0.5 + 0.5$ **6.** $n = 1.1 + 1.4$
7. $n = 1.1 + 1.5 + 1.0$ **8.** $n = 1.2 + 1.1 + 1.3$
9. $n = 1.2 + 1.2 + 1.4$ **10.** $n = 2.1 + 1.3 + 1.4$
11. $n = 2.1 + 2.2 + 2.2$ **12.** $n = 2.1 + 1.4 + 1.4$

3–10 D

Within each exercise the numbers are expressed in base six. Find each sum in base six:

1. 1.22	**2.** 2.05	**3.** 3.21	**4.** 4.25
2.13	2.11	2.42	4.33
5. 12.31	**6.** 53.25	**7.** 124.12	**8.** 33.405
24.32	42.14	35.45	13.241
9. 24.103	**10.** 40.024	**11.** 30.415	**12.** 21.403
13.224	15.553	15.524	33.505

3–10 E

If $n = 2.2_{six} - 1.4_{six}$, then $n = 0.4_{six}$. Within each exercise numbers are expressed in base six. Solve for n in base six:

1. $n = 1.2 - 1.1$ **2.** $n = 2.4 - 2.3$ **3.** $n = 4.3 - 2.2$
4. $n = 13.5 - 2.4$ **5.** $n = 22.4 - 2.3$ **6.** $n = 20.3 - 1.1$
7. $n = 1.4 - 0.5$ **8.** $n = 2.1 - 0.4$ **9.** $n = 3.2 - 0.4$
10. $n = 4.1 - 0.5$ **11.** $n = 2.3 - 1.4$ **12.** $n = 4.1 - 2.3$

3–10 F

Within each exercise numbers are expressed in base six. Subtract and give each difference in base six:

1. 4.21	**2.** 5.24	**3.** 5.13	**4.** 3.402
3.12	4.13	2.05	2.432
5. 13.13	**6.** 24.10	**7.** 45.32	**8.** 21.14
5.04	15.10	34.42	14.22

9. 35.42	**10.** 13.000	**11.** 44.002	**12.** 254.3402
12.34	4.143	35.443	145.4553

3–10 G

Consider this example in base six:

$$n = (5 \times 0.3)_{six} = [5 \times \tfrac{3}{6}]_{ten}$$
$$= \tfrac{15}{6} = 2\tfrac{3}{6} \quad \text{(in base ten)}$$
$$= 2.3_{six}.$$

Within each exercise numbers are expressed in base six. Find n in base six:

1. $n = 2 \times 0.2$	**2.** $n = 2 \times 0.3$	**3.** $n = 2 \times 0.4$
4. $n = 2 \times 0.5$	**5.** $n = 3 \times 0.3$	**6.** $n = 3 \times 0.4$
7. $n = 3 \times 0.5$	**8.** $n = 4 \times 0.3$	**9.** $n = 4 \times 0.4$
10. $n = 5 \times 0.4$	**11.** $n = 5 \times 0.5$	**12.** $n = 5 \times 1.2$

Vocabulary

The section in which each word appears is indicated in parentheses.

base (3–8)	ordered triple (Exercises 3–2 H)
complex decimal (3–2)	percent (3–7)
decimal fraction (3–1)	percentage (3–8)
mixed decimal (3–1)	rate (3–8)
nonterminating decimal (3–6)	scientific notation (3–9)
order relation (3–6)	terminating decimal (3–6)

Chapter Review

A

Solve for n, giving your answer in positional notation:

1. $\dfrac{3}{100} + \dfrac{5}{10} + \dfrac{7}{1000} = n$

2. $\dfrac{5}{1000} + \dfrac{6}{100} + \dfrac{4}{10} = n$

3. $\dfrac{5}{100} + \dfrac{7}{1000} + \dfrac{19}{10,000} = n$

Chapter Review continued on page 158.

4. $\dfrac{3}{5} + \dfrac{7}{10} + \dfrac{91}{100} = n$

5. $\dfrac{16}{100} + \dfrac{5}{10} + \dfrac{413}{1000} = n$

6. $\dfrac{8}{10,000} + \dfrac{5}{100} + \dfrac{7}{10} + \dfrac{8}{1000} = n$

7. $\dfrac{21}{1000} + \dfrac{15}{100} + \dfrac{2.9}{10} = n$

8. $\dfrac{34}{1000} + \dfrac{71}{100} + \dfrac{3.8}{10} = n$

9. $\dfrac{53.5}{1000} + \dfrac{7.8}{100} + \dfrac{5.9}{10} = n$

10. $\dfrac{7.64}{10} + \dfrac{4.9}{100} + \dfrac{63.8}{1000} = n$

B

Solve for n:

1. 27 tenths is n hundredths.

2. 270 hundredths is n tenths.

3. 251 tenths is n thousandths.

4. 251 thousandths is n tenths.

5. $\frac{3}{5}$ is n hundredths.

6. $\frac{7}{20}$ is n hundredths.

7. $\frac{8}{40}$ is n thousandths.

8. $\frac{17}{4}$ is n thousandths.

9. $\frac{17}{25}$ is n thousandths.

10. $\frac{24}{80}$ is n ten thousandths.

C

If a statement is true, mark it true. If it is false, write a replacement for the part underlined to make it true.

1. $\frac{1}{5} + \frac{2}{5} = \underline{(1 + 2)}$ fifths

2. $\frac{2}{7} + \frac{4}{7} = \underline{(2 + 4)}$ sevenths

3. $0.5 + 0.3 = \underline{(5 + 3)}$ tenths

4. $0.12 + 0.23 = \underline{(1 + 2)}$ tenths $+ (2 + 3)$ hundredths

5. $0.25 + 0.37 = \underline{(2 + 3) \times \frac{1}{10} + (5 + 7) \times \frac{1}{100}}$

6. $0.07 + 0.039 = \underline{(7 + 3) \times \frac{1}{10} + (0 + 9) \times \frac{1}{100}}$

7. $\frac{9}{10} \times \frac{11}{100} = \underline{9 \times 11 \times \frac{1}{10} \times \frac{1}{100}}$

8. $9 \times 11 \times \frac{1}{10} \times \frac{1}{1000} = \underline{99 \times 0.0001}$

9. $\frac{9}{10} \div \frac{3}{10} = \underline{9 \text{ ones} \div 3 \text{ ones}}$

10. $2.79 \div 0.09 = \underline{279 \text{ ones} \div 9 \text{ ones}}$

D

If a statement is true, mark it true. If it is false, write a replacement for the part underlined to make it true.

1. If $n = 3.15$, then $n \approx \underline{15}$.
2. If $n > 2.1$, then $\underline{n \times 5 > 10}$.
3. If $n < 3.09$, then $\underline{n \times 5 < 20}$.
4. If $n \approx 3.14$, then $\underline{2 \times n \approx 6.28}$.
5. If $n = 0.12\frac{1}{2}$, then $n = \underline{\frac{1}{8}}$.
6. If $10n = 0.666\ldots$, then $n = \underline{6.66}$.
7. If $n = 0.444\ldots$, then $n = \underline{\frac{4}{9}}$.
8. If $n = 26.5\%$, then $\underline{10n = 26.5}$.
9. If $p = 11\%$ of b and $b = 23$, then $\underline{p = 2.43}$.
10. If $p = 11\%$ of b and $p = 25.3$, then $\underline{b = 2300}$.

E

In Exercises 1–9 write in positional notation:

1. 3×10^0
2. 3×10^{-1}
3. 5.1×10^{-1}
4. 7×10^{-2}
5. 6.8×10^{-3}
6. 7.9×10^{-2}
7. 8.1×10^{-3}
8. 798×10^{-3}
9. 4.03×10^{-1}

10. Find the sum in base six: $0.32_{\text{six}} + 0.45_{\text{six}}$.

F

1. If 6% of a number is 24, find the number.
2. If 25 is 5% of a number, find the number.
3. If n is 27% of 3000, find n.
4. If 27 is $n\%$ of 90, find n.
5. If 80 is $n\%$ of 4000, find n.
6. A furniture salesman was paid a commission of 7% on his sales. Find the amount of his sales for a week when his commission was $189.00.
7. Suppose that $1\frac{1}{4}\%$ of the products in a factory are defective. Out of 10,000 products, how many are defective?
8. If $2\frac{1}{3}\%$ of b is 21, find b.
9. If $\frac{1}{2}\%$ of n is 6, find n.
10. A merchant sold goods at $112\frac{1}{2}\%$ of cost. Find the cost of an item for which the selling price is $4.50.

4 Geometric Concepts and Measurement

■ 4–1 GEOMETRIC FIGURES

The terms **point, line,** and **plane** are familiar to nearly everyone. We do not define these terms because the attempt involves words more complex than the terms themselves. We may think of a point as a mark on paper made by a sharp pencil; a line as a set of points such as those lying along the edge of a ruler; a plane as a flat surface such as a desk top or the surface of this page.

We name points with capital letters, such as P. We name a line by using two of its points. In Figure 4–1 $\overrightarrow{PQ}$ is read, "line PQ." We may also call this line $\overleftrightarrow{PS}$ or $\overleftrightarrow{QS}$. Often we name a line with a single letter, such as line L in Figure 4–2. A line extends indefinitely in either direction; we indicate this by the arrows shown.

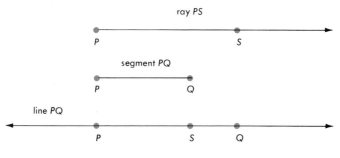

FIGURE 4–1

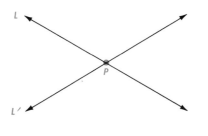

FIGURE 4-2

It is an **axiom of geometry** that through two points, one, and only one, line can be drawn. As a consequence we say that two points determine a line.

A **line segment** is a set of points on a line consisting of two endpoints and the points of the line between these endpoints. We name a segment by its endpoints. In Figure 4-1 P and Q are endpoints of line segment PQ. We write $\overline{PQ}$, which reads, "line segment PQ." Other line segments in Figure 4-1 are $\overline{QS}$ and $\overline{PS}$.

A **ray** consists of a point on a line (called the endpoint of the ray) and that part of the line on one side of the endpoint. In Figure 4-1 we have $\overrightarrow{PS}$ (read, "ray PS"), the ray with endpoint P. Ray $\overrightarrow{PS}$ contains all points on the line to the right of P, and thus includes points Q and S. Other rays in the figure are $\overrightarrow{PQ}$, $\overrightarrow{QP}$, and $\overrightarrow{SP}$.

A line is a set of points. A line segment or a ray is a special subset of such a set.

You know that the intersection of two sets is the set of all elements belonging to both sets. In Figure 4-2 the **intersection** of lines L and L' is the point P. We say that lines L and L' intersect at P. This concept can be written, "$L \cap L' = P$."

In Figure 4-3 lines K and K' are **coplanar** (lie in the same plane) and do not intersect; that is, $K \cap K' = \emptyset$, the empty set. Two lines which are coplanar and do not intersect are called **parallel lines.** We write $K \parallel K'$, read, "line K is parallel to line K'."

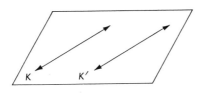

FIGURE 4-3

The set of points formed by the union of two rays having a common endpoint is called an **angle.** The common endpoint is called the **vertex** of the angle. The rays are called the **sides** of the angle. We use the symbol $\angle$ to mean *angle*.

We name an angle in several ways. To name the angle on the left in Figure 4–4, we write either $\angle EFG$ (read, "angle *EFG*") or $\angle GFE$ (read, "angle *GFE*"). Note that the letter at the vertex (in this case *F*) is placed in the middle when we write *EFG* or *GFE*. Also, we refer to angle *EFG* as $\angle F$, or $\angle 1$. Similarly, in the figure we have $\angle ABC$, or $\angle 2$, and $\angle CBD$, or $\angle 3$. Since there are two angles with vertex *B*, we do not refer to $\angle B$ because this would not distinguish clearly which angle is intended.

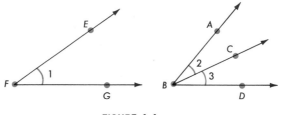

FIGURE 4–4

Exercises for Section 4–1

4–1 A

1. Give three examples of planes.
2. (a) On the surface of a flat sheet of paper, is it possible to draw two straight lines which will not meet no matter how far they are extended?
   (b) Is it possible to draw two such lines on the surface of a tin can (cylinder)? Explain.
   (c) Is it possible to draw two such lines on the surface of a ball (sphere)? Explain.
3. Figure 4–5 is the drawing of an ordinary box.
   (a) Name four pairs of parallel line segments.
   (b) Name four pairs of intersecting line segments.
   (c) What letter names the vertex of $\angle CED$? of $\angle HAB$? of $\angle ABG$? of $\angle GBA$?
   (d) Suppose we extend $\overline{CD}$ and $\overline{BH}$. Do they meet? Are they parallel? Can they lie in the same plane?

4. In Figure 4–5 find the following:
(a) $\overline{CD} \cap \overline{DF}$
(b) $\overline{AB} \cap \overline{AH}$
(c) $\overleftrightarrow{EF} \cap \overline{FG}$
(d) $\overline{CD} \cap \overleftrightarrow{EF}$

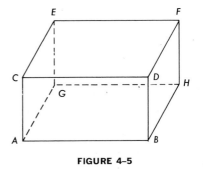

FIGURE 4–5

5. In Figure 4–6 $\overrightarrow{PR}$ represents the direction north. Name the direction represented by the following: (a) $\overrightarrow{PS}$ (b) $\overrightarrow{PT}$ (c) $\overrightarrow{PU}$.

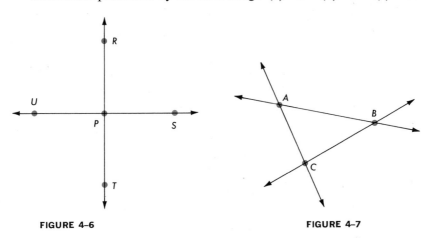

FIGURE 4–6   FIGURE 4–7

6. In Figure 4–7 points A and B determine a line; B and C determine a line; C and A determine a line. Draw 5 points, no 3 of which lie on the same line. Find the number of lines that the five points determine.

4–1 B

Name each angle in two ways.

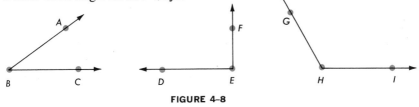

FIGURE 4–8

4-2 ANGLE MEASURE

With every angle, we can associate a number called the measure of
the angle. To make this association, we must choose a unit-angle.
The common unit-angle used is the **degree.** The instrument used to
measure an angle is called a **protractor.** In Figure 4–9 note the place-
ment of the protractor on $\angle ABC$. We say that the measure of
$\angle ABC$ is 65 (degrees). This can be shortened to $m(\angle ABC) = 65$.
We use the symbol ° for degree; thus 65° is read, "65 degrees." The
degree is subdivided into minutes and seconds:

$$1 \text{ degree } (1°) = 60 \text{ minutes } (60'),$$
$$1' = 60 \text{ seconds } (60''),$$
$$1° = 3600''.$$

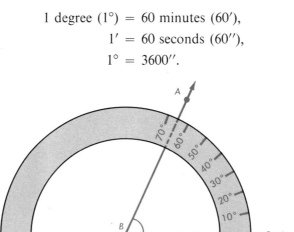

FIGURE 4–9

The measure of a **right angle** is 90. An angle which has a measure
greater than 0 but less than 90 is called an **acute angle.** An angle
which has a measure greater than 90 but less than 180 is called an
obtuse angle.

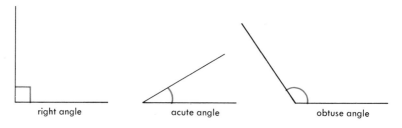

right angle   acute angle   obtuse angle

FIGURE 4–10

Two angles having the same measure are said to be **congruent.**
For example, if $m(\angle A) = 90$ and $m(\angle B) = 90$, then $\angle A \cong \angle B$
(read, "angle A is congruent to angle B"). When two lines intersect
and form right angles, the lines are said to be **perpendicular.**

Exercises for Section 4-2

4-2 A

Tell whether each measurement indicated is that of an acute angle,
a right angle, or an obtuse angle:

1. 90°
2. 37°
3. 89°
4. 2°
5. 105°
6. 75° 58′
7. 91° 30′
8. 89° 65′
9. 17° 49′
10. 109° 10′
11. 165° 48′
12. 179° 59′

4-2 B

In Figure 4-11 estimate whether each angle is an acute angle, a right
angle, or an obtuse angle.

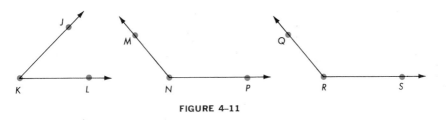

FIGURE 4-11

4-2 C

Use a protractor to measure each angle in Figure 4-11.

4-2 D

Use a protractor to draw angles with the given measures; label as
indicated:

1. 45°, $\angle ABC$
2. 69°, $\angle BDA$
3. 105°, $\angle PQR$
4. 14° 30′, $\angle EFG$
5. 5°, $\angle PST$
6. 175°, $\angle EFH$
7. 95° 30′, $\angle EST$
8. 148°, $\angle PQT$
9. 168°, $\angle ERT$
10. 158°, $\angle CAB$

4-2 E

In each exercise find the total of the measurements:

1. $63° 15'$, $72° 40'$ 2. $101° 35'$, $91° 20'$
3. $72° 18'$, $31° 40'$ 4. $16° 42'$, $37° 41'$
5. $45° 35'$, $45° 45'$ 6. $15° 17' 18''$, $60° 20' 22''$
7. $23° 41' 9''$, $58° 2' 51''$ 8. $40° 40' 40''$, $49° 19' 20''$
9. $131° 19' 51''$, $48° 40' 9''$ 10. $205° 18'$, $105° 40'$, $49° 2'$

4-2 F

1. Find the number of degrees through which the minute hand of a clock turns in 1 hour.
2. What is the measure of the angle made by the hands of the clock at 3:00?
3. The drawing shows points on the compass. Find the measure of the angle formed by the ray marked N and the ray marked NE; of the angle formed by the ray marked NW and the ray marked S.

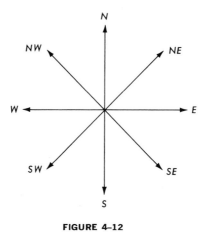

FIGURE 4-12

4. A man stood in one spot and faced east. He then turned clockwise until he faced north. Find the measure of the angle through which he turned.

In Exercises 5-8 refer to Figure 4-13 and use a protractor to find each measure:

5. $m(\angle ABC)$ 6. $m(\angle BCD)$
7. $m(\angle ADC)$ 8. $m(\angle DAB)$

9. In Exercises 5–8 find x if $x =$ $m(\angle ABC) + m(\angle BCD) +$ $m(\angle ADC) + m(\angle DAB)$.

10. Draw two more figures of the type used in Figure 4–13. Measure the angles in each drawing and find x as in Exercise 9.

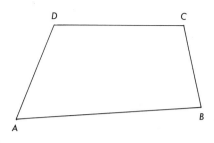

FIGURE 4–13

An Angle in Trigonometry

In trigonometry we consider *direction of turning* in defining an angle. In $\angle ABC$, $\overrightarrow{BC}$ is the initial side and $\overrightarrow{BA}$ is the terminal side. The arrow indicates that the direction of turning is counterclockwise. In $\angle DEF$, $\overrightarrow{ED}$ is the initial side and $\overrightarrow{EF}$ is the terminal side; the arrow indicates that the direction of turning is clockwise.

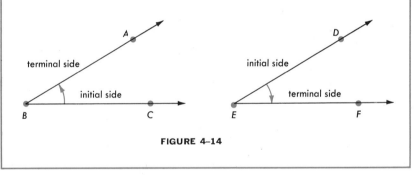

FIGURE 4–14

4–3 AXIOMS, MULTIPLICATION AND DIVISION

In order to work with formulas and to solve equations in general, we need some basic assumptions. Consider the formula $d = rt$. We wish to solve for r. Since d and rt represent the same number, we can **divide** both sides of the equation by t:

$$\frac{d}{t} = \frac{rt}{t}.$$

Thus $r = d/t$.

Now consider the formula $p/b = r$. We wish to solve for p. Since p/b and r represent the same number, we can **multiply** both numbers by b:

$$b \times \frac{p}{b} = b \times r.$$

Thus $p = br$.

The assumptions used in solving the two formulas are called axioms. We combine these assumptions in the following statement.

Axiom I. **Multiplying or dividing both sides of an equation by the same number (not zero) yields an equation having the same solution as the first equation.**

Note the use of Axiom I in the examples.

Example 1. Solve $3x = 15$.

$$3x = 15$$

$$\frac{3x}{3} = \frac{15}{3} \qquad \text{Divide both sides by 3.}$$

$$x = 5$$

Check: 3×5 does equal 15.

Example 2. Solve $\frac{1}{5}x = 2$.

$$\tfrac{1}{5}x = 2$$

$$5 \times \tfrac{1}{5}x = 5 \times 2 \qquad \text{Multiply both sides by 5.}$$

$$x = 10$$

Check: $\frac{1}{5} \times 10$ does equal 2.

Example 3. Solve for x: $ax = 5, a \neq 0$.

$$ax = 5$$

$$\frac{ax}{a} = \frac{5}{a} \qquad \text{Divide both sides by } a.$$

$$x = \frac{5}{a}$$

Check: $a \times \dfrac{5}{a}$ does equal 5, $a \neq 0$.

Example 4. Solve for x: $\dfrac{x}{a} = 5$, $a \neq 0$.

$$\frac{x}{a} = 5$$

$$a \times \frac{x}{a} = a \times 5 \qquad \text{Multiply both sides by } a.$$

$$x = 5a$$

Check: $\dfrac{5a}{a}$ does equal 5.

Sometimes it is helpful to multiply *and* divide in solving an equation, as the following example shows.

Example 5. Solve $\frac{3}{4}x = 15$.

$$\frac{3}{4}x = 15$$
$$3x = 60 \qquad \text{Multiply both sides by 4.}$$
$$x = 20 \qquad \text{Divide both sides by 3.}$$

Check: $\frac{3}{4} \times 20$ does equal 15.

Exercises for Section 4-3

4-3 A

Solve and check:

1. $3x = 12$
2. $5x = 40$
3. $7x = 50$
4. $2x = 75$
5. $13x = 65$
6. $9x = 48.6$
7. $3.75x = 72.750$
8. $12x = 48\frac{1}{2}$
9. $45x = 900$
10. $27x = 837$

4-3 B

Solve and check:

1. $\frac{1}{3}n = 7$
2. $\frac{1}{4}n = 20$
3. $\frac{1}{5}n = \frac{1}{3}$
4. $\frac{1}{5}n = 5$
5. $\frac{1}{5}n = \frac{1}{5}$
6. $\frac{1}{12}n = 5$
7. $\frac{1}{7}n = 7$
8. $\frac{1}{12}n = 24$
9. $\frac{1}{15}n = 18$
10. $\frac{1}{13}n = 23$

4–3 C

Solve and check:

1. $\frac{3}{4}y = 6$ 2. $\frac{2}{5}y = 45$ 3. $\frac{5}{8}y = 1$
4. $\frac{7}{8}y = \frac{7}{8}$ 5. $\frac{4}{15}y = 80$ 6. $1\frac{1}{2}y = 24$
7. $2\frac{3}{4}y = 22$ 8. $1.75y = 21$ 9. $\frac{5}{9}y = 455$

4–3 D

Solve for x:

1. $ax = 6$ 2. $bx = 9$ 3. $cx = d$

4. $\frac{x}{a} = 6$ 5. $\frac{x}{d} = 17$ 6. $\frac{x}{c} = d$

7. $\frac{c}{d}x = a$ 8. $\frac{cx}{d} = 1$ 9. $\frac{bx}{c} = a$

4–3 E

1. If 21 times a number is 4200, find the number. (*Note:* Let x stand for the number. Then $21x = 4200$.)
2. If 5.5 times a number is 2200, find the number.
3. If $\frac{3}{4}$ times a number is 300, find the number.
4. If $\frac{5}{8}$ times a number is 450, find the number.
5. Use the formula $d = rt$ to find t if $d = 100$ (miles) and $r = 40$ (miles per hour).
6. Use the formula $p/b = r$ to find p if $r = 0.06$ and $b = 1250$ (dollars).
7. The sum S of the measures of the angles of a quadrilateral is 360; the four angles are congruent. Use the formula $S = 4n$ to find the measure n of each angle. (*Note:* $360 = 4n$.)
8. A dealer sells clocks at s dollars each. His cost per clock is $\frac{3}{4}$ of his selling price. Find s if he pays \$114 for a clock. (*Note:* $\frac{3}{4}s = 114$.)
9. In Exercise 8 find s if the cost is \$123.
10. In Exercise 5 find r if $d = 2000$ and $t = 2\frac{1}{2}$.

4–3 F

1. In Figure 4–15 note that $7x$ is equal to 14. Find the coordinate of point A. Of point B. Of point C. (*Note:* The coordinate x is the number associated with point A.)

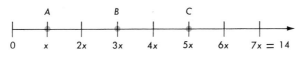

FIGURE 4-15

2. In Figure 4–16, $3\frac{1}{2}y$ is equal to 14. Find the coordinate of point D. Of point E. Of point F.

FIGURE 4-16

3. In Figure 4–17, $2\frac{1}{5}n = 22$. Find the coordinate of point G. Of point H. Of point I.

FIGURE 4-17

4. In Figure 4–18, $0.7t = 3.5$. Find the coordinate of point J. Of point K. Of point L. Of point M.

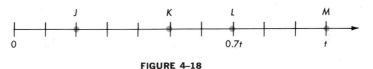

FIGURE 4-18

5. In Figure 4–18 find the coordinates of $J, K, L,$ and M if $0.4t = 2.4$.

4-4 THE ENGLISH SYSTEM OF LINEAR MEASUREMENT

Early units of measurement were of natural origin. The *cubit*, the distance from the tip of the elbow to the end of the middle finger, was used in early Biblical times. The Romans used a unit of measure called the *pace*. King Edward II declared that an *inch* was equal to 3 barleycorns chosen from the middle of an ear and placed end to end.

King Henry I established the *yard* as the distance measured from the tip of his nose to the end of his thumb when his arm was fully outstretched.

Less than two centuries ago, the French government appointed a committee to devise a better unit. The committee defined the **meter** as $\frac{1}{10,000,000}$ of the distance from the equator to the North Pole, measured along the meridian through Paris (a unit later refined in other ways). The metric system grew out of the committee's work and is now the standard system of measurement used in most of the world.

In the United States the English system of linear units is still in everyday use. The metric system, however, is recognized and is generally used in science.

Table A.

English System of Linear Measurement

12 inches (in.) = 1 foot (ft)

3 ft = 1 yard (yd)

$\left.\begin{array}{l} 5\frac{1}{2} \text{ yd} \\ \text{or } 16\frac{1}{2} \text{ ft} \end{array}\right\} = 1 \text{ rod (rd)}$

$\left.\begin{array}{l} 5280 \text{ ft} \\ \text{or } 320 \text{ rd} \end{array}\right\} = 1 \text{ mile (mi)}$

1.15^+ mi = 1 nautical mile

1 fathom = 6 feet

It is important that one be able to change units within a measurement system. From the table you see that if y stands for the number of yards in a measure and f for the number of feet in the measure, then $f = 3y$.

Example 1. Find the number of feet in $2\frac{1}{2}$ yards.

$$f = 3y$$
$$f = (3)(2\tfrac{1}{2})$$
$$f = 7\tfrac{1}{2} \text{ (feet)}$$

Note the use of Axiom I in Example 2.

Example 2. Find the number of yards in a measure of 27 feet.

$$f = 3y$$

$$27 = 3y \qquad \text{Substitute.}$$

$$\frac{27}{3} = \frac{3y}{3} \qquad \text{Divide both sides by 3.}$$

$$9 = y \qquad \text{Thus 27 feet} = 9 \text{ yards.}$$

Exercises for Section 4-4

4-4 A

Find the number of feet in each measurement:

1. 3 yd	**2.** 5 yd	**3.** 10 yd	**4.** 28 yd
5. $1\frac{1}{2}$ yd	**6.** $3\frac{2}{3}$ yd	**7.** $5\frac{7}{12}$ yd	**8.** $11\frac{1}{4}$ yd
9. 3.5 yd	**10.** 7.25 yd	**11.** $19\frac{2}{3}$ yd	**12.** 104 yd

4-4 B

Find the number of feet in each measurement:

1. 2.5 yd	**2.** 3.75 yd	**3.** 11.3 yd
4. 13.1 yd	**5.** 10 mi	**6.** 4.5 mi
7. 9.15 fathoms	**8.** 28.25 fathoms	**9.** 107.3 rd
10. 124.5 rd	**11.** 39.95 rd	**12.** 97.52 yd

4-4 C

Find the number of yards in each measurement:

1. 6 ft	**2.** 15 ft	**3.** 27 ft	**4.** 18 ft
5. 20 ft	**6.** 7 ft	**7.** 48 ft	**8.** 56 ft
9. 29 ft	**10.** 160 ft	**11.** 245 ft	**12.** 1420 ft

4-4 D

Let i equal the number of inches in a measurement, and let f equal the number of feet in the measurement. Write a formula to convert inches to feet. Use the formula to find the number of feet in each measurement:

1. 36 in.	**2.** 18 in.	**3.** 48 in.	**4.** 60 in.
5. 20 in.	**6.** 40 in.	**7.** 39 in.	**8.** 76 in.
9. 108 in.	**10.** 250 in.	**11.** 432 in.	**12.** 288 in.

4–4 E

Use your formula from 4–4 D to find the number of inches in each measurement:

1. 3 ft	**2.** 2.5 ft	**3.** 6.8 ft	**4.** 17 ft
5. 2.75 ft	**6.** 6.125 ft	**7.** $9\frac{1}{2}$ ft	**8.** $12\frac{2}{3}$ ft
9. $18\frac{1}{4}$ ft	**10.** $21\frac{1}{2}$ ft	**11.** $13\frac{3}{4}$ ft	**12.** $25\frac{5}{6}$ ft

4–4 F

Use the formulas $f = 5280m$, $y = 1760m$, and $r = 320m$ to find the number of miles in each measurement:

1. 2640 ft	**2.** 880 ft	**3.** 10,560 rd	**4.** 1056 ft
5. 3960 rd	**6.** 13,200 ft	**7.** 6336 ft	**8.** 15,840 ft
9. 1760 yd	**10.** 3520 yd	**11.** 880 yd	**12.** 440 yd

4–4 G

1. Arrange in order of size: 16 feet, $5\frac{1}{2}$ yards, $\frac{2}{3}$ rod, 190 inches.
2. Find the total number of inches in these lengths of steel bars: $2\frac{1}{2}$ feet, 17 inches, $1\frac{1}{2}$ yards, $\frac{1}{2}$ yard.
3. Arrange in order of size: 21.75 feet; $7\frac{1}{3}$ yards; 249 inches; 7 yards, 1 foot, 3 inches.
4. Use a ruler to find the length of each line segment in Figure 4–19 to the nearest $\frac{1}{4}$ inch.
5. Find the length of each line segment in Figure 4–19 to the nearest $\frac{1}{8}$ inch.
6. Find the length of each line segment in Figure 4–19 to the nearest $\frac{1}{16}$ inch.

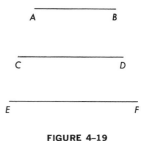

FIGURE 4–19

7. The dimensions of a box are 2 feet 9 inches, 1 foot, and 1 foot 3 inches. Give these dimensions in (a) feet only; (b) inches only.
8. A surveying party found the length of a plot of land to be $48\frac{1}{2}$ rods. Find the measure in yards.
9. An airport runway is 483 rods long. Find this distance to the nearest 0.1 mile.
10. A furlong is 220 yards. Find the number of furlongs in $2\frac{3}{8}$ miles.

■ 4–5 THE METRIC SYSTEM

Today most of the world uses the metric system of measurement. This system is based on our decimal system of numeration.

Table B.

Metric System of Linear Measurement

10 millimeters (mm) = 1 centimeter (cm)

10 centimeters = 1 decimeter (dm)

10 dm, 100 cm, or 1000 mm = 1 meter (m)

10 meters = 1 dekameter (dkm)

10 dekameters = 1 hectometer (hm)

10 hm, or 1000 m = 1 kilometer

Most often, we use only these linear units: millimeter, centimeter, meter, and kilometer. The units relate in this way:

10 millimeters = 1 centimeter,

100 centimeters = 1 meter,

1000 meters = 1 kilometer.

We often need to convert units from one system to another. Table C gives some useful relationships.

Table C.

Linear Equivalents (to the nearest 0.001)

1 inch = 2.540 centimeters

1 foot = 0.305 meter

1 yard = 0.914 meter

1 mile = 1.609 kilometers

1 centimeter = 0.394 inch

1 meter = 3.281 feet

1 meter = 1.094 yards

1 kilometer = 0.621 mile

The following approximations should make clearer the relationship between the two systems.

$$1 \text{ inch} \approx 2.5 \text{ centimeters}$$
$$1 \text{ meter} \approx 1 \text{ yard 3 inches}$$
$$1 \text{ kilometer} \approx 0.6 \text{ mile}$$

The ruler shown in Figure 4–20 is laid off in both inches and centimeters.

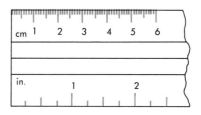

FIGURE 4–20

By an act of Congress in 1886 the relationship between metric and English systems of linear measure was defined as

$$1 \text{ yard} = \tfrac{3600}{3937} \text{ meter}$$

or

$$1 \text{ meter} = 39.37 \text{ inches.}$$

Let i stand for the number of inches in a measurement, and let c stand for the number of centimeters in the measurement. Then $c = 2.540i$, to the nearest 0.001.

Example. Find the number of inches in a measurement of 20 centimeters.

$$c = 2.540i$$
$$20 = 2.540i$$
$$i = \frac{20}{2.540}$$
$$i = 7.874 \text{ (inches)}$$

Exercises for Section 4–5

4–5 A

In each exercise c is given in centimeters. Find c as a number of inches:

1. $c = 2.54$ **2.** $c = 12.7$ **3.** $c = 5.08$
4. $c = 100$ **5.** $c = 10.16$ **6.** $c = 27.94$
7. $c = 49.530$ **8.** $c = 6.152$ **9.** $c = 38$

4–5 B

In each exercise i is given in inches. Find i as a number of centimeters:

1. $i = 10$ **2.** $i = 12$ **3.** $i = 36$
4. $i = 40$ **5.** $i = 60$ **6.** $i = 100$
7. $i = 17.5$ **8.** $i = 24.8$ **9.** $i = 39.75$

4–5 C

Arrange in order of size:

1. 1 yd; 1 m; 105 cm   **2.** 2 ft; $\frac{3}{4}$ yd; $\frac{2}{3}$ m
3. $1\frac{1}{2}$ km; 1 mi; 6000 ft   **4.** 5 ft; $1\frac{3}{4}$ yd; $1\frac{1}{2}$ m
5. 10 in.; 20 cm; $\frac{1}{5}$ m   **6.** 110 cm; 40 in.; $1\frac{1}{10}$ m
7. 350 mm; 14.5 in.; $\frac{1}{3}$ m   **8.** 5 km; 3 mi; 10,000 ft
9. 70 km; 40 mi; 20,000 fathoms   **10.** 3 mm; 0.15 in.; 0.25 cm

4–5 D

1. A bicyclist found that he was averaging about $12\frac{1}{2}$ miles per hour. Find his speed in kilometers per hour.
2. In a recent Olympic race the 10,000-meter run was won in 28.54 minutes. Find the speed of the winning runner in meters per minute.
3. Find the number of miles in 10,000 meters.
4. Use the data from Exercises 2 and 3 to calculate the runner's speed in miles per minute. Give your answer to the nearest 0.01.
5. The width of the film in a camera is 35 millimeters. Find this width in inches.
6. In Mexico a speed limit sign along a highway reads, "75 kilometers per hour." Express this speed in miles per hour.

Exercises 4–5 D continued on page 178.

7. The acceleration of gravity at sea level is about 9.8 meters per second per second. Express this acceleration as inches per second per second.

8. To determine atmospheric pressure scientists use a column of mercury. At sea level this column is 76 centimeters high. Find this height to the nearest $\frac{1}{100}$ inch.

9. In some nations the 100-yard dash is an event in track meets; in others the 100-meter dash is a comparable event. Which is the longer race? By how many inches?

10. Find the number of millimeters in 10 yards. Write your answer in scientific notation.

4–5 E

Mark each of the following true or false:

1. Five centimeters is about 2 inches.
2. The average man is about 3 meters tall.
3. A penny is about 2 millimeters thick.
4. One foot is about 30 centimeters.
5. One yard is exactly 39.37 inches.
6. The doors in most houses are almost 400 centimeters high.
7. Most athletes can jump as high as 2 meters 50 centimeters.
8. A football field is about $91\frac{1}{2}$ meters long.
9. Five kilometers is a little more than 3 miles.
10. On the average, women are about 221 centimeters tall.

■ 4–6 AXIOM II

Consider the formula $S = P + C$. Since S and $P + C$ represent the same number, we may write $S - C = P + C - C$; that is, $S - C = P$. We have now solved the formula for P.

Next, consider the formula $S - P = C$. We wish to solve for S. We write $S - P + P = C + P$; that is, $S = C + P$. We have now solved the formula for S.

The following axiom is useful in solving such equations.

Axiom II. **Adding the same number to (or subtracting the same number from) both sides of an equation yields an equation having the same solution as the first equation.**

These examples demonstrate the use of Axiom II.

Example 1. Solve for x: (a) $x + 2 = 15$; (b) $x + a = 15$; (c) $x - 7 = 20$; (d) $x - a = 20$.

(a) $x + 2 = 15$
$x = 13$ Subtract 2 from both sides.

(b) $x + a = 15$
$x = 15 - a$ Subtract a from both sides.

(c) $x - 7 = 20$
$x = 27$ Add 7 to both sides.

(d) $x - a = 20$
$x = 20 + a$ Add a to both sides.

Often, as in Example 2, we need to use more than one axiom to solve an equation.

Example 2. Solve $3x + 2 = 17$.

$$3x + 2 = 17$$
$$3x = 15 \qquad \text{Axiom II}$$
$$x = 5 \qquad \text{Axiom I}$$

Example 3. Solve $\frac{2}{3}y - 5 = 16$.

$$\frac{2}{3}y - 5 = 16$$
$$\frac{2}{3}y = 21 \qquad \text{Axiom II}$$
$$2y = 63 \qquad \text{Axiom I}$$
$$y = 31\frac{1}{2} \qquad \text{Axiom I}$$

Exercises for Section 4–6

4–6 A

Solve for n:

1. $n - 2 = 15$ **2.** $n - 5 = 5$ **3.** $n - 1\frac{1}{2} = 6$
4. $n - 8 = 80$ **5.** $n - 4\frac{1}{2} = 6\frac{2}{3}$ **6.** $n - 17.5 = 1.05$
7. $n - 0.35 = 0.70$ **8.** $n - 610 = 40$ **9.** $n - 47\frac{1}{2} = 9\frac{1}{4}$

4-6 B

Solve for x:

1. $x + 7 = 7$
2. $x + 18 = 30$
3. $x + 1 = 4\frac{3}{5}$
4. $x + \frac{2}{3} = 3\frac{7}{12}$
5. $x + 1.75 = 6.05$
6. $x + 19 = 37.07$
7. $x + 25 = 700$
8. $x + 95.7 = 325.6$
9. $x + 4\frac{1}{2} = 17.325$

4-6 C

Solve:

1. $x - 3 = 16.5$
2. $x + 17 = 48$
3. $y - 5 = 70.5$
4. $n + 21 = 24$
5. $n - 21 = 24$
6. $n + 7\frac{1}{2} = 18\frac{2}{3}$
7. $n - 17 = 49$
8. $n + 12 = 81\frac{1}{4}$
9. $n - 6 = 75$

4-6 D

Solve for x:

1. $2x - 1 = 5$
2. $3x - 6 = 18$
3. $5x - 10 = 45$
4. $3x + 7 = 22$
5. $8x + 15 = 87$
6. $9x + 27 = 325$
7. $\frac{1}{3}x - 6 = 8$
8. $\frac{1}{5}x + 10 = 85$
9. $\frac{1}{4}x - 60 = 424$

4-6 E

Solve:

1. $\frac{2}{3}x + 6 = 18$
2. $\frac{3}{4}n - 5 = 85$
3. $\frac{4}{5}y + 10\frac{1}{2} = 32\frac{1}{2}$
4. $2\frac{1}{2}n - 1 = 16$
5. $3\frac{1}{2}b + 2 = 18$
6. $\frac{5n}{2} - 5 = 17$
7. $\frac{3n}{5} + 6\frac{1}{2} = 48\frac{3}{4}$
8. $5\frac{1}{4}n + 20\frac{1}{8} = 87\frac{3}{4}$
9. $16\frac{1}{2}m - 48 = 726\frac{1}{2}$
10. $2\frac{1}{2}n + 5 = 10$

4-6 F

1. The cost C of home payments plus the cost M of maintaining the home equals the total cost T of housing. Write a formula and solve for C.
2. In Exercise 1 find C if $M = 45.50$ and $T = 131.45$.
3. The weight w of a truck plus the weight p of the pay load equals the gross weight g. Write a formula and solve for p.

4. In Exercise 3 find p if $w = 15{,}000$ and $g = 22{,}450$.
5. The cost c of a purchase plus the sales tax s equals the total charge t. Write a formula and solve for c.
6. In Exercise 5 find s if $c = 14.05$ and $t = 14.61$.
7. The payment p on a loan plus the interest, $\frac{1}{2}\%$ of p, equals the total payment T. Write a formula for T.
8. In Exercise 7 find p if $T = 90.45$.
9. In Exercise 7 find p if $T = 112.56$.
10. The sum s of the measures of the angles of a polygon with n sides is $180n$ minus 360. Find the number of sides if $s = 1620$.

▪ 4-7 PERIMETER

Many applications of arithmetic relate to figures from geometry. We will now study the characteristics of some of the more common geometric figures in a plane.

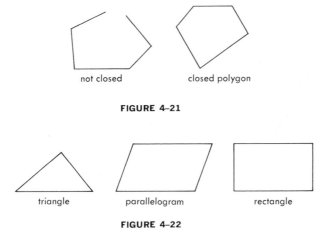

not closed   closed polygon

FIGURE 4-21

triangle   parallelogram   rectangle

FIGURE 4-22

A polygon is a plane closed figure whose sides are line segments. A triangle (symbol, $\triangle$) is a polygon with three sides. A quadrilateral is a polygon with four sides. A quadrilateral whose opposite sides are parallel is called a parallelogram. A parallelogram whose adjacent sides are perpendicular is a rectangle. A square is a rectangle with all sides equal in length.

The sum of the lengths of the sides of a polygon is called its perimeter.

Example 1. Find the perimeter p of a rectangle 14 feet long and $3\frac{1}{2}$ feet wide.

$$p = 3\tfrac{1}{2} + 3\tfrac{1}{2} + 14 + 14$$
$$p = 35 \text{ (feet)}$$

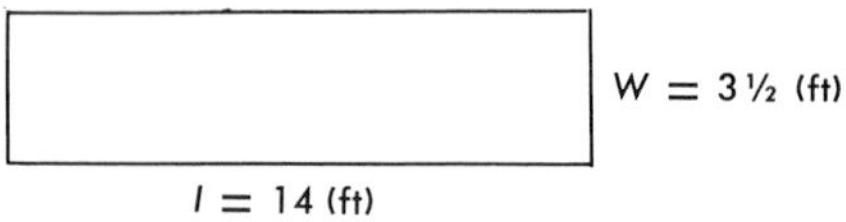

W = 3 ½ (ft)

l = 14 (ft)

FIGURE 4–23

If the length of a rectangle is l units and the width is w units then the perimeter p can be expressed as in I.

I. $p = 2l + 2w$

Example 2. The perimeter of a rectangle is 48 feet and its width is 4 feet. Find the length.

$$p = 2l + 2w$$
$$48 = 2l + (2)(4) \qquad \text{Substitute the known values.}$$
$$40 = 2l \qquad\qquad\quad \text{Axiom II}$$
$$l = 20 \text{ (feet)} \qquad\quad \text{Axiom I}$$

A circle is a set of points in a plane; each point is a given distance from a given point called the center (point O). The given distance from the center is called the radius (plural, radii). Also, a line segment with one endpoint on the circle and with the center as the other endpoint is called a radius (for example, radius OC). A line segment whose endpoints lie on the circle is a chord ($\overline{AB}$, read "chord AB"). A diameter of a circle is a chord through the center of the circle (for example, $\overline{DOE}$). Also, we refer to the length of such a chord as the diameter of the

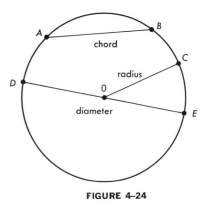

FIGURE 4–24

circle. Two points on a circle and the part of the circle between these form an **arc** of the circle (for example, arc AB, often written $\overset{\frown}{AB}$).

From their definitions we see that the diameter d equals twice the radius r.

$$\textbf{II.} \qquad d = 2r$$

The distance around a circle is called the **circumference.** The ratio of the circumference c to its diameter d is about 3.14.

$$\frac{c}{d} \approx 3.14.$$

This constant, denoted by the Greek letter π, is of great importance to man. In higher mathematics the value of π has been calculated to hundreds of decimal places. We have

$$\pi = 3.14159 \text{ (to the nearest } 0.00001).$$

We derive a formula for the circumference of a circle as follows:

$$\frac{c}{d} = \pi,$$

$$\textbf{III.} \qquad c = \pi d, \qquad \text{Axiom I}$$
$$\textbf{IV.} \qquad c = 2\pi r. \qquad \text{Substitute } 2r \text{ for } d.$$

Exercises for Section 4–7

4–7 A

Find the perimeter of a rectangle whose dimensions are given:

1. 20 ft, 3 ft   **2.** $19\frac{1}{2}$ ft, 7 ft   **3.** 37.25 ft, 16.5 ft
4. 9 yd, $3\frac{1}{2}$ yd   **5.** 17 in., 15 in.   **6.** 4 rd, 2 rd
7. 9 m, 3 m 52 cm   **8.** 12 yd 2 ft, 5 yd 1 ft   **9.** 26 rd, 165 ft

4–7 B

In Exercises 1–9, find the perimeter of a square whose side has the given length:

1. 15 in.   **2.** $6\frac{1}{2}$ ft   **3.** 21.75 yd
4. $\frac{3}{4}$ mi   **5.** 24 rd   **6.** 19.75 cm
7. 6 ft 9 in.   **8.** 2 yd 1 ft 5 in.   **9.** 8 m 47 cm

10. Write a formula for the perimeter p of a square whose side has a measurement of s units.

4-7 C

In Exercises 1–9, find the perimeter of a triangle whose sides have the given lengths:

1. 12 in., 8 in., 5 in.
2. 7.2 yd, 9 yd, 8.6 yd
3. 9 m, 14 m, 17 m
4. 12 cm, 8.7 cm, 9.3 cm
5. 6 ft, 3 yd, 10 ft 5 in.
6. 27 mm, 18 mm, 2 cm
7. 5 yd, 6.5 yd, 27 ft
8. 5 ft 3 in., 4 ft 9 in., 6 ft

9. Write a formula for the perimeter p of a triangle whose sides are a, b, and c units long.

4-7 D

Use 3.14 for π and find the circumference of a circle with diameter given:

1. 1.7 mi
2. 4 in.
3. $3\frac{1}{2}$ yd
4. 3.2 m
5. 4.5 cm
6. 50 mm
7. 16 ft
8. 1 ft
9. 1 in.

4-7 E

Find the circumference of a circle with radius given:

1. 6 ft
2. 7 yd 2 ft
3. 19 ft 7 in.
4. 10 in.
5. 8 cm
6. 1 m
7. 120 ft
8. 75.5 rd
9. 400 yd

4-7 F

1. A farmer built a fence in a field in the shape of a quadrilateral. The lengths of the sides were 65 feet, 120 feet 9 inches, 87 feet 8 inches, and 100 feet 7 inches. Find the total length of the fence.
2. A sheet of rectangular notebook paper is about $8\frac{1}{2}$ inches wide by 11 inches long. Find its perimeter.
3. The perimeter of a square field is 222 yards 2 feet. Find the length of one side.
4. A baseball diamond is a square, 90 feet on a side. Find the perimeter.
5. A homeowner's lot has the shape of a quadrilateral whose sides are 125 feet, 78 feet, 129 feet, and 73 feet. Find the cost to fence this lot if fencing costs 15¢ per running foot.

6. A pond at a university is circular and has a diameter of 50 feet. A walk 6 feet wide encircles the pond. Find the length of the outside edge of this walk.

7. The perimeter of a rectangular room is 90 feet. The room is 16 feet wide. Find its length.

8. The wheel of a bicycle is $27\frac{1}{2}$ inches in diameter. How far will the bicycle go in 10 complete revolutions of the wheel?

9. Find the perimeter of a dollar bill to the nearest $\frac{1}{8}$ inch.

10. Find the distance around the door shown in Figure 4–25. The top is one-half of a circle.

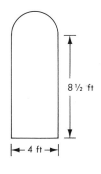

8 ½ ft

|← 4 ft →|

FIGURE 4–25

4–7 G

1. The diameter of a circle is 28 inches. Find its radius.

2. Find the ratio of the measures of two diameters of the same circle.

3. The earth is about 93,000,000 miles from the sun. Assume that the earth has a circular orbit and compute the length of one orbit.

4. Describe the figure one would get by drawing 5 circles with the same center and same radius.

5. An angle with its vertex at the center of a circle is called a central angle (see $\angle AOB$ in Figure 4–26). A circle of radius 10 inches has a central angle of 90°. Find the length of $\overset{\frown}{AB}$ intercepted by this angle.

6. From the drawing for Exercise 5 find the length of arc AB for a central angle of 60°.

7. The circumference of a toy wagon wheel is 12.56 inches. Find the diameter of the wheel. (Use 3.14 for π.)

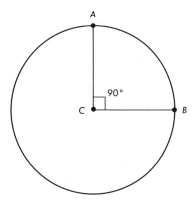

FIGURE 4–26

Exercises 4–7 G continued on page 186.

8. A bicycle wheel makes 1 complete revolution while traveling 81.64 inches along a straight line. Find the diameter of the wheel.
9. The circumference of a baseball is 9 inches. Find its diameter.
10. The maximum circumference allowed in a regulation bowling ball is 27 inches. Find the diameter of such a ball.

4-7 H

Refer to Figure 4–27 and use a protractor to find these measures:

1. $m(\angle e)$ 2. $m(\angle x)$ 3. $m(\angle f)$
4. $m(\angle g)$ 5. $m(\angle p)$ 6. $m(\angle n)$
7. $m(\angle h)$ 8. $m(\angle y)$ 9. $m(\angle z)$

10. Find $m(\angle e) + m(\angle f) + m(\angle g)$.
11. Find $m(\angle x) + m(\angle h) + m(\angle y)$.
12. Find $m(\angle z) + m(\angle n) + m(\angle p)$.

(*Note:* From Exercises 10–12 you may observe that the sum of the angles of a triangle is about 180°. In fact this is a theorem of geometry: The sum of the measures of the angles of any triangle is 180 (degrees).)

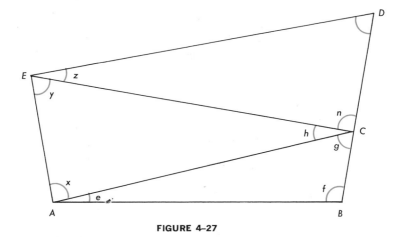

FIGURE 4–27

Theorem

A theorem is a statement to be proved. In books on higher mathematics proofs for theorems are usually required. In this textbook we generally accept the truth of a theorem without proof.

4–8 AREAS OF PLANE FIGURES

To measure the area of a surface we choose a square, 1 unit on a side. We then determine the number of squares contained in the given surface. For example, Figure 4–28 represents a rectangle 6 inches long and 3 inches wide.

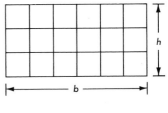

FIGURE 4–28

The rectangle contains 6 × 3, or 18, squares, each 1 inch on a side. We say the rectangle has (encloses) an area of 18 square inches. The area of a rectangle can be found by multiplying its base b by its altitude h (the height).

$$\textbf{V.} \qquad A = bh$$

Rule V holds even if the lengths of the sides are not whole numbers.

The vertices of a polygon are the points in which the sides intersect. Each vertex is labeled with a capital letter. We refer to a polygon by naming its vertices. In Figure 4–29 we have parallelogram $ABCD$.

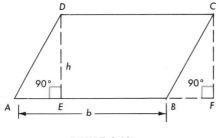

FIGURE 4–29

A rectangle is used to derive the formula for the area of a parallelogram. In Figure 4–29 think of cutting off triangle ADE and placing it on triangle BFC. (It can be shown that these two triangles have the same shape and size.) This forms rectangle $EFCD$, whose area is equal to that of the parallelogram. Thus we assume the area of the parallelogram can be found by the following formula.

$$\textbf{VI.} \qquad A = bh$$

Notice in Figure 4–29 that the altitude h is the perpendicular distance between the base and the side opposite it.

To any triangle we can add another triangle of the same size and shape to form a parallelogram. In Figure 4-30 triangle *ABC* and triangle *BDC* combine to form parallelogram *ABCD*.

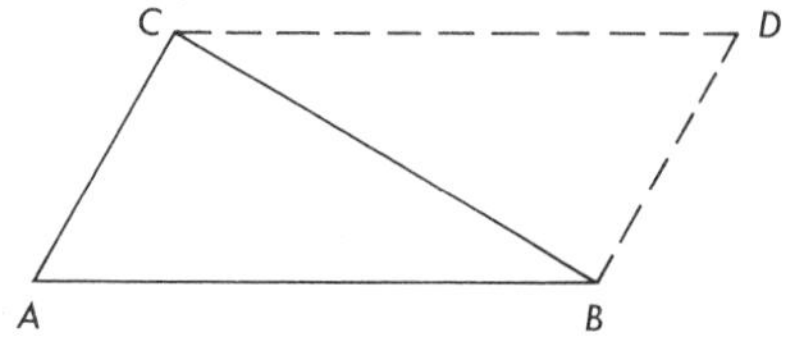

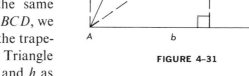

FIGURE 4-30

Since the parallelogram *ABCD* has area $A = bh$, then VII is the formula we use to find the area of triangle *ABC*.

VII. $A = \frac{1}{2}bh$

A **trapezoid** is a quadrilateral having one pair (and only one pair) of parallel sides. We find a formula for the area of a trapezoid by dividing the figure into two triangles having the same altitude. In trapezoid *ABCD*, we draw $\overline{AC}$. This divides the trapezoid into two triangles. Triangle *ACD* has b' as its base and h as its altitude. Triangle *ABC* has b as its base and h as its altitude. The trapezoid then has area

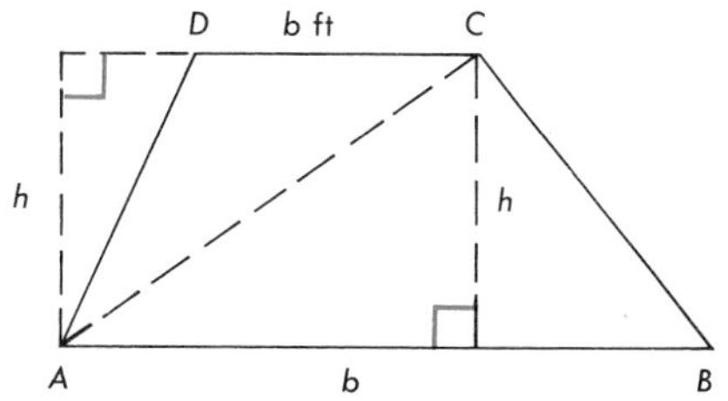

FIGURE 4-31

$$A = \text{area } \triangle ACD + \text{area } \triangle ABC,$$
$$A = \frac{1}{2}b'h + \frac{1}{2}bh.$$

Formula VIII follows by the distributive law.

VIII. $A = \frac{1}{2}h(b' + b)$

When we speak of the area of a circle, we refer to the area of the surface enclosed by the circle. It can be proved that IX is the formula for the area of a circle with radius r.

IX. $A = \pi r^2$

Example. Find the area of a circle whose radius is 10 inches.

$$A = \pi r^2$$
$$A = 3.14 \times 10^2$$
$$A = 314 \text{ (square inches)}$$

Exercises for Section 4–8

4–8 A

Find the area of a rectangle whose dimensions are as follows:

1. 10 ft, 5 ft
2. $3\frac{1}{2}$ in., 10 in.
3. 2 yd, 5 yd
4. 9 ft, 12 ft 6 in.
5. 7 m, 12 m
6. $5\frac{1}{4}$ in., $10\frac{1}{2}$ in.
7. 10 cm, 25 cm
8. 1 m 30 cm, 2 m 50 cm
9. 205 yd, 325 yd
10. 7 rd, 160 rd

4–8 B

Find the area of a trapezoid whose dimensions are as follows:

1. altitude, 5 ft; bases, 6 ft and 8 ft
2. altitude, $2\frac{1}{2}$ ft; bases, 6 ft and 8 ft
3. altitude, 10 in.; bases, 1 in. and 18 in.
4. altitude, 1 yd; bases, 2 yd and 5 yd
5. altitude, $2\frac{1}{4}$ ft; bases, 4.35 ft and 6.75 ft
6. altitude, 2 m; bases, 3 m and 4.5 m
7. altitude, 10 cm; bases, 40 cm and 2 m
8. altitude, 7 yd; bases, $6\frac{1}{4}$ yd and $8\frac{1}{3}$ yd

4–8 C

Find the area of a triangle whose dimensions are as follows:

1. altitude, 6 ft; base, 8 ft
2. altitude, 6 in.; base, 10 in.
3. altitude, $1\frac{1}{2}$ ft; base, $2\frac{1}{4}$ ft
4. altitude, 4 ft 3 in.; base, 6 ft 5 in.
5. altitude, 6 yd; base, 31 ft
6. altitude, 3 ft 7 in.; base, 6 ft
7. altitude, $2\frac{1}{2}$ m; base, 8 m
8. altitude, 6 m 40 cm; base, 5 m 85 cm

4–8 D

Find the area enclosed by a circle with the given dimensions:

1. radius, 6 in.
2. radius, 4 ft
3. radius, 15 m
4. radius, 1 ft
5. radius, 2 ft 6 in.
6. diameter, 8 yd
7. diameter, 40 ft 8 in.
8. diameter, 3.14 yd
9. diameter, 18.75 cm
10. diameter, 55 m

4–8 E

1. Find the area of a rectangular playing field which is 120 feet long and 78 feet wide.
2. A circular fish pond has a diameter of 8 feet. Find the area of the surface of the pond.
3. Find the width of a rectangular field which is 363 feet long and contains 1 acre. (*Note:* 1 acre = 43,560 square feet, or 160 square rods)
4. A living room has 300 square feet of floor space. Find the number of square yards of carpet needed to cover this floor.
5. Find the number of square yards in 1 acre.
6. Find the number of square inches in 1 square foot.
7. Find the total area of the wall shown in Figure 4–32.
8. The gate in a dam is in the shape of a trapezoid. The parallel sides are 15 feet and 24 feet long; the distance between them is 12 feet. Find the area of the surface of this gate.
9. One square mile of land is called a section. Find the number of acres in a section.

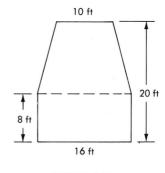

FIGURE 4–32

10. The radii of two circles are 10 inches and 20 inches. Find the ratio of the area of the larger circle to the area of the smaller circle.

4–8 F

In each exercise find the area represented by the shaded region.

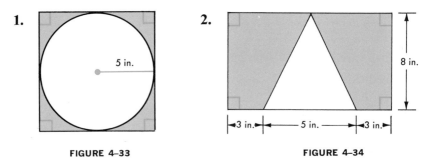

1.

FIGURE 4–33

2.

FIGURE 4–34

3.

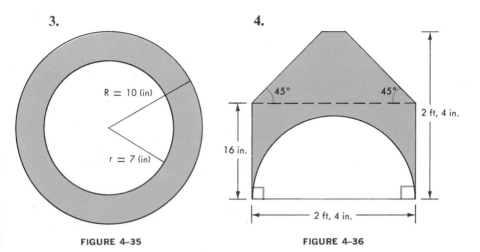

FIGURE 4–35

4.

FIGURE 4–36

4–8 G

1. The shaded region of Figure 4–37 is called a **sector** of circle *P*. In higher mathematics it is shown that the area *A* of the sector is $A = \frac{1}{2}br$; here *r* is the radius of the circle and *b* is the length of $\widehat{AB}$. Find the area of the sector if $r = 10$ (inches) and $b = 8$ (inches).

2. Find the area of a sector whose dimensions in inches are as follows:

   (a) $r = 10$,
   $b = 6$.
   (b) $r = 20$,
   $b = 12$.

3. In Figure 4–38 consider the circle with its interior divided into six equal sectors. The circumference of the circle is called *C*.

Exercises 4–8 G continued on page 192.

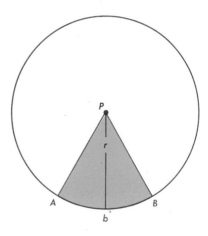

FIGURE 4–37

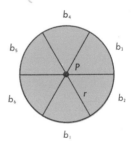

FIGURE 4–38

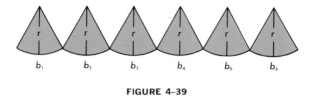

FIGURE 4-39

Next consider these sectors "spread out," as in Figure 4-39. Note that the total area A of the sectors is

$$A = \tfrac{1}{2}b_1r + \tfrac{1}{2}b_2r + \cdots + \tfrac{1}{2}b_6r. \qquad \text{Explain.}$$

That is,

$$A = \tfrac{1}{2}r(b_1 + b_2 + \cdots + b_6). \qquad \text{Explain.}$$
$$A = \tfrac{1}{2}r \times C. \qquad \text{Explain.}$$

4. In Exercise 3 find the area of the circle if:

$$r = 7,$$
$$b_1 = 6,$$
$$b_2 = 7,$$
$$b_3 = 8,$$
$$b_4 = 9,$$
$$b_5 = 7,$$
$$b_6 = 7.$$

Dimensions are in inches.

5. The formula for the circumference C of a circle is

$$C = 2\pi r.$$

In Exercise 3 we have

$$A = \tfrac{1}{2}r \times C.$$

Thus

$$A = \tfrac{1}{2}r \times (2\pi r). \qquad \text{Explain.}$$

That is,

$$A = \pi r^2. \qquad \text{Explain.}$$

6. In Exercise 4 use the formula $A = \pi r^2$ to find the area.

Sector

A sector is somewhat like an isosceles triangle: two of its sides are congruent line segments (see Figure 4–39). The third side is an arc. Note that the area of any triangle can be found by use of the formula $A = \frac{1}{2}bh$. Thus it seems reasonable to assume that a similar formula applies to a sector where r is the "height" of the sector. The formula, $A = \frac{1}{2}br$, is, in fact, true.

■ 4–9 SURFACE AREA OF SOLIDS

Figure 4–40 represents a rectangular solid. The solid is bounded by six faces, each of which is a rectangle. The opposite faces are parallel. To find the total surface area of a rectangular solid, we add the areas of the six faces. A box which is l units long, w units wide, and h units high has total surface area S, given by the following formula.

X. $S = 2lw + 2wh + 2lh$

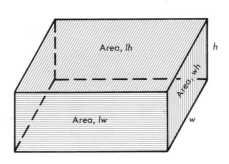

FIGURE 4–40

Example 1. Find the surface area of a box whose dimensions are 20 feet, 10 feet, and 8 feet.

$$S = 2lw + 2wh + 2lh$$
$$S = (2)(20)(10) + (2)(10)(8) + (2)(20)(8)$$
$$S = 400 + 160 + 320 = 880 \text{ (square feet)}$$

Figure 4–41 represents a **right circular cylinder.** The curved surface of the cylinder is called the **lateral surface.** The circular plane surfaces are called **bases.** The perpendicular distance between the bases is the **height** (altitude) of the cylinder. The **lateral area** (area of the lateral surface) is the product of the height and the circumference of a base (formula XI).

XI. $A = Ch$, or $A = 2\pi rh$

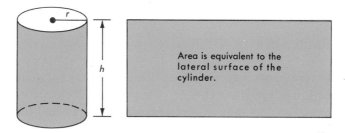

FIGURE 4–41

Since the area of each base is πr^2, then the total surface area S of the cylinder is given by the following formula.

XII. $S = 2\pi r^2 + 2\pi rh$

Example 2. Find the total surface area of a right circular cylinder with $r = 7$ (inches) and $h = 10$ (inches). Use $3\frac{1}{7}$ for π.

Method 1

$A = 2\pi rh$	The lateral area formula
$A = 2 \times \frac{22}{7} \times 7 \times 10$	Substitute in the formula.
$A = 440$	Lateral area is 440 square inches.
$B = \pi r^2$	Formula for area of base B
$B = \frac{22}{7} \times 7^2$	Substitute.
$B = 154$	The area of a base is 154 square inches.
$T = (2 \times 154) + 440$	We take (2×154) since the cylinder has 2 bases.
$T = 748$ (square inches)	

Method 2

$$A = 2\pi r^2 + 2\pi rh$$
$$A = 2(\tfrac{22}{7})(7^2) + 2(\tfrac{22}{7})(7)(10)$$
$$A = 748$$

By the distributive property, we know that

$$2\pi r^2 + 2\pi rh = 2\pi r(r + h).$$

Method 3 is based on this simplified form.

Method 3

$$A = 2\pi r[r + h]$$
$$A = 2(\tfrac{22}{7})(7)[7 + 10]$$
$$A = 748$$

Exercises for Section 4-9

4-9 A

Find the area of a rectangular solid with these dimensions:

1. 20 ft, 12 ft, 6 ft
2. 8 in., 8 in., 8 in.
3. 10 in., 6 in., 6 in.
4. 4 cm, 3 cm, 2 cm
5. $8\frac{1}{2}$ yd, 4 yd, 3 yd
6. $3\frac{1}{4}$ ft, $2\frac{1}{4}$ ft, 1 ft
7. 4.7 m, 3.5 m, 3 m
8. 60 ft, 18 yd, 10 yd
9. 18 in., 3 ft, 4 ft
10. 27 ft, 4 yd, 3 ft
11. 3.5 mm, 3.5 mm, 9 mm
12. 12 yd, 11 yd, 45 ft

4-9 B

Find (a) the lateral area and (b) the total surface area of a cylinder with these dimensions:

1. radius 5 in., height 8 in.
2. radius 6 in., height $10\frac{3}{4}$ in.
3. radius $2\frac{1}{2}$ ft, height 10 in.
4. radius 1 yd, height $3\frac{1}{2}$ yd
5. radius 1 ft, height 10 ft
6. radius $2\frac{1}{2}$ in., height 20 ft
7. radius 6 cm, height 5 m
8. radius 8 mm, height 32 cm
9. radius 14 in., height 11 in.
10. radius $4\frac{1}{2}$ ft, height $3\frac{1}{2}$ ft
11. radius 14 mm, height 1.25 mm
12. radius $\frac{2}{3}$ in., height $\frac{5}{8}$ in.

4-9 C

In these exercises use 3.14 for π.

1. Find the total surface area of an apple box which is $1\frac{1}{2}$ feet long, 1 foot wide, and 1 foot deep.

2. An oil storage tank in the shape of a cylinder is 15 feet high and 24 feet across the base. The lateral surface will be painted with a special type of paint. One gallon of this paint covers 150 square feet. How many gallons of paint will be needed to give the tank 1 coat?

3. A can of soup in the shape of a cylinder has a radius of $1\frac{5}{16}$ inches and is 4 inches high. Find the area of paper needed to make a label to cover the lateral surface of the can.

4. A cube is a rectangular solid with all edges equal in length. Find the total surface area of a cube with edges 8 inches long.

5. Find the total area of the walls of a swimming pool which is 36 feet long and 18 feet wide. It is 3 feet deep at one end and 9 feet deep at the other end. The floor is one plane.

6. A pipe 8 inches in diameter and 12 feet long contains hot water. How many square feet of asbestos paper are needed to wrap this pipe?

7. Which has the greater area: a cylinder with a base diameter of 10 inches and height of 10 inches, or a cube whose edges are each 10 inches? Find the difference in their total surface areas.

8. A cube-shaped carton is made of cardboard. The edge of the cube is 2 feet 4 inches long. Find the amount of cardboard needed to make this carton. Add 10% of the total area for folds and waste.

■ 4-10 SURFACE AREA—SPHERE, PYRAMID, CONE

Consider a fixed point P and distance r. The set of all points whose distance from P is r is a sphere with radius r. The intersection of a sphere with a plane through its center (as plane s) is a circle with the same center and radius as the sphere. We call such a circle a great circle of the sphere. (See Figure 4-42.) In higher mathematics we prove that the area S of a sphere is equal to the area enclosed by four great circles (formula XIII).

$$\textbf{XIII.} \qquad S = 4\pi r^2$$

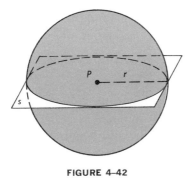

FIGURE 4–42

Example 1. Find the approximate area of the moon. Use $r \approx 1080$ (miles).

$$A = 4\pi r^2$$
$$A = 4 \times 3.14 \times 1080^2$$
$$A = 14{,}649{,}984 \text{ (square miles)}$$

The area is about 15,000,000 square miles.

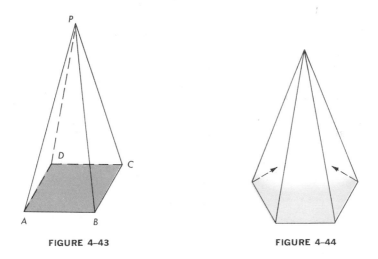

FIGURE 4–43   FIGURE 4–44

Consider Figure 4–43. The **base** $ABCD$ is a square region. The **faces** are triangular regions (PAB, PBC, PCD, and PAD). The solid enclosed by the base and these faces is called a **pyramid.** The base of a pyramid may be a polygon with any number of sides; the faces are always triangles (see Figure 4–44).

The area of the surface of a pyramid is the sum of the areas of the base B and the faces T_1, T_2, T_3, and so on.

XIV. $A = B + T_1 + T_2 + T_3 + \cdots$

Example 2. The base of a pyramid is a square with sides 10 inches long. Each face is a triangle with height 12 inches. Find the area of the pyramid.

$A = B + T_1 + T_2 + T_3 + T_4$

In this case, $T_1 = T_2 = T_3 = T_4$.

   Thus,

$$A = B + 4T.$$

We have

$A = 10^2 + 4(\tfrac{1}{2} \times 10 \times 12),$

$A = 340$ (square inches).

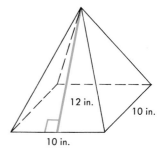

FIGURE 4–45

Next consider a region R enclosed by a right triangle. Think of rotating this region about side BC. By this rotation, we describe a right circular cone. The base of the cone is a circle whose radius r is equal to the length of $\overline{AC}$. The slant height s of the cone is equal to the length of $\overline{AB}$.

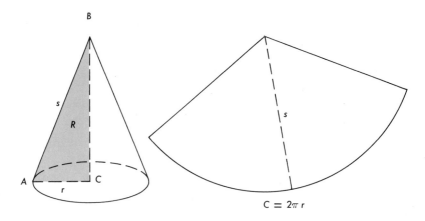

FIGURE 4–46

We may think of the area of the curved surface, the lateral area, as the area of a sector with radius s. The area of the base is the area of a circle with radius r. The formula for the total area A is

$$A = \pi r^2 + \tfrac{1}{2}sC,$$

or, since

$$C = 2\pi r,$$

then

$$A = \pi r^2 + (\tfrac{1}{2}s \times 2\pi r).$$

Hence XV is the formula for the total surface area of a cone.

XV. $A = \pi r^2 + \pi r s$

We may use the distributive property and write $A = \pi r(r + s)$.

Example 3. Find the area of a right circular cone with $r = 7$ (inches) and $s = 10$ (inches). Use $3\tfrac{1}{7}$ for π.

> The area of the base is $\pi \times 7^2$.
> The lateral area is $\pi \times 7 \times 10$.
> $A = (\pi \times 7^2) + (\pi \times 7 \times 10)$.
> $A = 374$
> The area is about 374 square inches.

Exercises for Section 4–10

4–10 A

The base of a pyramid is a square with side x inches. The height of a triangular face is s inches. Find the total area of a pyramid, given the ordered pair (x, s):

1. (10, 20)   **2.** (6, 9)   **3.** (9, 15)   **4.** (11, 20)
5. (7, 9)   **6.** (24, 30)   **7.** (1.5, 3)   **8.** (2.5, 4)

(*Note:* In each exercise above $s > \tfrac{1}{2}x$. Can you explain why this inequality must be true?)

4–10 B

The base of a cone has radius x inches. The slant height of the cone is s inches. Use 3.14 for π and find the total area of a cone, given the ordered pairs (x, s) in Exercises 4–10 A.

4-10 C

In Exercises 1–6 use $3\frac{1}{7}$ for π and find the area of a sphere with the given radius:

1. 7 ft   **2.** 10 ft   **3.** 14 ft
4. 21 ft   **5.** 70 mi   **6.** 700 mi

7. Find the area of a sphere with radius 2000 miles. Give your answer to two significant digits.

4-10 D

In these exercises use 3.14 for π.

1. Find the total area of a cone with slant height 12 feet and radius of the base 4 feet.
2. Find the total surface area of a basketball which has a diameter of 9.55 inches. Give your answer to the nearest hundredth.
3. The radius of the earth is about 4000 miles. Assume that the earth is a sphere and find the total area. Express your answer in scientific notation.
4. Find the total surface area of the gas tank shown in Figure 4–47. Each end has the shape of half a sphere.

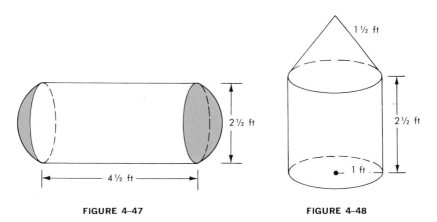

FIGURE 4–47   FIGURE 4–48

5. A metal cap is built as shown in Figure 4–48. Find the total area of this figure. Do not count the base.
6. Find the ratio of the surface area of a sphere with a radius of 5 inches to the surface area of a cone with base radius of 3 inches and slant height of 5 inches.

7. Which of the following has the greater total area: a cone with radius 10 inches and slant height 20 inches or a sphere with radius 10 inches? Find the difference in the total surface areas of the cone and the sphere.

8. The solid in Figure 4–49 is called a **frustum of a cone.** A small cone that has a height of 10 inches was cut off a larger cone to form the frustum shown at the right. Find the total surface area of this frustum.

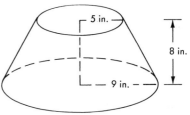

FIGURE 4–49

■ 4-11 VOLUME

To find the volume of a geometric figure, we choose some cube as a unit. Then we determine the number of these cubes within the geometric figure. This number is called the **volume.**

To determine the volume of the rectangular solid whose dimensions are shown, we choose a cubic inch as the unit. By counting the cubes, we see that there are four rows with (2 × 3) cubes in each row. The volume is 4 × (2 × 3) = 24 (cubic inches). In general, we have formula XVI for determining the **volume V of a rectangular solid** that is *l* units long, *w* units wide, and *h* units high.

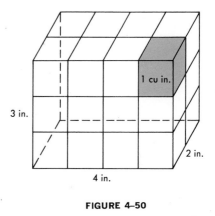

FIGURE 4–50

$$\textbf{XVI.} \qquad V = lwh$$

To find the **volume of a circular cylinder,** we find the product of its circular base and its height.

$$\textbf{XVII.} \qquad V = \pi r^2 \times h$$

Example. Find the volume of a cylinder with $r = 7$ (inches) and $h = 10$ (inches).

$$V = \pi r^2 \times h$$
$$V = (\tfrac{22}{7} \times 7^2) \times 10$$
$$V = 1540 \text{ (cubic inches)}$$

It can be shown that the **volume of a pyramid or a cone** is $\tfrac{1}{3}$ the product of the area of the base and the height.

XVIII. $V = \tfrac{1}{3}Bh$

In Figure 4–51 the base is a square with $s = 8$ (inches). The height is 9 inches. Hence $B = 8^2$, or 64. Then $V = \tfrac{1}{3} \times 64 \times 9$, that is, 192 (cubic inches).

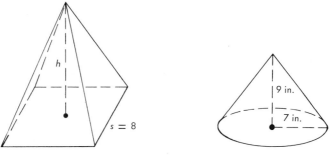

FIGURE 4-51   FIGURE 4-52

In Figure 4–52, $B = \pi \times 7^2 = 154$ (square inches). Thus $V = \tfrac{1}{3} \times 154 \times 9 = 462$ (cubic inches).

The **volume of a sphere** is $\tfrac{1}{3}$ the product of its radius r and its area $4\pi r^2$:

$$V = \tfrac{1}{3} \times r \times 4\pi r^2$$

Thus XIX is the formula for the volume of a sphere.

XIX. $V = \tfrac{4}{3}\pi r^3$

Thus for a sphere with radius 7 inches, $V = \tfrac{4}{3} \times \tfrac{22}{7} \times 7^3$. Hence $V = 1437\tfrac{1}{7}$ (cubic inches) approximately.

Exercises for Section 4–11

4–11 A

Find the volume of a rectangular solid with the given dimensions:

1. 6 ft, 3 ft, 2 ft
2. 4 ft, 4 ft, 4 ft
3. 1 yd 2 ft, 3 yd, 2 yd
4. 2 ft 6 in., 1 ft 8 in., 2 ft
5. 40 ft, 6 ft, 8 ft
6. $12\frac{1}{2}$ yd, $6\frac{3}{4}$ ft, 5 ft

4–11 B

1. Find the number of cubic feet in a box which is 8 feet by 3 feet by 4 feet.
2. A steel drum in the shape of a cylinder is $3\frac{1}{4}$ feet long with radius 1 foot. Find the number of gallons this drum can hold. Use 1 cubic foot $\approx$ 7.5 gallons.
3. Find the number of cubic inches in 1 cubic foot.
4. Find the number of cubic feet in 1 cubic yard.
5. The bed of a certain truck is the shape of a rectangular solid 4 feet by 5 feet by 8 feet. Find the weight of a load if the bed is filled with sawdust which weighs 12 pounds per cubic foot.
6. Find the ratio of the volume of a cube whose edge is 6 inches long to the volume of a cube whose edge is 3 inches long.
7. Find the volume of a cone with radius $2\frac{1}{2}$ inches and height 6 inches. (Use 3.14 for π.)
8. Find the weight of a cylindrical steel rod 10 feet long with a diameter of 1 inch. Steel weighs about 490 pounds per cubic foot. (Use 3.14 for π.)
9. A sphere with diameter 10 inches is fitted in a cubical metal box whose inside edges are 10 inches long. Find the volume of water needed to fill the rest of the box. (Use 3.14 for π.)
10. A section of a concrete culvert is shown below. Use the dimensions given to find the volume of the concrete. (Use 3.14 for π.)

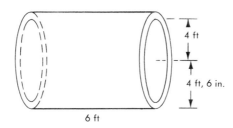

6 ft   4 ft   4 ft, 6 in.

FIGURE 4–53

4–11 C

In higher mathematics we show that the **Prismoidal Formula** can be used to find the volume of many solids. In the formula V represents the volume; h, the height; B, the area of one base; B', the area of the other base; M, the area of the midsection. The formula is

$$V = \frac{h}{6}(B + 4M + B').$$

1. Consider the rectangular solid in Figure 4–54.

(a) Does $B = B'$?

(b) Does $M = B = B'$?

(c) Substitute in the prismoidal formula. Does

$$V = \frac{h}{6}(B + 4B + B)$$

$$= \frac{h}{6}(6B)?$$

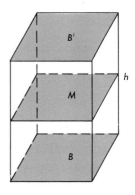

FIGURE 4–54

(d) Simplify the result found in (c). Is your answer the formula for the volume of a rectangular solid?

2. Consider a triangle with base b and height h. Consider a second triangle with base $\frac{1}{2}b$ and height $\frac{1}{2}h$.

(a) For the larger triangle, does $A = \frac{1}{2}bh$?

(b) For the smaller triangle, does $A = \frac{1}{2} \times \frac{1}{2}b \times \frac{1}{2}h$? Does $A = \frac{1}{8}bh$?

(c) Simplify $\dfrac{\frac{1}{8}bh}{\frac{1}{2}bh}$.

(d) From your work in (a), (b), and (c), do you find that the area of the smaller triangle is $\frac{1}{4}$ the area of the larger triangle?

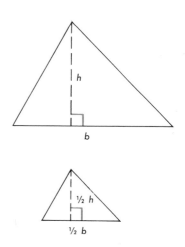

FIGURE 4–55

3. From your work in Exercise 2, you may assume that in Figure 4–56
$M = \frac{1}{4}B$. Also note that B' is a point. Thus the area $B' = 0$.
Substitute in the Prismoidal Formula.

(a) Does $V = \dfrac{h}{6}[B + 4(\frac{1}{4}B) + 0]$?

(b) Simplify the work in (a). Do you have the formula for the
volume of a pyramid?

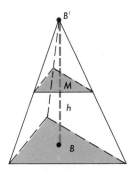

FIGURE 4–56

4. Consider the cone in Figure 4–57. The midsection $M = \frac{1}{4}B$.
(a) Does $B = \pi r^2$?
(b) Does $M = \frac{1}{4}\pi r^2$?
(c) Substitute in the Prismoidal Formula. Does

$$V = \frac{h}{6}[\pi r^2 + 4(\frac{1}{4}\pi r^2) + 0]?$$

(d) Simplify the result in (c). Do you get the formula for the
volume of a cone?

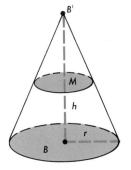

FIGURE 4–57

Exercises 4–11 C continued on page 206.

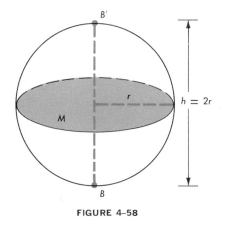

FIGURE 4–58

5. Consider the sphere in Figure 4–58. The midsection M is a great circle. The bases are the two points B and B'.
(a) Does $M = \pi r^2$?
(b) Since B is a point, does $B = 0$?
(c) Since B' is a point, does $B' = 0$?
(d) Substitute in the Prismoidal Formula. Does

$$V = \frac{2r}{6}(0 + 4\pi r^2 + 0)?$$

(e) Simplify the result in (d). Do you get the formula for the volume of a sphere?

Vocabulary

The section in which each word appears is indicated in parentheses.

acre (Exercises 4–8 E)
acute angle (4–2)
altitude (4–8)
angle (4–1)
arc (4–7)
axiom of geometry (4–1)
base (4–8, 4–10)
bases (4–9)
chord (4–7)
circle (4–7)

circumference (4–7)
congruent (4–2)
coplanar (4–1)
degree (4–2)
diameter (4–7)
faces (4–10)
frustum of a cone
    (Exercises 4–10 D)
great circle (4–10)
height (4–9)

Chapter Review

A

Refer to Figure 4–59, and mark each statement true or false.

1. Lines x and y appear to be parallel.
2. Angles a, c, f, and h appear to be obtuse angles.
3. Angles i and j appear to be right angles.
4. Point A and the part of line x to the right of point A form a ray.
5. Points A and B, combined with the points of line x that lie between A and B, form a line segment.
6. Angles b and e appear to be congruent.
7. The set $x \cap y$ is an empty set.
8. Ray BA and ray AB are identical rays.
9. Segment AB is a subset of ray AB.
10. It appears that

$$m(\angle b) > m(\angle c).$$

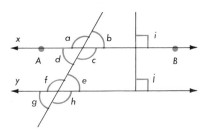

FIGURE 4–59

B

Solve and check:

1. $13n = 32.5$
2. $\frac{1}{4}n = 20$
3. $\frac{1}{3}n = 17$
4. $1.3n = 65$
5. $2.8n = 112$
6. $2x - 7 = 103$
7. $3x + 41 = 68$
8. $16x - 90 = 70$
9. $1.6x - 900 = 700$

10. Use the formula $f = 16.5r$ to find the number f of feet in 22 rods (r stands for the number of rods).

C

1. Use a protractor to draw angle ABC if $m(\angle ABC) = 49$.
2. A pilot flies d miles in t hours at an average speed of 610 miles per hour. Find d if $t = 4.5$.
3. In Exercise 2 find d in kilometers. Use 1 kilometer $= 0.62$ miles. (*Hint:* Should your answer be more, or less, than the answer for Exercise 2?)
4. The diameter d of a wheel is 48 inches. Find the distance which the wheel will move along a road while making one turn. (Use 3.14 for π.)
5. The circumference of a steel ball is 6.28 inches. Find the number of such balls which may be fitted into a box 10.2 inches by 16.2 inches by 2.1 inches.
6. Find the total area of a rectangular solid 5.5 feet by 6 feet by 8 feet.
7. In Exercise 6 find the volume of the solid.
8. In Exercise 5 find the area of 1 ball.
9. Find the volume of a cylindrical can with diameter 2 inches and height 10 inches. Use 3.14 for π. If 1 gallon is 231 cubic inches, will this can hold more than $\frac{1}{2}$ gallon?
10. Find the volume of a steel ball with radius 5 inches. Use 3.14 for π. Find the weight of the ball if steel weighs 0.28 pounds per cubic inch.

D

If a statement is true, mark it true. If it is false, write a replacement for the part underlined to make it true.

1. The sides of an angle are rays.
2. The sides of a rectangle are lines.
3. If $f = 3y$, then $f < y$.

4. If $c = \pi d$, then $\underline{d > c}$.

5. A distance of 15 miles is about $\underline{24\ kilometers}$.

6. A speed of 80 kilometers per hour $\underline{would\ be}$ unusually fast for a car on a public highway.

7. If $\frac{1}{7}x - 83 = 267$, then $x = \underline{2450}$.

8. If the radius of a circle is 1 inch, then the area is π $\underline{inches}$.

9. For a triangle with base b and height h, $b > 2$ and $h > 16$. If A represents the area, then $\underline{A > 16}$.

10. For a sphere with radius r and volume V, $r = 10$. Then $\underline{V > 1100}$.

REVIEW OF CHAPTERS 1–4

A

In Exercises 1–8 solve for n:

1. $n = 2\frac{1}{4} + 3\frac{2}{5} + 3\frac{7}{10}$ **2.** $n = \frac{5}{7} + \frac{3}{4} + \frac{5}{12}$

3. $n = 2\frac{1}{2} + 3\frac{4}{5} + 2\frac{5}{6} + 3\frac{7}{15}$ **4.** $n - 243 = 476$

5. $n + 243 = 476$ **6.** $\dfrac{n}{8} = 4\dfrac{1}{2}$

7. $\dfrac{n}{6} = 10.5$ **8.** $\dfrac{n}{5} = 23.2$

9. Find $n(A)$ if $A = \{a, b, c, d\} \cup \{r, s, t, u, v\}$.

10. If $n = 7$ tenths $+ 2$ tenths, does $n = (7 + 2)$ tenths? Explain.

11. If 5 times a number n is 55, find the number n.

12. If $\frac{2}{3}$ of a number n is 114, find the number n.

B

1. Does 0.07 plus 18 thousandths equal $(70 + 18)$ thousandths? Explain.

2. Does $0.07 + 0.018 = (70 + 18)$ thousandths? Explain.

3. Does $\frac{6}{10} + \frac{7}{100} + \frac{19}{1000} = (600 + 70 + 19)$ thousandths? Explain.

4. Does $0.5 + \frac{41}{100} + 2\frac{1}{2} = (50 + 41 + 250)$ hundredths? Explain.

5. Does $5.5 \div 0.11 = 550 \div 11$? Explain.

6. Solve for n: $n = 21.9 \times 90.8$.

7. Solve for n: $n = 1.728 \div 0.12$.

Review of Chapters 1–4 continued on page 210.

8. Solve for n: $\dfrac{3.4}{6} \times \dfrac{n}{n} = \dfrac{34}{60}$.

9. If 5 times a number n equals 30, find the number n.

10. If 0.4 times a number n equals 28, find the number n.

11. In a piece of metal 0.3 of the weight is aluminum. If the piece weighs 36 pounds, find the weight of the aluminum in it.

12. In a piece of metal 0.3 of the weight is aluminum. The weight of the aluminum is 9 pounds. Find the weight of the piece.

C

Express as a decimal:

1. 27%	2. 43%	3. 98%	4. 52%
5. 2.4%	6. 95.5%	7. 150%	8. 2000%

Express as a number of percent:

9. 0.41	10. 0.05	11. 2.5	12. 0.5
13. 0.8	14. 125	15. 204	16. 2000

17. Find $\frac{1}{2}\%$ of 2340 pounds.

18. Of 19,000 voters, 51% voted for a law. How many voted for the law?

19. Of a number n of workers, 40% worked on the day shift. The number working on the day shift was 2000. Find n.

20. Express n in scientific notation:
    (a) $n = 2348$ (b) $n = 23.48$
    (c) $n = 0.2348$ (d) $n = 23 \times 79$

21. Tell the number of significant digits in each number:
    (a) 12.06   (b) 0.0060
    (c) 11,250   (d) 1.0605

5 Interpretation of Data; Coordinates

■ **5-1 BAR AND LINE GRAPHS**

To communicate ideas about a collection of data we often use a type of diagram called a **graph.** The most common graphs used in periodicals and books are the bar graph, the line graph, and the circle graph.

The bar graph is most often used to show comparisons. We will make a bar graph from the data given in the following table. This table shows the growth in the amount of bonds owned by all life insurance companies in the United States.

Period	Amount of Bonds Owned By U.S. Life Insurance Companies
First	0.21 billion dollars
Second	0.42 billion dollars
Third	1.33 billion dollars
Fourth	1.82 billion dollars
Fifth	3.75 billion dollars
Sixth	5.20 billion dollars
Seventh	9.58 billion dollars
Eighth	13.51 billion dollars
Ninth	16.50 billion dollars
Tenth	17.43 billion dollars

Each period in the table represents 5 years. Thus the span covered is 50 years. During this time we see that the amount of bonds owned

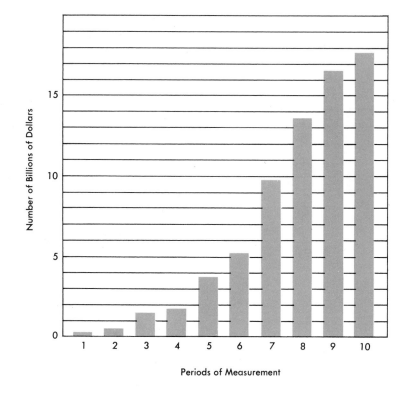

Periods of Measurement

FIGURE 5–1

increased from about $\frac{1}{5}$ of a billion to 17 billion dollars. The vertical line along the left side of this figure is called the **vertical axis;** the horizontal line across the bottom, the **horizontal axis.** Each unit on the vertical axis stands for 1 billion dollars. The bars are numbered along the horizontal axis in the order of time.

A bar graph is made in the following way.

    1. *Choose appropriate units for the two axes and label them.*

    2. *Make each bar (rectangle) the same width.*

    3. *Space the bars equally.*

    4. *Give a clear, concise title to the graph.*

To make a line graph we use squared graph paper and choose scales for each axis. In the line graph of Figure 5–2 the horizontal axis represents the time of day. Each square represents a 1-hour

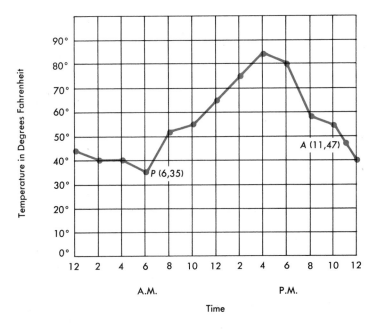

FIGURE 5-2

change. The vertical axis begins at 0° and each square stands for 5°. The temperature measurements were made every 2 hours for a 24-hour period starting at 12:00 A.M.

Each point on the temperature graph represents an ordered pair of numbers. These numbers are called the coordinates of the point. The first coordinate is measured on the horizontal axis; the second coordinate is measured on the vertical axis. The point labeled P has the coordinates $(6, 35)$. We write $P(6, 35)$, which means "a point P with first coordinate 6 and second coordinate 35."

The points are connected in order by line segments which form a broken line. We often think of the entire picture as the graph. However, in mathematics we refer to this broken line as the graph. We assume that every point on the graph has meaning. For example, a temperature measurement was not made at 11:00 P.M. However, we can read $A(11, 47)$ and assume that the temperature was about 47° at 11:00 P.M.

For each point on the broken line graph in Figure 5-2, there is a pair of coordinates which are approximately correct for the time and temperature. Hence we say that the graph is continuous.

Exercises for Section 5–1

5–1 A

For these exercises refer to Figure 5–1 and to the table for that graph.
In Exercises 1–5 find the ratio of the value of bonds owned:

1. In the second period to bonds owned in the first period.
2. In the third period to bonds owned in the first period.
3. In the fifth period to bonds owned in the first period.
4. In the seventh period to bonds owned in the fourth period.
5. In the tenth period to bonds owned in the third period.
6. Find the range of years covered by this graph. (*Note:* Each period is 5 years. The range is the number of years represented on the graph.)
7. Find the range in billions of dollars shown on the graph.
8. Which 5-year period showed the greatest gain? Find the amount of this gain.

5–1 B

Use Figure 5–2 to answer the following:

1. Find the range of the temperatures shown. (*Note:* The range is the difference between the highest and lowest temperatures.)
2. Find the approximate temperature at 5:00 P.M.
3. Was there a general trend of the temperature as time progressed from 6:00 A.M. to 4:00 P.M.?
4. Find the temperature at these times:
   (a) 10:00 A.M.   (b) 10:00 P.M.
5. Use the 13 measured temperatures to get the median temperature.
6. From your data in Exercise 5, find the average temperature.

5–1 C

1. The following is a list of the number of metric tons of silver mined by each of the 10 leading producers in the world during a recent year.

Mexico	1281.8	Australia	554.6
United States	1130.5	West Germany	478.2
Peru	1120.2	Japan	277.2
Canada	953.9	Bolivia	117.0
U.S.S.R.	700.0	Yugoslavia	116.7

Round off each figure to the nearest 10 metric tons and make a bar graph for these data.

2. Suppose that a line graph were made of the data in Exercise 1 (see Figure 5–3). Would each point on the graph have meaning? Consider points *A* and *B*. Would a line graph be a proper representation of the data? Explain.

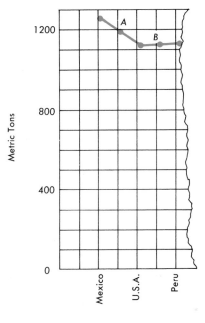

FIGURE 5–3

3. In a class of 100 men the measure *d* from the tip of the nose to the tip of the outstretched hand was found for each man. The table shows the results. Measurements are given to the nearest 0.2 inch. Make a bar graph of the data. Use *n* for the vertical scale.

Measure	37.2	37.0	36.8	36.6	36.4	36.2	36.0	35.8	35.6
Number *n* of men	3	5	12	16	18	17	13	11	5

4. In Exercise 3 for which value of *d* is *n* greatest? For which value of *d* is *n* least? Does *n* tend to decrease as *d* gets farther from 36.4? (*Note:* The English measurement 1 yard was derived from the measure *d*.)

5–1 D

1. Use the following census figures of a small city to make a line graph. Round off the population figures to the nearest hundred.

Year	Population
First	4952
Second	5725
Third	5908
Fourth	5402
Fifth	4633
Sixth	6675
Seventh	6995
Eighth	6237
Ninth	7064
Tenth	9957
Eleventh	10,873
Twelfth	12,804
Thirteenth	13,095
Fourteenth	16,587

2. Would a bar graph be a proper representation of the data in Exercise 1? Explain.

5–2 THE CIRCLE GRAPH

The circle graph is used to compare the parts of a collection of data to each other and to the whole.

To make a circle graph:

1. *From the data used, list the numbers corresponding to the parts. Find the total.*

2. *Find the percent p of the total which each part represents.*

3. *Find p × 360 to determine the measure of the central angle used for each sector of the circle.*

4. *Use a protractor to draw each sector.*

5. *Label each sector and give the graph a title.*

Consider the rules for making a circle graph as you study the example.

Example. A family budgeted their monthly income of $650 as follows: food, $175; housing, $125; transportation, $30; savings, $150; clothing, $60; other expenses, $110. Make a circle graph.

Refer to steps 1–3 in studying this chart. The percents and the angle measures in the table have been calculated to the nearest whole number. (*Note:* The total in the last column is adjusted to give 360° since the graph is an approximation. In this table the measure for *clothing* was rounded up to 33°.)

Item	Amount in Dollars	Part of the Whole	Central Angle in Degrees
Food	175	$\frac{175}{650} = 27\%$; 27% of 360 = 97	97
Housing	125	$\frac{125}{650} = 19\%$; 19% of 360 = 68	68
Transportation	30	$\frac{30}{650} = 5\%$; 5% of 360 = 18	18
Savings	150	$\frac{150}{650} = 23\%$; 23% of 360 = 83	83
Clothing	60	$\frac{60}{650} = 9\%$; 9% of 360 = 33	33
Other expenses	110	$\frac{110}{650} = 17\%$; 17% of 360 = 61	61
Totals	650	100%	360

Using a protractor and the data from the chart, we draw the circle graph shown in Figure 5–4.

FIGURE 5–4

Exercises for Section 5–2

5–2 A

1. A work force is composed of these groups: 6 farmers, 3 mechanics, 2 electricians, 4 carpenters, and 9 laborers. The force was employed to assist a small new nation in getting established. Find the percent of the whole force which each of the 5 groups represents.
2. From Exercise 1 find the measures of the respective central angles for a circle graph.
3. Use the data from Exercises 1 and 2 to make a circle graph.
4. Sources of the United States' Budget Dollar for a recent year were individual income tax, 50 cents; corporation income tax, 30 cents; excise tax, 8 cents; borrowing, 2 cents; other, 10 cents. Make a circle graph, using these data.

5–2 B

1. At a certain highway intersection, the direction of travel was noted for 200 vehicles. The data are shown in the table.

Direction of Travel	Number of Vehicles
Turn east	33
Turn west	64
Continue through	103

Make a circle graph.
2. How might the data of Exercise 1 be useful to the Highway Planning Department?
3. The employees in one business office are grouped as shown in the following table:

Classification	Number
Management	3
Engineers	7
Clerks	4
Sales people	15

Make a circle graph.

5-2 C

1. A family spends their monthly income of $575 as follows: food, $135; housing, $105; clothing, $25; transportation, $25; recreation, $25; savings, $100; other items, $160. Make a circle graph.
2. The annual report from a company showed the following: net sales, $100,000; cost of goods sold, $70,000; selling expenses, $17,000; financial expenses, $2000; office expenses, $6000; net profit, $5000. Make a circle graph, using these data.

■ 5-3 GRAPH OF A LINEAR EQUATION

Each line graph you have studied has consisted of a sequence of segments arranged in a broken line. There are many formulas each of which has only one straight line as its graph. For example, if an object is traveling at 5 miles per hour, the relationship between distance d and time t can be represented as

$$d = 5t.$$

The table shows a number of ordered pairs (t, d). Note that if we assign a value to t, we obtain a fixed value for d. Thus if $t = 6$, then $d = 5 \times 6$, or 30.

t	1	2	3	4	5	6	10	12
d	5	10	15	20	25	30	50	60

In the formula $d = 5t$, we say that the value of d depends upon the value of t. Therefore we call d a **dependent variable.** We may assign any value of a set of numbers to t. Thus we call t the **independent variable.**

On graph paper plot the independent variable t on the horizontal axis; plot the dependent variable d on the vertical axis. The point marked 0 is called the **origin;** its coordinates are $(0, 0)$. To locate the point corresponding to $(2, 10)$ move 2 units to the right from the origin on the horizontal axis; then move 10 units up and parallel to the vertical axis. In the same manner locate another point with coordinates given in the table (such as $(4, 20)$). Draw a straight line through these points.

Each point on the graph (Figure 5–5) has an ordered pair of numbers (t, d) as its coordinates. This ordered pair is a solution of the formula $d = 5t$. Thus for point A we have $(8, 40)$, which is a solution of $d = 5t$. On the other hand, each solution of $d = 5t$ is an ordered pair which determines a point on the graph. For example, any ordered pair in the table determines such a point. Thus there is a one-to-one correspondence between the ordered pairs which satisfy the formula and the points on the line.

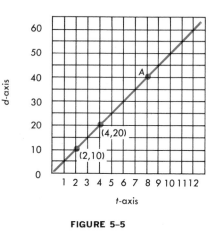

FIGURE 5-5

Any equation of the general form $ax + by + c = 0$ where a, b, and c are constants (a and b not both zero) has a straight line as its graph. For example, the graph of $2x + 3y + 5 = 0$ is a line. Equations whose graphs are straight lines are referred to as **linear equations.**

In a formula such as $d = 3t$ the set of numbers from which the independent variable t is chosen is called the **domain.** The set of numbers for the dependent variable d is called the **range.** The formula $d = 3t$ may stand for the distance d a man can walk in time t. If the man can walk at this pace for at most 10 hours, then the domain of the formula can be written as $0 \leq t \leq 10$. The range will then be $0 \leq d \leq 30$.

Exercises for Section 5-3

5-3 A

In the study of electricity we can use the graph in Figure 5–6 to relate voltage and resistance in a 5-ampere direct current circuit.

1. From the graph estimate the voltage when the resistance is:
    (a) 1.5   (b) 3   (c) 4.5   (d) 9
2. Estimate the resistance when the voltage is:
    (a) 0   (b) 5   (c) 7.5   (d) 32.5
3. Find the increase in voltage for an increase in resistance from:
    (a) 3 to 4   (b) 5 to 6   (c) 8 to 9

4. From Exercise 3 does the voltage seem to increase a fixed amount for each unit increase in the resistance?

5. Let E stand for voltage and R stand for resistance. Which of the following formulas is the formula for the graph of the line: $E = 2R$, $E = 5R$, $E = 6R$, or $E = 7R$? (*Note:* Try some coordinates of points on the line in the formulas.)

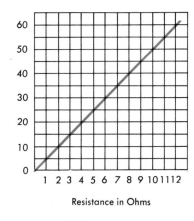

Resistance in Ohms

FIGURE 5-6

5-3 B

In Exercises 1–8 draw a pair of axes on graph paper and locate the points corresponding to these ordered pairs:

1. $A(1, 3)$ **2.** $B(2, 5)$ **3.** $C(4, 1)$ **4.** $D(3, 1)$
5. $E(5, 2)$ **6.** $F(1, 4)$ **7.** $G(2\frac{1}{2}, 5)$ **8.** $H(5, 2\frac{1}{2})$

9. Consider your graphs for Exercises 1–8.
   (a) Points A and D correspond to $(1, 3)$ and $(3, 1)$. Are these different points?
   (b) Are B and E different points?
   (c) Are C and F different points?
   (d) Are G and H different points?
   (e) Refer to your answers to parts (a) through (d). Why does the order in a pair of numbers make a difference? Explain.

5-3 C

In Exercises 1–6 use graph paper and a set of axes to plot the points corresponding to these ordered pairs:

1. $(2, 2)$ **2.** $(4, 3)$ **3.** $(0, 1)$
4. $(5, 3\frac{1}{2})$ **5.** $(6, 4)$ **6.** $(8, 5)$

7. Do these points seem to lie along a straight line?
8. Verify that the coordinates (x, y) listed in Exercises 1–6 are solutions of the equation $y = \frac{1}{2}x + 1$.
9. In Exercises 1–8 connect the points with a straight line. Find the coordinates of the point where the line intersects the vertical axis.

5-3 D

1. A truck is traveling at a steady speed of 60 miles per hour. Write a formula showing the distance d which the truck will travel in time t.
2. Use the formula from Exercise 1 to find ordered pairs (t, d) when the time t is:
   (a) $\frac{1}{2}$ hour   (b) 2 hours
   (c) $2\frac{1}{4}$ hours   (d) 4 hours
3. On a set of axes similar to those in Figure 5-5, page 220, plot the points corresponding to the ordered pairs found in Exercise 2. Draw the graph. (*Note:* Let each square for distance on the vertical axis stand for 20 miles.)
4. From your graph in Exercise 3 estimate the distance which the truck traveled after $3\frac{1}{2}$ hours. Check your estimate with the formula.

5-3 E

Make a list of 3 or 4 ordered pairs for each formula and graph the result.

1. $C = 6r$ 2. $p = 2l + 4$
3. $y = 2x + 2$ 4. $d = 2r$
5. $F = \frac{9}{5}C + 32$ 6. $I = 0.05p$

5-3 F

1. For a freely falling body, $v = 16t$ where t stands for time in seconds; v, for velocity in feet per second. Make a line graph. (*Note:* In the formula we assume the body falls from rest; that is, it has initial velocity of zero and no force acts upon it except gravity.)
2. In Exercise 1 find v when t is:
   (a) 1   (b) 5
   (c) 10   (d) 15
3. Consider your answers in Exercise 2. Does the falling body gain speed quickly?
4. From your graph in Exercise 1 find t when $v = 200$ (feet per second). (*Note:* 200 feet per second is approximately 135 miles per hour.)

■ 5-4 GRAPH OF A NONLINEAR FORMULA

Whenever any variable of a formula has an exponent other than 1, the graph of the formula will be a curve rather than a straight line.

At sea level a free-falling object will fall d feet in t seconds, where $d = 16t^2$. To draw the graph of this formula we determine a set of ordered pairs as we did for the line graph. We choose an arbitrary value for t; then we substitute it in the formula to determine the corresponding value for d. Thus if $t = 0$, then

$$d = 16 \times 0^2 = 0;$$

if $t = \frac{1}{2}$, then

$$d = 16 \times \left(\tfrac{1}{2}\right)^2 = 4.$$

t	0	$\frac{1}{2}$	1	2	$2\frac{1}{2}$	3	4
d	0	4	16	64	100	144	256

In Figure 5-7 the points have been plotted and a curve has been fitted to them. There is a one-to-one correspondence between the points on the curve and the ordered pairs that were determined from the formula.

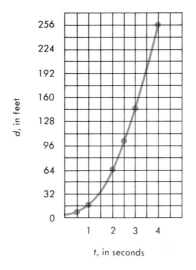

FIGURE 5-7

Exercises for Section 5–4

5–4 A

More water vapor can be held by warm air than by cold air.
The graph shows the relationship between the number of grains of
water vapor in a cubic foot of air and the temperature. Thus at
50° F a cubic foot of air can hold about 4 grains of water. (*Note:*
1 grain = $\frac{1}{7000}$ pound)

Use Figure 5–8 to find the amount of water vapor in a cubic foot
of air for the given Fahrenheit temperatures.

1. 10°	**2.** 16°	**3.** 28°	**4.** 35°
5. 40°	**6.** 52°	**7.** 87°	**8.** 82°

In Exercises 9–14 use Figure 5–8 to find the temperature at which
a cubic foot of air can hold the amount of water vapor given.

9. 1.5 grains	**10.** 4.0 grains	**11.** 5.0 grains
12. 7.6 grains	**13.** 10.5 grains	**14.** 13.2 grains

15. Find the temperature at which water vapor measured in grains
is $\frac{1}{2}$ that at temperature 90°.

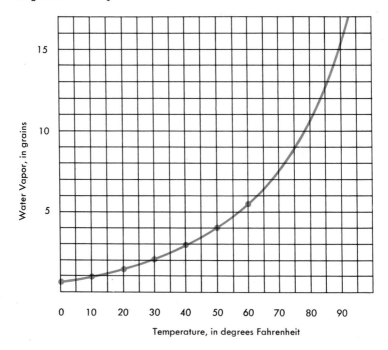

FIGURE 5–8

5–4 B

At a certain altitude an object will fall d feet in t seconds, where $d = 12t^2$. For this formula find d when t is:

1. 0	**2.** $\frac{1}{2}$	**3.** 1	**4.** $1\frac{1}{2}$
5. 2	**6.** $2\frac{1}{2}$	**7.** 3	**8.** $3\frac{1}{2}$

9. Plot the ordered pairs derived from Exercises 1–8 on a sheet of graph paper.
10. Draw a curve through the points in Exercise 9.

5–4 C

A car weighs 2600 pounds. The force F (in pounds) necessary to keep it from skidding on a curve of radius 1000 feet is $F = 2.6v^2$. In the formula v is the speed of the car in feet per second. In Exercises 1–8 speeds are given in feet per second (fps). Find F:

1. 0	**2.** 5	**3.** $7\frac{1}{2}$	**4.** 10
5. 12	**6.** 20	**7.** 25	**8.** 30

9. Plot the ordered pairs from Exercises 1–8.
10. Fit a curve to the points plotted in Exercise 9.

5–4 D

Plot the graph of each formula:

1. $d = 10t^2$	**2.** $K = 5v^2$	**3.** $A = S^2$
4. $L = 5 + d^2$	**5.** $K = \frac{1}{2}l^2$	**6.** $d = 2 + \frac{1}{2}t^2$
7. $A = 3r^2$	**8.** $N = \frac{1}{2} + l^2$	**9.** $T = 2g^2 + 1$

5–4 E

1. If $16 = 4^2$, then we say that 4 is a **square root** of 16. If $25 = 5^2$, then 5 is a square root of 25. In general if $y = x^2$, then x is a square root of y. We use the **square root symbol**, $\sqrt{}$, and write $x = \sqrt{y}$. Use the formula $y = x^2$ and complete the table of values. (See graph page 226.)

x	0	1	2	3	4	5	6	7	8	9	. . .	20
y	0	1	4			25						400

Exercises 5–4 E continued on page 226.

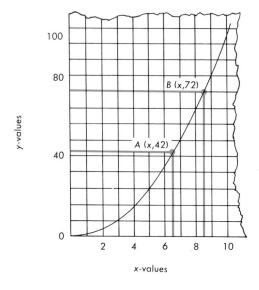

FIGURE 5-9

2. Use a full sheet of graph paper and plot the points in the table of Exercise 1. Draw a smooth curve.

3. Refer to your drawing for Exercise 2.
   (a) Find x when $y = 42$. See point A.
   (b) Find x when $y = 72$. See point B.
   (c) Is $\sqrt{42} \approx 6\frac{1}{2}$?
   (d) Is $\sqrt{72} \approx 8\frac{1}{2}$?
   (e) Is $\sqrt{110} \approx 10\frac{1}{2}$?

In Exercises 4-11 use your drawing for Exercise 2 to find the approximate square roots:

4. $\sqrt{8}$ **5.** $\sqrt{12}$ **6.** $\sqrt{52}$

7. $\sqrt{90}$ **8.** $\sqrt{210}$ **9.** $\sqrt{156}$

10. $\sqrt{342}$ **11.** $\sqrt{240}$ **12.** $\sqrt{180}$

13. A builder plans to build a square room with floor area of 120 square feet. Use your graph to find the length of 1 side. (*Note:* $120 = x^2$)

14. A family plans to lay a wall-to-wall carpet in a square room with floor area of 272 square feet. Use your graph to find the length of 1 side of the carpet.

■ 5-5 PROBABILITY

A certain professional basketball player scores free throws on 63% of his attempts. Hence he averages 63 out of 100 attempts. We say that his *probability* of making a free throw is $\frac{63}{100}$, or 63%.

The operators of a factory found that 1.3% of their products did not meet required specifications. So, on the average, 13 out of 1000 of their products should be rejected. The probability of producing a reject is $\frac{13}{1000}$, or 1.3%.

If an evenly balanced coin is flipped many times, it will tend to fall with a head up one-half the time. The probability of obtaining a head is $\frac{1}{2}$, or 50%.

We think of **probability** as the ratio of the favorable ways an event can happen to the total of the ways it can happen. Suppose that an event can happen in n different, equally likely ways. Suppose also that s of these ways represent a condition we consider a **success.** Then the probability p that this condition will occur is given in I.

$$\text{I.} \qquad p = \frac{s}{n}$$

Example 1. Find the probability of obtaining a 3 or a 6 in 1 roll of a die. The die has 6 faces and each face has a different number of spots on it from 1 through 6. A 3 can show up in 1 way or a 6 can show up in 1 way. Thus the probability of obtaining a 3 or a 6 is

$$p = \frac{1 + 1}{6} = \frac{2}{6} = \frac{1}{3}.$$

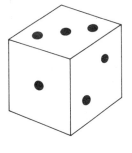

FIGURE 5-10

The probability that an event will happen is always between 0 and 1 inclusive ($0 \le p \le 1$). If the event cannot possibly happen, the probability is 0. If the event must happen, the probability is 1.

The **odds in favor** of an event happening is the ratio of the number of successful ways it can happen to the number of unsuccessful ways it can happen.

Example 2. A box contains 8 blue buttons and 4 red buttons.

(a) Find the probability of drawing at random a blue button.

$$p = \frac{8}{4 + 8} = \frac{8}{12} = \frac{2}{3}$$

(b) Find the odds x for drawing a blue button against drawing a red button.

$$x = \tfrac{8}{4} = 2, \text{ or 2 to 1}$$

Exercises for Section 5-5

5-5 A

In one throw of a die find the probability of obtaining:

1. 6	**2.** 3 or 5	**3.** 4
4. 2 or 4	**5.** 1, 2, or 3	**6.** 4, 5, or 6
7. an odd number	**8.** an even number	**9.** 8

5-5 B

A box contains 5 red marbles, 7 white marbles, 2 blue marbles, and no others. Find the probability of selecting on the first draw a marble which is:

1. white	**2.** blue
3. red	**4.** red or blue
5. red or white	**6.** blue or white
7. red, white, or blue	**8.** green

5-5 C

1. A marksman can hit a target 88% of the time from 300 feet away. In 850 shots how many times will he hit the target?
2. A letter of the alphabet is chosen at random. Find the probability that the letter is a vowel. (*Note:* The vowels are $a, e, i, o, u,$ and sometimes w and y. Consider that the number of vowels is 7.)
3. Find the probability that the letter chosen in Exercise 2 comes before n in the alphabet.
4. Two coins are tossed. Make a list of all possible outcomes. (*Note:* The coins may fall four ways: both coins heads up, (H, H); first coin heads and second coin tails, (H, T); first coin tails and second coin heads, (T, H); and both coins tails, (T, T).)

5. Two coins are tossed. Determine the probability that both coins come up heads. (*Note:* How many different ways can the coins come up?)

6. Two coins are tossed. Find the probability of getting at least 1 tail.

7. Find the odds in favor of getting a tail in Exercise 5.

8. One card is to be drawn from a well-shuffled deck of playing cards. Find the probability that it will be a club. (*Note:* There are 52 cards in a deck: 13 clubs, 13 spades, 13 hearts, and 13 diamonds.)

9. Find the probability that the card drawn in Exercise 8 will be a queen.

10. A ball is to be drawn out of a box containing 3 red and 2 white balls. Find the probability that the ball will be white.

5-5 D

1. A grocer placed razor blades on a shelf in the middle of his store. He found that 1 customer out of 20 purchased razor blades.
   (a) Find in percent the probability of a sale of razor blades.
   (b) Find the number of such sales to be expected on a day when the grocer had 1000 customers.

2. The grocer in Exercise 1 changed his display and placed razor blades at each cash register. He found that 3 customers out of 15 purchased razor blades.
   (a) Find in percent the probability of a sale of razor blades.
   (b) Find the number of such sales to be expected on a day when he had 1000 customers.

3. A grocer found that out of 100 sales of canned peaches 73 cans were Brand X. Find the probability that when a can of peaches is sold, it is Brand X.

4. In Exercise 2 explain the usefulness of the given probability.

5. In Exercise 3 explain the usefulness of the given probability.

6. Before an election, a poll of a small sample of voters was taken. The poll showed that 47 out of 100 people would vote for Jones; the rest would vote for Smith. Find the odds in favor of Smith's winning the election. (*Note:* In such cases a small sample is selected in a manner which should make it representative of all voters.)

Exercises 5–5 D continued on page 230.

7. It was estimated that the need for a product in one locality was 20 units per day. Brand A, one of several brands competing for this market, was advertised on a local radio station. Before radio advertising, sales of Brand A were 8 units per day; after radio advertising, 11 units per day.

   (a) Find the odds that before radio advertising, a sale of the product would be Brand A.

   (b) Find the odds after radio advertising.

8. In Exercise 7 does it appear that radio advertising helped sales?

9. From Exercise 7 do you think that the results of radio advertising might cause competitors of Brand A to advertise? Explain.

10. A radio station started a program of telephone conversations. It was found that this program had 53% of the listening audience.

   (a) Find the odds that a local listener was tuned to this program.

   (b) What would you expect competing stations to do? Explain.

■ 5-6 STATISTICS

Statistics is the science that relates to collecting, organizing, analyzing, and interpreting numerical data. For example, out of a random group of people, there will probably be a large variation in heights, weights, and so on. We may wish to characterize a group as a whole with regard to some one of these measures.

A **measure of central tendency** is one kind of statistic which is frequently used. The three most common measures of central tendency are the mean, the mode, and the median.

The **mean** is equal to the sum of all the measures in a set divided by the number n of the measures. Let X_i stand for the set of n measures; that is, $X_i = X_1, X_2, \ldots, X_n$. The symbol

$$\sum_{i=1}^{n} X_i$$

means the sum of the n measures; that is,

$$\sum_{i=1}^{n} X_i = X_1 + X_2 + X_3 + \cdots + X_n.$$

II. $\qquad m = \dfrac{\sum\limits_{i=1}^{n} X_i}{n}$, where m is the mean

Example 1. On a history test a class made scores of 59, 70, 72, 66, 66, 85, 90, and 68. Find the mean test score.

$$m = \frac{\sum\limits_{i=1}^{8} X_i}{n} = \frac{(59 + 70 + 72 + 66 + 66 + 85 + 90 + 68)}{8}$$
$$= \frac{576}{8} = 72$$

To find the median of a set of measures, arrange them in order of size. If there is an odd number of measures in the set, then the median is the middle measure. If there is an even number of measures, then the median is the mean of the two measures that are nearest the middle.

Example 2. Find the median of these heights of players on a junior varsity basketball team: 72 inches, 75 inches, 71 inches, 78 inches, and 81 inches.

$$71, 72, 75, 78, 81$$
The median is 75.

Example 3. Find the median of the scores from Example 1.

$$59, \quad 66, \quad 66, \quad 68, \quad 70, \quad 72, \quad 85, \quad 90$$
The median is $\dfrac{68 + 70}{2} = 69$.

The mode of a set of measures is the measure which occurs most often. There may not be a mode or there may be several in a group of measures.

Example 4. Find the mode of the scores from Example 1.

The mode is 66

since it occurs twice and each of the others occurs only once.

Example 5. Find the mode in this set of test scores: 8, 9, 8, 7, 7, 10, and 11.

> The score 7 occurs twice.
> The score 8 occurs twice.
> The set has two modes, 7 and 8.
> We say that this set is bimodal.

The mean, mode, and median are statistical measures (statistics) used to give a general idea about any set of measures. Another commonly used statistic is the range. The range in a set of measures is the difference between the smallest measure and the largest one. Thus the range in Example 2 is 81 − 71, or 10.

Exercises for Section 5–6

5–6 A

Find the mean, the median, the mode, and the range for each set of measures:

 1. 16, 20, 18, 16, 14
 2. 31, 30, 31, 32, 40, 37
 3. 87, 80, 81, 76, 50, 70, 50, 52
 4. 75, 55, 60, 85, 90, 55, 75, 82, 75
 5. 5, 6.5, 7.5, 7, 6.5, 8.5, 9, 6.5, 7, 8.5
 6. 25, 31, 24, 19, 25, 36, 18, 25, 24

5–6 B

The members of a physical education class ran the 100-yard dash. Their times are listed in seconds as 10.8, 11.4, 13, 10.6, 13.1, 14.3, 10.4, 15.1, 16.1, 11.9, 10.6, 12.1, 11.8, 16.4, 10.6, 16.1, 14.8, 10.6, and 13.9.

 1. Find the mean time.
 2. Find the median time.
 3. Find the mode.
 4. Find the range.
 5. Which of the three measures of central tendency do you believe gives the best idea about the "average" time of the class? Explain.

6. Which measure would give a false impression about the running speed of the "average" student in this class? Explain.

7. Another physical education class had a time range of 0.9 seconds for the 100-yard dash. Could you say that this second class had a mean time higher than the first class? Explain.

5–6 C

1. What can you say about the distribution of the remainder of the salaries if the median salary paid by a certain automobile-manufacturing company is $5800?

2. A salesman made total weekly sales of $148.50, $136, $140.75, $130.95, $139.50, $141.25, $172.50, $136.45, and $168.45 for a period of 9 weeks. Find his mean weekly sales.

3. A student had a range of 45 points on 6 history tests. The total score possible for each test was 100 points. Do you believe that this student's test scores were very consistent? Explain.

4. A certain instructor gives a grade of B for mean test scores of 82–90. Should a student with test scores of 80, 70, 95, 88, and 79 get a B for the course? Explain.

5. The heights of a group of people are: 6 feet 4 inches, 6 feet, 5 feet 11 inches, 5 feet 9 inches, 6 feet 1 inch, 5 feet 10 inches, and 6 feet 3 inches. Find the mean height.

6. A waitress said that she had an average (mean) of $3.78 a day in tips for the last 14 working days. Find the total amount she received in tips.

7. An agriculture student had 5 rectangular plots of ground on which to do research. The plots had the following dimensions: 9 feet by 11 feet, $8\frac{1}{2}$ feet by 10 feet, 7.9 feet by 12 feet, $10\frac{1}{2}$ feet by $10\frac{1}{2}$ feet, and 11 feet by $12\frac{1}{3}$ feet. Find the mean area of these plots of ground.

8. To figure grade point average we count each semester hour of A as 4 points; of B, 3 points; of C, 2 points; of D, 1 point; of F, 0 points. Find the grade point average, to the nearest hundredth, of a student who received 6 hours of B, 6 hours of C, and 3 hours of D.

9. Use the data in Exercise 8 to find the grade point average of a student who had the following record: 6 hours of A, 8 hours of B, 24 hours of C, and 4 hours of D.

Exercises 5–6 C continued on page 234.

10. A store manager kept this record of the number of customers in his store for certain hours of the day.   Each tally represents 1 customer.

9:00–10:00 A.M.	////
10:00–11:00 A.M.	⁄⁄⁄⁄ ⁄⁄⁄⁄ /
11:00–12:00 A.M.	⁄⁄⁄⁄ ⁄⁄⁄⁄ ⁄⁄⁄⁄
12:00–1:00 P.M.	⁄⁄⁄⁄ ⁄⁄⁄⁄ ⁄⁄⁄⁄ //
1:00–2:00 P.M.	⁄⁄⁄⁄ ⁄⁄⁄⁄
2:00–3:00 P.M.	⁄⁄⁄⁄ ⁄⁄⁄⁄ ⁄⁄⁄⁄ ⁄⁄⁄⁄
3:00–4:00 P.M.	⁄⁄⁄⁄ ⁄⁄⁄⁄ ⁄⁄⁄⁄ ⁄⁄⁄⁄ ⁄⁄⁄⁄
4:00–5:00 P.M.	⁄⁄⁄⁄ ⁄⁄⁄⁄ ⁄⁄⁄⁄ ⁄⁄⁄⁄ ⁄⁄⁄⁄ ⁄⁄⁄⁄ ⁄⁄⁄⁄
5:00–6:00 P.M.	⁄⁄⁄⁄ ⁄⁄⁄⁄ ⁄⁄⁄⁄ ⁄⁄⁄⁄ ⁄⁄⁄⁄ ⁄⁄⁄⁄ ⁄⁄⁄⁄ ⁄⁄⁄⁄ ///

(a) During what period of time does he need the greatest number of sales workers? The least? Explain.

(b) What time would you suggest for lunch hour? Explain.

(c) Should the manager consider opening his store later in the morning and closing later in the evening? Explain.

(d) During what hour of the day does the mode of customers occur?

(e) Find the mean number of customers per hour. Is the mean a helpful statistic for the manager? Explain.

11. In Exercise 10 the manager chose to give a door prize during each hour from 9:00 A.M. to 2:00 P.M. Do you think this a good plan? Explain.

12. In Exercise 10 the manager employed student helpers daily from 4:00 P.M. to 6:00 P.M. Does this seem a wise judgment for him to make? Explain.

5–6 D

1. Use the facts from 5–6 C, Exercise 10, to make a bar graph. See Figure 5–11.

2. On your graph for Exercise 1 draw a line showing the mean number of customers per hour.

3. From your graph in Exercises 1 and 2, list each hour for which the number of customers was below average.

4. In 5–6 B make a bar graph of the times for students in the 100-yard dash. Draw a line across the graph showing the mean.

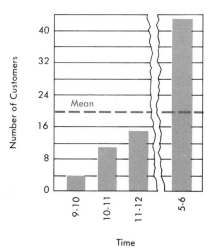

Time

FIGURE 5-11

5-6 E

One afternoon a filling-station owner kept a record of gasoline sales as shown. As each sale was made he placed a tally in the appropriate interval. Thus for a sale of 16.7 gallons he placed a tally by the interval headed 16.0 − 20.0. For a sale of 6.1 gallons he placed a tally by the interval headed 4.0 − 8.0.

We assume that the sales in each interval would average around the midpoint. Thus $(16.0 + 20.0)/2 = 18.0$ (gallons), the midpoint for the top interval. Then the total of these sales is approximately (3×18.0) gallons, or 54 gallons.

Each tally represents a **frequency**. We call the table a **frequency table.**

Interval	Mid-point, m	Number of Sales, f		$f \times m$	Cumula-tive Fre-quencies
16.0 − 20.0	18.0	///	= 3	54.0	33
12.0 − 16.0	14.0	//// /	= 6	84.0	30
8.0 − 12.0	10.0	//// //// //	= 12	120.0	24
4.0 − 8.0	6.0	//// ///	= 8	48.0	12
0 − 4.0	2.0	////	= 4	8.0	4
			$n = 33$	$S = 314.0$	

Exercises 5–6 E continued on page 236.

1. Use the formula $m = S/n$ to find the mean of gasoline sales.
2. Find the mode of gasoline sales. (*Note:* Give the midpoint m for the interval with largest frequency f.)
3. Note the column headed Cumulative Frequencies (page 235). We find these figures by adding the values of f: $4 + 8 = 12$, $12 + 12 = 24$, and so on. Find the median sale in this way: (1) The middle frequency is the seventeenth sale from the bottom; that is, the fifth sale in the interval $8.0 - 12.0$. (2) Assume that this sale is $\frac{5}{12}$ of the way between 8.0 gallons and 12.0 gallons: $\frac{5}{12} \times 4.0 = \frac{20}{12}$, or about 1.7. (3) Median $= 8.0 + 1.7 = 9.7$.

    Because rounding off is involved, the answers derived from the table are approximate. Give the median of gasoline sales to the nearest gallon.

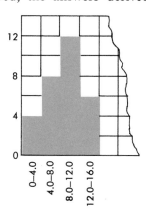

4. Make a graph of the data on gasoline sales. As suggested in Figure 5-12, leave no space between bars. Such a graph is called a **frequency polygon.**
5. A butcher kept the following frequency table on sales of steak. The intervals are given in pounds.

FIGURE 5-12

Interval	Mid-point, m	Number of Sales, f		$f \times m$	Cumulative Frequencies
$1.0 - 1.2$	1.1	$//$	$= 2$	2.2	35
$0.8 - 1.0$	0.9	$\cancel{HHH}$	$= 5$	4.5	33
$0.6 - 0.8$	0.7	$\cancel{HHH}\ ////$	$= 9$	6.3	28
$0.4 - 0.6$	0.5	$\cancel{HHH}\ \cancel{HHH}\ \cancel{HHH}$	$= 15$	7.5	19
$0.2 - 0.4$	0.3	$////$	$= 4$	1.2	4
			$n = 35$	$S = 21.7$	

Find the mean of the weights. Use the formula $m = S/n$ and give your answer to the nearest 0.1 pound.

6. In Exercise 5 find the median. Give your answer to the nearest 0.1 pound.
7. In Exercise 5 find the mode.
8. Make a frequency polygon from the data in Exercise 5.
9. Assume that the table in Exercise 5 gives a fair sample of the butcher's sales and that the butcher prepackages his meat.
   (a) What percent r of his packages should contain steaks weighing between 1.0 and 1.2 pounds? (*Note:* $r = \frac{2}{35}$)
   (b) As in (a) find r for weights between 0.8 and 1.0 pound.
   (c) Find r for each of the other intervals in the table.

■ 5–7 LATITUDE AND LONGITUDE

In order to locate points on the surface of the earth, man uses a coordinate system. Consider a plane, as p or p', through the center of the earth. Such a plane intersects the earth's surface in a great circle (a circle with its center at the center of the earth). In Figure 5–13 the intersection of plane p with the earth's surface represents the equator; points N and S represent the North and South poles.

Imaginary semicircles (as arc NAS) with endpoints at the poles are called meridians. Thus a meridian is one-half of a great circle. A plane q parallel to the plane of the equator (plane p) intersects the earth in a circle called a parallel of latitude. Such a circle is called a small circle of the sphere, since its center is not the center of the sphere.

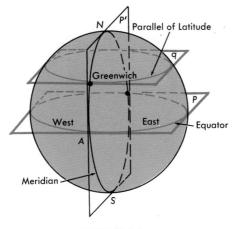

FIGURE 5–13

One of the meridians is called the *zero semicircle* and is named the **prime meridian.** This meridian passes through Greenwich, England. All points west of the prime meridian as far as the *international date line*, one-half the way around the world, are called **west longitude.** The points east of the prime meridian to the date line are called **east longitude.** The equator is the *zero circle* for latitude. Points north of the equator are called **north latitude** and points south of it are called **south latitude.**

The longitude of a point on the surface of the earth is determined by the measure of a central angle (see $\angle ACB$ in Figure 5–14) of the equator. The measure of a central angle (see $\angle BCP$) of a meridian is the latitude of the point.

In Figure 5–14 let us assume that the circle through NAS is the prime meridian. Hence point P has longitude 15° west since $\angle ACB$ has a measure of 15°. Angle PCB is a central angle of the

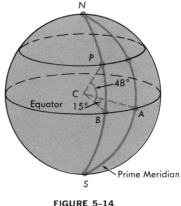

FIGURE 5-14

meridian through P.   Point P has latitude 48° north since $\angle PCB$ has a measure of 48°.

An arc of a circle has a degree measure which is the measure of its central angle. In Figure 5–14 arc AB, symbolized as $\overset{\frown}{AB}$, has a measure of 15 arc degrees.

One minute of arc on a great circle of the earth equals 1 **nautical mile.** A nautical mile is approximately 6080 feet, or 1853 meters. A **knot** is a unit of speed; it is 1 nautical mile per hour.

In our study we shall consider that the shape of the earth is spherical, even though this is not precisely true.   Thus our answers are approximate.

Example 1. Find the length of $\overset{\frown}{PB}$ in Figure 5–14.   First, $\overset{\frown}{PB}$ has a measure of 48°. We express 48° in minutes.

$$48 \times 60 = 2880$$

Thus $\overset{\frown}{PB}$ has a length of 2880 nautical miles (about 3300 land miles).

Example 2. Find the difference d in longitude between point A at 41° E and point B at 12° W.

$$d = 41 + 12 = 53$$

The difference is 53°.

Exercises for Section 5-7

5-7 A

Find the differences in longitude between A and B:

1. A, 42° W; B, 75° W   **2.** A, 19° E; B, 164° E
3. A, 10° W; B, 10° E   **4.** A, 15° W; B, 175° E
5. A, 17°35′ E; B, 106°15′ E
6. A, 24°44′5″ W; B, 37°32′40″ W
7. A, 19°27′ E; B, 31°36′ W
8. A, 62°19′40″ W; B, 18°25′47″ E

5-7 B

Find the differences in latitude between A and B:

1. A, 12° N; B, 43° N   **2.** A, 47° S; B, 87° S
3. A, 16° S; B, 42° N   **4.** A, 53° N; B, 74° S
5. A, 42°17′ N; B, 71°19′ N
6. A, 68°27′15″ N; B, 83°43′9″ N
7. A, 21°37′48″ N; B, 19°27′55″ S
8. A, 82°18′18″ S; B, 70°30′49″ N

5-7 C

Find the distance in nautical miles between A and B:

1. A, (17° N, 43° W); B, (28° N, 43° W)
2. A, (12° N, 51° W); B, (75° N, 51° W)
3. A, (28°17′ S, 101° E); B, (19°43′ S, 101° E)
4. A, (13°19′ N, 90°40′ W); B, (19°13′ N, 90°40′ W)
5. A, (21° S, 9° E); B, (11°30′ N, 9° E)
6. A, (4°4′11″ N, 7° W); B, (7°7′4″ N, 7° W)
7. A, (57° S, 18′11″ E); B, (11° S, 18′11″ E)
8. A, (90° N, 0° E); B, (90° S, 0° E)

5-7 D

1. Find the latitude of the North Pole. Of the South Pole.
2. Find the latitude of a city which is $\frac{1}{4}$ the way from the equator to the South Pole.
3. Which parallels of latitude fulfill the definition of a great circle?
4. Determine the longitude of the international date line.
5. Cities C and B lie on the same meridian. City B is 975 nautical miles north of city C. Find the latitude of B if C has latitude 24°30′ N.
6. Find the latitude of a city which is 31°43′ north of the South Pole.
7. Starting from 30° W, a ship steamed west along the equator at 15 knots. Find the longitude of the ship in 32 hours.
8. A ship steamed from 60° S, 120° W to 37° S, 120° W in 3 days and 9.6 hours. Find the speed to the nearest tenth of a knot.

5-7 E

This table gives the approximate longitudes of some cities.

City	Longitude
Berlin, Germany	14° E
Denver, Colorado	105° W
San Francisco, California	122° W
Honolulu, Hawaii	157°52′ W
Rome, Italy	12°30′ E
New York, New York	74° W
Yokohama, Japan	139°40′ E

Find the difference in longitude between:

1. Berlin and Honolulu
2. Rome and Berlin
3. Denver and San Francisco
4. New York and Yokohama
5. San Francisco and Yokohama
6. Honolulu and New York
7. Yokohama and Rome
8. Rome and New York

5-7 F

To find the shortest path between two points on the earth, as points A and B, stretch a piece of string between them on a globe, as shown in Figure 5–15. Then measure the length of string used (see $\overparen{A'B'}$).

This measure, in minutes, is the number of nautical miles from A to B. (*Note:* In geometry it is shown that a string stretched, between two points, as from A to B in Figure 5–15, describes an arc of a great circle. Also it is shown that this is the shortest distance between the two points.

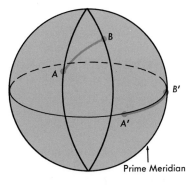

FIGURE 5–15

1. In Figure 5–15 $m(\widehat{A'B'}) = 42$ (degrees). Find the distance AB in nautical miles.

2. Suppose we have found that $m(\widehat{A'B'}) = 28\frac{1}{2}$ (degrees). Find the distance AB in nautical miles.

Use a globe and a piece of string to find the approximate great-circle distance from:

3. San Francisco to New York   4. Los Angeles to New York
5. New York to London   6. Denver to Paris
7. New Orleans to Berlin   8. Seattle to Chicago
9. Rome to New York   10. Honolulu to Paris

◼ 5–8 TIME

Man bases his measurements of time primarily on the movements of the bodies of the solar system.

One year is the time required for the earth to make 1 complete revolution about the sun. One day is the time required for the earth to make 1 complete rotation on its axis. One week is the time required for the moon to make $\frac{1}{4}$ of its journey around the earth. These times are approximate.

More accurately, it takes the earth about $365\frac{1}{4}$ days to complete its trip around the sun. For convenience we round this off to 365. Every fourth year (leap year) an extra day is added to the month of February to make up for this rounding off.

Since the earth makes 1 complete turn in 24 hours, any point on the surface of the earth passes through an arc of 360° in 24 hours, or an arc of 15° in 1 hour.

As the sun "crosses" each meridian, the solar time for all points along that meridian is noon. However if each community tried to use its own solar time, much confusion would arise. This is avoided by the establishment of standard time zones for approximately every 15° of arc around the world. These begin at the prime meridian. As one moves westward the time in each new time zone entered is 1 hour earlier than the last.

Figure 5–16 shows five standard time zones. The boundaries do not follow the meridians but are adjusted to fit local situations. As we move from east to west, note that these standard time zones are Atlantic, Eastern, Central, Mountain, and Pacific.

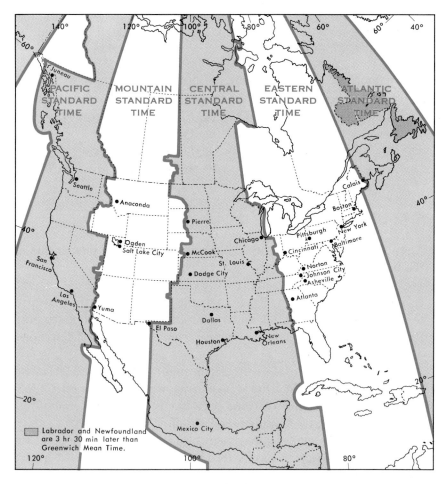

FIGURE 5–16

Suppose two people take a trip starting on the prime meridian at 11:59 P.M. on Sunday. Person A moves westward and B moves eastward. They meet 7 days later halfway around the world at the 180° meridian. Person A has turned his watch back 1 hour for each 15° of arc through which he has traveled. Thus his time is 11:59 A.M. Sunday. Person B has turned his watch forward a total of 12 hours, 1 hour for each 15° of arc through which he has traveled. Thus his time is 11:59 A.M. Monday.

We see that just east of the 180° meridian it is one day later than it is just west of it. For this reason the 180° meridian is called the **international date line.** People who cross it westward gain a day; those who cross it eastward lose a day.

Exercises for Section 5-8

5-8 A

1. When it is 1:00 P.M. EST, what is the time in the Pacific zone? Central zone? Mountain zone? (*Note:* EST means eastern standard time; CST means central standard time; and so on.)
2. Name the time zone in which each of these cities is found: New York, Los Angeles, Denver, Chicago, and Boston.
3. A football game starts at 2:00 P.M. in Pittsburgh, Pennsylvania. Find the time (PST) at which a person can start watching the game live on television in Seattle.
4. An airplane left San Francisco at 4:45 P.M. (PST) and arrived in New York at 4:15 A.M. (EST) the next day. How long did the trip take?
5. When it is noon in Greenwich, it is 6:00 P.M. in Calcutta. Find the approximate longitude of Calcutta.
6. The difference in longitude between two cities is 105°. Find the difference in time.
7. When it is 4:00 P.M. in Greenwich, find the time in Natal, Brazil, longitude 35°13′ W.
8. Honolulu, Hawaii, is near the 157° West meridian and Sydney, Australia, is near the 151° East meridian. When it is Wednesday in Sydney, what day is it in Honolulu?
9. It is 11:00 P.M. Friday in New York. Determine the time and the day in Seattle.
10. If it is 1:30 A.M. Tuesday in Los Angeles, determine the time and day in New Orleans.

5-8 B

Use the table from Exercise 5–7 E to determine the difference in time between the cities.

1. Berlin and Rome   2. Denver and San Francisco
3. New York and Honolulu   4. San Francisco and Honolulu
5. Berlin and Yokohama   6. New York and San Francisco
7. Rome and Yokohama   8. Denver and Honolulu

5-8 C

Find the time of flight.   (*Note:* Lv means "leave" and Ar means "arrive.")

1. Lv New York, 6:01 A.M. EST—Ar Los Angeles, 7:05 A.M. PST
2. Lv Denver, 7:45 A.M. MST—Ar Detroit, 12:32 P.M. EST
3. Lv St. Louis, 6:15 P.M. CST—Ar Seattle, 8:05 P.M. PST
4. Lv Kansas City, 12:04 P.M. CST—Ar El Paso, 3:00 P.M. CST
5. Lv Los Angeles, 10:55 P.M. PST—Ar New York, 6:05 A.M. EST

■ 5-9 GRAPHS OF INEQUALITIES

Consider the inequality $x > 5$. We can show this graph *on a number line*, as in Figure 5–17. The colored part of the line is the graph. The hollow dot at "5" indicates that the point is not a part of the graph, since $x > 5$ shows that x cannot equal 5.

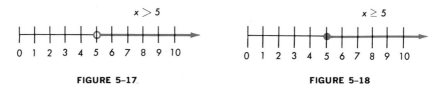

FIGURE 5-17   FIGURE 5-18

Now consider the graph of $x \geq 5$ (x is greater than or equal to 5). Here, $x = 5$ is a part of the graph. The solid dot at "5" indicates this.

On a coordinate plane we graph $x > 5$, as shown in Figure 5–19. The dashed vertical line through point A indicates that this line is not a part of the graph. The graph is the shaded region of the picture.

Figure 5–20 shows the graph of $x \geq 5$. The solid vertical line through point B indicates that this line is a part of the graph. The graph is this line plus the shaded region of the picture.

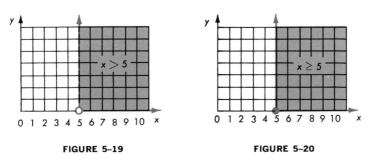

FIGURE 5–19   FIGURE 5–20

The inequality $1 < x < 5$ (read as "x is greater than 1 and x is less than 5") describes an **open interval,** and is graphed on a number line in Figure 5–21. The graph consists of all points between A and B, not including A and B.

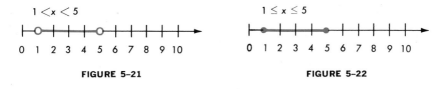

FIGURE 5–21   FIGURE 5–22

On the number line the inequality $1 \leq x \leq 5$ describes a **closed interval,** and its graph is shown in Figure 5–22.

In Figure 5–23, the doubly-shaded region is the graph of the system of the two inequalities

$$\begin{cases} 2 < x < 4, \text{ and} \\ 1 < y < 3. \end{cases} \quad (1)$$

That is, the graph is the intersection of two regions: the region where all values of x are between 2 and 4 with the region where all values of y are between 1 and 3. Thus it is the region within rec-

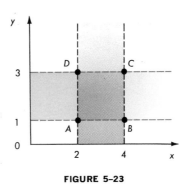

FIGURE 5–23

tangle $ABCD$. The coordinates of any point in this intersection satisfy both inequalities in (1). For example, $(3, 2)$ is such a point since

$$\begin{cases} 2 < 3 < 4, \text{ and} \\ 1 < 2 < 3. \end{cases}$$

In Figure 5-24 the doubly-shaded region is the graph of the system of the two inequalities

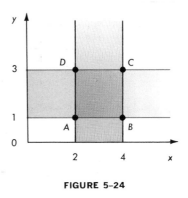

FIGURE 5-24

$$\begin{cases} 2 \leq x \leq 4, \text{ and} \\ 1 \leq y \leq 3. \end{cases} \quad (2)$$

That is, the graph of (2) includes the region within rectangle $ABCD$ and also the rectangle. The coordinates of any point in this intersection satisfy both of the inequalities in (2). For example, (4, 3) is such a point since

$$\begin{cases} 2 \leq 4 \leq 4, \text{ and} \\ 1 \leq 3 \leq 3. \end{cases}$$

Exercises for Section 5-9

5-9 A

On a number line sketch the graph of each inequality:

1. $x > 3$ **2.** $x > 6$ **3.** $x > 4\frac{1}{2}$

4. $x \geq 2$ **5.** $x \geq 3\frac{1}{2}$ **6.** $x \geq 4.5$

7. $2 < x < 7$ **8.** $3.5 \leq x \leq 7.8$ **9.** $2.8 \leq x \leq 8.7$

10. $3 \leq x < 12$. Note that $x = 12$ is not a part of this graph.

5-9 B

As in Figures 5-23 and 5-24, make a graph of each of the following systems of inequalities:

1. $\begin{cases} 2.5 < x < 5.5, \text{ and} \\ 3.4 < y < 4.8 \end{cases}$ **2.** $\begin{cases} 2.5 \leq x \leq 6.5, \text{ and} \\ 3.4 \leq y \leq 5.8 \end{cases}$

3. $\begin{cases} 4.2 \leq x \leq 7.2, \text{ and} \\ 4.5 \leq y \leq 8.6 \end{cases}$ **4.** $\begin{cases} 5.8 \leq x < 9.6, \text{ and} \\ 6.2 \leq y < 8.5 \end{cases}$

5. $\begin{cases} 5.6 < x < 8.1, \text{ and} \\ 3.1 \leq y \leq 4.6 \end{cases}$ **6.** $\begin{cases} 4.1 \leq x < 5.3, \text{ and} \\ 2.6 < y \leq 4.5 \end{cases}$

7. $\begin{cases} 3.1 \leq x \leq 4.6, \text{ and} \\ 5.6 < y < 8.1 \end{cases}$ **8.** $\begin{cases} 3.6 < x \leq 4.2, \text{ and} \\ 3.6 \leq y < 4.2 \end{cases}$

5-9 C

In each exercise make a graph of the interval on a number line.

1. During 1 year, the price of 1 grade of pine lumber ranged from a low of 18 cents to a high of 26.5 cents per square foot.
2. During 1 year the range in the average work week in a factory was: low, 38.8 hours; high, 41.6 hours.
3. During 1 day in San Francisco the range in temperature was: low, 46°; high, 67°.
4. During 1 year the range in the popularity of the President was: low, 52%; high, 63%.
5. During 1 semester the range in a student's test scores was: low, 76; high, 98.
6. During 1 month the range of production in a factory was: low, 28 units; high, 44 units.
7. The engineer said, "We must keep the pressure in this boiler between 40 and 50 pounds."
8. The car owner said, "I want the pressure in my tires between 28 and 30 pounds."
9. A city water company reports that pressure in its water lines is between 80 and 90 pounds per square inch.
10. A pilot flies his plane between 550 and 650 miles per hour.

5-9 D

1. The foreman said, "In 4 to 5 hours we should produce 15 to 20 units." Make a graph, using one axis for time t. Use the other axis for number of units u.
2. The space flight director said, "For $40 \leq t \leq 50$, in minutes, this machine should travel between 2800 and 2900 miles." Label a t-axis and a d-axis, and make a graph.
3. With a sales staff of 8 to 10 people, a merchant can make sales of $30,000 to $40,000 per month. Let x be the number on his sales staff; y, the number of dollars of sales. Make a graph.
4. In Exercise 2 find the range of values for d.
5. A driver's average speed is about 50 miles per hour. He makes a vacation trip on which he plans to drive at least 2 hours per day, and at most, 9 hours per day. Make a graph of the formula $d = 50t$, where $2 \leq t \leq 9$. The graph should be a line segment.

Vocabulary

The section in which each word appears is indicated in parentheses.

bimodal (5–6)

broken line (5–1)

closed interval (5–9)

continuous (5–1)

coordinates (5–1)

dependent variable (5–3)

domain (5–3)

east longitude (5–7)

equator (5–7)

frequency (Exercises 5–6 E)

frequency polygon
   (Exercises 5–6 E)

frequency table (Exercises 5–6 E)

graph (5–1)

horizontal axis (5–1)

independent variable (5–3)

international date line (5–8)

knot (5–7)

linear equations (5–3)

mean (5–6)

measure of central tendency (5–6)

median (5–6)

meridians (5–7)

mode (5–6)

nautical mile (5–7)

north latitude (5–7)

odds in favor (5–5)

open interval (5–9)

origin (5–3)

parallel of latitude (5–7)

prime meridian (5–7)

probability (5–5)

range (5–3, 5–6)

small circle (5–7)

south latitude (5–7)

square root (Exercises 5–4 E)

square root symbol
   (Exercises 5–4 E)

statistics (5–6)

success (5–5)

vertical axis (5–1)

west longitude (5–7)

Chapter Review

A

1. Make a broken line graph of the data in 5–1 C, Exercise 3, page 215.

2. A factory produced a special breakfast cereal. The managers planned to spend income from the product in this way: 10% for advertising, 50% for manufacturing costs, 12% for gross profit, and 28% for other costs. Make a circle graph.

3. Let r represent the rate of interest on an installment loan; C, the interest charge on the loan. Suppose that the loan is for $100, and that the borrower pays it off in 12 equal monthly installments.

Then approximately, $r = \frac{24}{1300}C$. Make a line graph. Use values of C from 0 to 30. (*Note:* If $C = 10$, then $r = \frac{24}{1300} \times 10 \approx$ 18.5%.)

4. Refer to your graph in Exercise 3.
   (a) Is your graph a line segment?
   (b) Find an approximation of r for $C = 18$.
   (c) Find an approximation of r for $C = 27$.
   (d) Do your answers in (b) and (c) seem high?
5. In Exercise 3 which is the independent variable? The dependent variable?
6. In Exercise 3 what is the domain of the independent variable?

B

1. The blacksmith said, "I will shoe your horse for this charge: for the first nail, 1 cent; for the second nail, 2 cents; for the third nail, 4 cents; for the fourth nail, 8 cents; and so on." At this rate the cost C for driving the nth nail is given by the formula $C = 2^{n-1}$. Make a table of values for $n = 1, 2, \ldots, 16$. (*Note:* Some ordered pairs (n, C) are $(1, 1)$, $(2, 2)$, $(3, 4)$, $(4, 8)$, $(5, 16)$, and $(6, 32)$.)
2. From your table in Exercise 1 make a graph for $n = 1, 2, \ldots,$ 7, 8. Note that the graph is nonlinear.
3. A tank contains 80 balls. The balls are numbered $1, 2, 3, \ldots, 80$. A ball is picked at random from the tank. Find the probability that its number is 79.
4. A company planted 100 flower seeds as a test, and 94 grew. Find the probability that a seed selected at random will grow.
5. From a random sample of buyers it was found that 79 buy Brand A bacon, 93 buy Brand B, and 28 buy Brand C. Base your judgment on this sample, and find the probability that a customer for bacon selects:
   (a) Brand A   (b) Brand B   (c) Brand C
6. During 1 week the count of customers in a store was 16,000. The number of sales of Brand X window cleaner was 80. Based on these figures, what is the probability that a customer selected at random will buy Brand X window cleaner?

Chapter Review continued on page 250.

7. In making an index for a book one author found the following
   numbers of entries for the letters of the alphabet.

a	63	n	38
b	9	o	13
c	55	p	63
d	50	q	2
e	35	r	35
f	22	s	60
g	15	t	34
h	3	u	4
i	32	v	16
j	0	w	4
k	2	x	3
l	15	y	4
m	42	z	3

(a) Find the median.   (b) Find the mean.
(c) Find the mode.   (d) Find the range.

6 The Arithmetic of Finance

■ **6–1 INTEREST**

Money paid for the use of borrowed money is called **interest.** To the borrower, interest is an expense; to the lender, an income. The money borrowed or loaned is called the **principal.** The ratio of the interest per unit of time to the principal is called the **rate** of interest. The rate is usually given as a number of percent. Unless it is otherwise stated, the rate of interest is most commonly quoted for a period of 1 year.

Let p stand for the principal; r, for the rate of interest; t, for the number of units of time for which the loan is made. The interest I is found by using formula I.

$$\text{I.} \qquad I = prt$$

Example 1. Find the interest on a loan of \$200 for 4 years at $3\frac{1}{2}\%$ per year.

$$I = prt$$
$$I = (200)(0.035)(4)$$
$$I = 28$$

The interest is \$28.

Example 2. Find the interest on $150 for 6 months at $\frac{1}{2}\%$ per month.

$$I = prt$$
$$I = (150)\left(\frac{\frac{1}{2}}{100}\right)(6)$$
$$I = 4.50$$

The interest is $4.50.

In general, banks and other money-lending institutions use a 360-day year as a basis for calculating interest for a number of days less than a year.

Example 3. Find the interest on a loan of $500 for 120 days at a rate of 4%.

$$I = prt$$
$$I = (500)(0.04)(\tfrac{120}{360})$$
$$I = 6.67$$

The interest is $6.67, to the nearest cent.

The United States Government uses a 365-day year. Interest figured on this basis is sometimes called **exact interest.** Unless otherwise stated, we will use a 360-day year in this book.

The **amount** A is the sum of the principal and the interest, as in formula II.

II. $A = P + I$

Example 4. Find the exact interest and the amount on $800 borrowed on June 1 and paid the following August 5, at 5%.

We start with June 2 and count the number of days up to and including August 5. Interest is not charged for the first day.

$$I = prt$$
$$I = (800)(0.05)(\tfrac{65}{365})$$
$$I = 7.22$$

The interest is $7.22.

$$A = P + I$$
$$A = 800 + 7.22$$
$$A = 807.22$$

The amount is $807.22.

Exercises for Section 6-1

6-1 A

Find the interest on a loan of $1000 for:

1. 1 year at 4%
2. 3 years at 4%
3. $4\frac{1}{2}$ years at 4%
4. 6 years at $3\frac{1}{2}$%
5. 8 years at $5\frac{3}{4}$%
6. 3 months at 2%
7. 5 months at $3\frac{1}{2}$%
8. 60 days at $4\frac{1}{4}$%
9. 75 days at 6%
10. 130 days at 10%

6-1 B

1. Find the interest on a loan of $750 for 1 year 5 months at 5%.
2. Find the interest on a loan of $12,300 for 8 years at $5\frac{1}{2}$%.
3. Find the interest on a loan of $1750 for 1 year 80 days at $3\frac{1}{4}$%.
4. An investment of $600 paid $24 in interest for 1 year. Find the rate of interest. $\left(\textit{Note:} \text{ Rate} = \dfrac{\text{Interest per unit of time}}{\text{Principal}} \text{ ; that is, } r = \dfrac{I}{p}. \text{ Hence } r = \dfrac{24}{600}. \right)$
5. A loan of $6000 for 1 year cost a man $210 in interest. Find the rate of interest.
6. Find the annual rate of interest if the principal is $1250 and the interest is $55 per year.
7. Find the principal when the annual rate of interest is 3% and the interest is $210 per year. (*Note:* 3% of $P = I$)
8. A man borrowed $1725 for 5 years at $4\frac{1}{2}$%. At the end of the 5-year period he wrote a check for the loan and all of the interest. What was the amount of the check?
9. Find the total amount of a loan for $620 for 2 years and 4 months. The rate is $5\frac{1}{2}$%.
10. How much money should be invested at $4\frac{1}{2}$% to earn $382.50 per year?

6-1 C

In each exercise find the exact interest on a loan of $900 with the given rate and time. Assume that no leap year is involved.

1. 3% from June 5 to September 5 of the same year
2. $4\frac{1}{2}$% from January 1 to May 15 of the same year
3. $3\frac{1}{4}$% from January 1 to June 1 of the same year
4. $3\frac{3}{4}$% from March 5 to May 30 of the same year
5. $4\frac{1}{4}$% from November 1 to March 15 of the next year
6. $5\frac{5}{8}$% from December 15 to May 15 of the next year

6-1 D

In the example we find the interest on $700 at 6% for 60 days.

$$I = prt$$
$$I = (700)(0.06)(\tfrac{60}{360}) = (700)(\tfrac{6}{100})(\tfrac{60}{360})$$
$$I = (700)(\tfrac{1}{100}) = 7$$

Notice that the product rt, $\frac{6}{100} \times \frac{60}{360}$, is $\frac{1}{100}$. Thus to find the interest on any amount p for 60 days at 6%, we take 1% of p.

Find the interest on the following amounts invested at 6% for 60 days:

1. $600	2. $1575	3. $2270	4. $975
5. $18,600	6. $8450	7. $475	8. $765

9. Find the interest on the amounts in Exercises 1–8 at 6% for 120 days. Write a simple formula.
10. An amount p is invested at 6% for 90 days. Write a simple formula for the interest due on this investment. The total interest is what percent of the amount p?

6-1 E

In Exercises 1–4 find the interest on a loan of $500:

1. For 1 month if r is $\frac{1}{2}$% per month.
2. For 1 month if r is $1\frac{1}{2}$% per month.
3. For 1 quarter if r is 3% per quarter.
4. For 1 half year if r is $3\frac{1}{2}$% per half year.
5. A home owner's loan of $4000 draws interest at $\frac{1}{2}$% per month on the unpaid balance. Each month the owner pays $30 to the

principal. He also pays the interest. Thus his loan record book looks like this:

Month	Unpaid Balance B	Interest I for Month	Payment P for Month
First	$4000	$\frac{1}{2}\% \times 4000 = 20$	$30 + 20 = 50$
Second	$3970	$\frac{1}{2}\% \times 3970 = I$	$30 + I = P$

(a) For each month does B decrease by 30?
(b) Does I decrease from month to month?
(c) Does $P + I$ decrease?
6. In Exercise 5 continue a table for B, I, and P for the first 6 months.

6-1 F

1. Consider the formula $I = prt$, where $p = 1$ and $r = 8\%$; that is, $I = 0.08t$. Make a graph of $I = 0.08t$, using $t = \{$real numbers from 0 to 10 inclusive$\}$.
2. On your drawing for Exercise 1, graph $I = 0.06t$.
3. From Exercises 1 and 2, you have the graphs of $I = 0.08t$ and $I = 0.06t$. Find the ratio of I on the first graph to I on the second if t is:
   (a) 1   (b) 2   (c) 3   (d) 10
4. In Exercise 1 or Exercise 2, is the interest on $2 twice the interest on $1? Is the interest on $5 five times the interest on $1? Is the interest on $1000 one thousand times the interest on $1? Is the interest on K dollars K times the interest on $1?
5. Suppose that $I = 0.08t$, as in Exercise 1:
   (a) Does I increase as time increases?
   (b) Is $I < t$?

▨ 6-2 SEQUENCES AND SERIES

A set of numbers for which the order is given is called a **sequence.** Thus the set

$$1, \quad 4, \quad 7, \quad 10$$

is a sequence. Each member of the set is called a **term** of the sequence. In this sequence note that $4 - 1 = 3$, $7 - 4 = 3$, and $10 - 7 = 3$. The **common difference** between consecutive terms is 3. A sequence

in which such a common difference d exists throughout is called an
arithmetic sequence.

Arithmetic Sequence	Common Difference
2, 4, 6, 8, 10	$d = 2$
0, 5, 10, 15, 20, 25	$d = 5$
5, 12, 19, 26, 33, 40	$d = 7$

The indicated sum of the terms of a sequence is called a **series.** This
sum can be found for an arithmetic sequence, as shown in the
examples.

Example 1. Find S if $S = 3 + 7 + 11$.

$$S = 3 + 7 + 11$$
$$\underline{S = 11 + 7 + 3} \qquad \text{Commutative and associative}$$
$$2S = 14 + 14 + 14 \qquad \text{properties of addition}$$
$$2S = 3 \times 14 \qquad\qquad 14 + 14 + 14 = 3 \times 14$$
$$S = \tfrac{3}{2} \times 14 \qquad\qquad \text{Division axiom}$$
$$S = 21 \qquad\qquad\quad \tfrac{3}{2} \times 14 = 21$$

Of course, in Example 1 we can find $3 + 7 + 11$ more quickly by
adding. Now consider the same method to find the sum of the arithmetic sequences in Examples 2 and 3.

Example 2. Find S if $S = 8 + 12 + 16 + 20$.

$$S = 8 + 12 + 16 + 20$$
$$\underline{S = 20 + 16 + 12 + 8}$$
$$2S = 28 + 28 + 28 + 28$$
$$2S = 4 \times 28$$
$$S = \tfrac{4}{2} \times 28$$
$$S = 56$$

Here again, we may find S more quickly by adding. But Example 3
is more difficult.

Example 3. Find S if $S = 2 + 4 + 6 + \cdots + 18 + 20$.

$$
\begin{aligned}
S &= 2 + 4 + 6 + \cdots + 18 + 20 \\
S &= 20 + 18 + 16 + \cdots + 4 + 2 \\
\hline
2S &= 22 + 22 + 22 + \cdots + 22 + 22
\end{aligned}
$$

$2S = 10 \times 22$ Note that there are
$S = \frac{10}{2} \times 22$ 10 addends, each of
$S = 110$ which is 22.

Let n stand for the number of terms; a, for the first term; l, for the last term. It can be shown (see Exercises 6–2 B) that the sum S of an arithmetic series is found by formula III.

III. $S = \dfrac{n}{2}(a + l)$

In Example 3, $a = 2$, $l = 20$, and $n = 10$. Thus

$$S = \tfrac{10}{2}(2 + 20),$$
$$S = 5(22) = 110.$$

Exercises for Section 6–2

6–2 A

As in the examples, solve for S:
1. $S = 5 + 10 + 15$
2. $S = 7 + 14 + 21$
3. $S = 12 + 24 + 36$
4. $S = 9 + 18 + 27$
5. $S = 23 + 46 + 69$
6. $S = 7 + 12 + 17 + 22 + 27$
7. $S = 6 + 10 + 14 + 18 + 22$
8. $S = 2 + 4 + 6 + \cdots + 10 + 12$
9. $S = 3 + 6 + \cdots + 18 + 21$
10. $S = 32 + 28 + \cdots + 8 + 4$

6–2 B

1. Consider the sequence a, $a + d$, $a + 2d$. The common difference is d. This sequence can be written as a series in either one of two ways.

$$S = \quad a \quad + \quad (a + d) + \quad (a + 2d) \quad (1)$$
$$S = \quad (a + 2d) + \quad (a + d) + \quad a \quad (2)$$

Adding lines (1) and (2) we get

$$2S = \quad (2a + 2d) + \quad (2a + 2d) + \quad (2a + 2d), \quad (3)$$

or

$$2S = [a + (a + 2d)] + [a + (a + 2d)] + [a + (a + 2d)]. \quad (4)$$

Let l represent the last term of the sequence; that is, $l = a + 2d$. Now we may write:

$$2S = (a + l) + (a + l) + (a + l), \quad (5)$$
$$2S = 3(a + l), \quad (6)$$
$$S = \frac{3}{?}(a + l). \quad (7)$$

Find the correct replacement for the question mark in (7).

2. Find S if $S = a + (a + d) + \cdots + (a + 5d)$. Use l for the last term.

3. Find S if $S = a + (a + d) + \cdots + (a + 6d)$. Use l for the last term.

4. Find S if $S = a + (a + d) + \cdots + (a + 8d)$. Use l for the last term.

5. Let n represent the number of terms in each sequence of Exercises 1–4. Thus in Exercise 1, $n = 3$. For each exercise does

$$S = \frac{n}{2}(a + l)?$$

6–2 C

1. Consider the following sequence:

$$2, 4, \ldots, 8, 10, 12.$$

In the reverse order we may write

$$2, 4, \ldots, 12 - 4, 12 - 2, 12.$$

In the same way consider the arithmetic sequence a, $a + d$, $a + 2d, \ldots, l - 2d, l - d, l$. From this, we have

$$
\begin{array}{rl}
S = & a \quad + (a + d) + (a + 2d) + \cdots + (l - 2d) + (l - d) + l \\
S = & l \quad + (l - d) + (l - 2d) + \cdots + (a + 2d) + (a + d) + a \\
\hline
2S = & (a + l) + (a + l) + (a + l) + \cdots + (a + l) + (a + l) + (a + l)
\end{array}
$$

If there are n terms in the sequence, then:

(a) Does $2S = n \times (a + l)$?   (b) Does $S = \dfrac{n}{2}(a + l)$?
Explain.

2. Use the formula $S = \frac{1}{2}n(a + l)$ to find S in 6–2 A, Exercises 1–10. (*Note:* This formula is the formula for finding the sum of the terms of an arithmetic sequence.)

■ 6-3 THE COST OF INSTALLMENT PURCHASES

When we buy on credit, we usually pay an extra charge. Whether this charge is called "interest," "carrying charge," or "service fee," it increases the cost of what we buy. The differences in the costs of credit among finance plans are great. The costs can be compared by calculating each one as an annual interest rate.

In IV we have the formula for the approximate annual interest rate r on an installment purchase.

$$\textbf{IV.} \qquad r = \frac{24C}{B(n + 1)}$$

The interest charge C is the installment price minus the cash price. The balance owed B is the cash price minus the down payment; n is the total number of monthly payments.

Example 1. A man bought a refrigerator and paid for it in 24 monthly installments of $17.50 each. The cash price was $350 and there was no down payment. Find the interest rate.

$$C = (24)(17.50) - 350 = 70$$
$$r = \frac{(24)(70)}{350(24 + 1)}$$
$$r = 0.192$$

The interest rate is 19.2%.

When installments are made on a weekly basis, the formula for the annual rate of interest is V.

$$\text{V.} \qquad r = \frac{104C}{B(n + 1)}$$

Example 2. A student bought a motorcycle for $20 down and $7.50 a week for 14 weeks. The cash price was $120. Find the annual interest rate.

$$C = [14(7.50) + 20] - 120 = 5.00$$
$$B = 120 - 20 = 100$$

Using the formula

$$r = \frac{104C}{B(n + 1)}$$

we get:

$$r = \frac{(104)(5.00)}{(100)(15)}$$
$$= 0.347.$$

The interest rate is 34.7%.

Exercises for Section 6-3

6-3 A

Give interest rates to the nearest 0.1%.

1. A family bought a refrigerator which they paid for in 28 monthly installments of $16.50 each. The cash price was $400.
   (a) Find the interest charge C.
   (b) Find the interest rate r.
2. In Exercise 1 the family could have paid $40 down and made 24 monthly payments of $17.00 each. Find C and r for this plan.
3. A housewife bought a vacuum cleaner on the installment plan for 10 monthly payments of $7.50 each. The cash price was $65. Find the interest rate.
4. A student bought a used car. He paid $300 in cash and the rest in 18 monthly installments of $30.77 each. The cash price was $808. What interest rate did he pay?

5. A stereo set was sold on the installment plan for a down payment of $60 and 11 monthly payments of $12 each. The cash price was $170. Find the interest rate.

6. A television set can be bought for $395 cash, or for $60 down and $30 per month for 12 months. Find the rate of interest charged on the installment plan.

7. A college student bought a coat for $8 down and 9 weekly payments of $6.35 each. The cash price of the coat was $64. Find the rate of interest paid.

8. A family bought a dining room set for $335 cash. They could have bought the set by paying $35 down and the rest in 14 monthly payments of $22.60 each.
(a) How much did they save by paying cash?
(b) Find the rate of interest on the loan.

9. A student bought a typewriter by paying $12 down and 10 monthly payments of $12 each. The cash price was $118. Find the rate of interest.

10. The cash price of a French horn was $195. A music student bought the horn by paying $50 down and 11 monthly installments of $14.50 each. Find the rate of interest.

6-3 B

Give interest rates to the nearest 0.1%.

1. A set of books sells for $37.50 cash, or $5 down and $2.50 a week for 14 weeks. Find the interest rate.

2. A man borrowed $200. He paid the loan in 8 weekly payments of $25.25 each. Find the annual interest rate.

3. A student bought a used car on the installment plan. The cash price was $850. The student paid $100 down and $37.50 per month for 22 months. Find the interest rate.

4. A hardware store had a sale on electric sanders, allowing a discount of 10% off the list price of $59. The sander could be bought for 10 payments of $6.10 a month.
(a) How much does one save by paying cash?
(b) Find the interest rate on the installment plan, using

$$B = 0.90 \times 59.$$

Exercises 6–3 B continued on page 262.

5. A college girl bought a wristwatch which had a cash price of $87.50. She paid $10 down and $7.50 per week for 11 weeks. Find the interest rate.

6. The annual interest rate on an installment loan of $1000 for 10 months was $8\frac{1}{2}\%$. The loan was paid in equal monthly payments. Find the interest charge C by solving

$$0.085 = \frac{24C}{(1000)(10 + 1)}.$$

7. A merchant claimed that he charged only 6% as an interest rate on installment buying. A dining room set which cost $220 cash could be bought for $20 down and $21.20 per month for 10 months. Find the actual annual rate.

8. Store A offers a kitchen furniture set for $19.00 down and 12 payments of $13.50 each. Store B offers the same set for $17 down and 46 weekly payments of $3.60 each. How much can a buyer save by taking the better offer?

9. In Exercise 8 find and compare the annual interest rates of each offer. Both stores had the same cash price of $175 for the set.

10. A man can buy an electric stove for $450 cash, or $50.00 down and the rest in 12 installments of $35.50 each. He has the cash for the down payment. He can borrow the rest from a friend for $4\frac{1}{2}\%$ interest and pay it back at the end of 12 months.

    (a) How much would he save by borrowing from the friend?

    (b) Compare the annual interest rate of the store with that of the friend.

6–3 C

1. Consider an installment loan with $B = 5$, to be paid off in 5 monthly payments of $1.00 each. This may be thought of as

1 loan of $5.00 for 1 month;

1 loan of $4.00 for 1 month;

1 loan of $3.00 for 1 month;

1 loan of $2.00 for 1 month;

1 loan of $1.00 for 1 month.

The installment loan of $5 is equivalent to a loan of $(1 + 2 + 3 + 4 + 5)$ dollars for 1 month. Solve for p if

$$p = 1 + 2 + 3 + 4 + 5.$$

2. If r is the annual rate of interest, then $r/12$ is the monthly rate. In Exercise 1 consider the formula $I = prt$.

   (a) Does $I = (1 + 2 + 3 + 4 + 5) \times \dfrac{r}{12} \times 1$?

   (b) Does $I = \dfrac{r}{12} \times p$?

   (c) Find I if $r = 12\%$.

3. In Exercise 2, $I = (r \times p)/12$.

   (a) Does $12I = rp$? Explain.

   (b) Does $\dfrac{12I}{p} = r$? Explain.

4. In Exercise 1 find p, using the formula $p = \dfrac{n}{2}(a + l)$.

5. Use the formula of Exercise 3(b), $r = 12I/p$, to find r if:

   (a) $I = 0.50$ and $p = 15$

   (b) $I = 0.75$ and $p = 15$

   (c) $I = 1.00$ and $p = 15$

6. Use the formula

$$r = \frac{24C}{B(n + 1)}$$

   to find r if:

   (a) $C = 0.50$, $B = 5$, and $n = 5$

   (b) $C = 0.75$, $B = 5$, and $n = 5$

   (c) $C = 1.00$, $B = 5$, and $n = 5$

7. Compare your answers in Exercises 5 and 6.

*6–3 D

1. Consider an installment loan with balance owed B. The loan is to be paid off in n monthly payments of B/n dollars each. Then (see 6–3 C, Exercise 1) this may be thought of as

   1 loan of B dollars for 1 month;

   1 loan of $B - \dfrac{B}{n}$ dollars for 1 month;

   1 loan of $B - \dfrac{2B}{n}$ dollars for 1 month;

   $\vdots$

   1 loan of $\dfrac{B}{n}$ dollars for 1 month.

The installment loan of B dollars is equivalent to a loan p of

$$\left[B + \left(B - \frac{B}{n} \right) + \left(B - \frac{2B}{n} \right) + \cdots + \frac{B}{n} \right]$$

dollars for 1 month. Solve for p, using the formula

$$p = \frac{n}{2}(a + l).$$

(*Hint:* $a = B$ and $l = B/n$) So,

$$p = \frac{n}{2}\left(B + \frac{B}{n} \right).$$

That is,

$$p = \frac{n}{2}\left(\frac{Bn}{n} + \frac{B}{n} \right).$$

Then

$$p = \frac{n}{2}\left[\frac{B(n + 1)}{n} \right].$$

Simplify.

2. From Exercise 1 you should have

$$p = \frac{B}{2}(n + 1).$$

Then if r is the annual rate of interest, $r/12$ is the monthly rate.
Substitute in the formula

$$I = p \times r \times t.$$

$$I = \frac{B}{2}(n + 1) \times \frac{r}{12} \times 1 \qquad \text{Substitute.}$$

$$I = \frac{B(n + 1) \times r}{24} \qquad \text{Multiply.}$$

$$24I = B(n + 1) \times r \qquad \text{Explain.}$$

$$\frac{24I}{B(n + 1)} = r \qquad \text{Explain.}$$

Since C is the interest charge, we can write

$$r = \frac{24C}{B(n+1)},$$

which is formula III in Section 6–2.

6–4 EARNING MONEY

Most people earn their incomes from the sale of their services. Some are paid a wage (a certain amount per hour); others receive a salary (a fixed amount per month or per year). In addition, many salesmen are paid a commission, which is based on a percent of the dollar value of their sales.

Certain deductions are made from pay. The total pay before deductions is called the **gross income.** The **take-home pay** is the net income after all deductions have been made.

The **Federal Social Security** law requires that an employer must withhold a certain percent of a portion of each employee's pay. The employer matches this amount for each employee.

Example 1. In a certain year each person paid 4.2% of the first $6600 he earned as Social Security tax. Find the amount paid by (a) worker A who earned $8400 for the year; (b) worker B who earned $5400 for the year.

(a) Worker A paid 4.2% of $6600.

$$(0.042)(6600) = 277.2$$

He paid $277.20.

(b) Worker B paid 4.2% on his entire income.

$$(0.042)(5400) = 226.8$$

He paid $226.80.

A certain amount is withheld from wages for the **Federal Income Tax.** The amount withheld depends on the number of exemptions claimed and on the total pay. Usually, one exemption may be claimed for each dependent of an employee as defined in the Tax Guide.

The Federal Government often changes the rates of income tax and the amounts withheld.

Weekly Payroll Period

(a) Single person—
*If the amount A is: The amount of income tax
                                                            to be withheld shall be:

Not over $4 0

Over—But not over		Of excess over
$ 4—$13	$0.00, plus 14%	$4
$ 13—$23	$1.26, plus 15%	$13
$ 23—$85	$2.76, plus 17%	$23
$ 85—$169	$13.30, plus 20%	$85
$169—$212	$30.10, plus 25%	$169
$212	$40.85, plus 30%	$212

(b) Married person—
*If the amount A is: The amount of income tax
                                                            to be withheld shall be:

Not over $4 . . . .

Over—But not over		Of excess over
$ 4—$23	$0.00, plus 14%	$4
$ 23—$85	$2.66, plus 15%	$23
$ 85—$169	$11.96, plus 17%	$85
$169—$340	$26.24, plus 20%	$169
$340—$423	$60.44, plus 25%	$340
$423	$81.19, plus 30%	$423

---

*Multiply the number of exemptions claimed by $13.50 and subtract this product from the gross weekly income to find the amount A.

Example 2. Find the income tax withheld for 1 week for a married man who claims 3 exemptions and earns $95 per week.

$$A = 95 - (3)(13.50) = 54.50$$

From the table (b), the tax T to be withheld on $54.50 is found by taking $2.66 plus 15% of the amount over $23.

$$T = 2.66 + 0.15 \, (54.50 - 23.00)$$
$$= 2.66 + 4.73 = 7.39$$

The weekly tax withheld is $7.39.

Exercises for Section 6-4

6-4 A

Find the gross weekly earnings in each exercise. For all time over 40 hours, use $1\frac{1}{2}$ times the regular rate.

1. 42 hours at $1.80 per hour
2. 38 hours at $2.20 per hour
3. 48 hours at $2.25 per hour
4. 41 hours at $3.40 per hour
5. 49 hours at $2.40 per hour
6. 52 hours at $2.10 per hour
7. 39 hours at $3.85 per hour
8. 46 hours at $4.55 per hour

6-4 B

In 6-4 A, Exercises 1-8, find the Social Security tax at 4.2% of gross income.

6-4 C

The number of hours worked in 1 week and the rate of pay are given in each exercise. For time over 40 hours, use $1\frac{1}{2}$ times the rate given. Assume that Social Security is withheld at a rate of 4.2%. Find the amount withheld for each.

1. 40 hours at $2.00 per hour
2. 40 hours at $1.50 per hour
3. 42 hours at $2.10 per hour
4. 43 hours at $2.05 per hour
5. 44 hours at $3.20 per hour
6. 46 hours at $2.80 per hour
7. 42 hours at $1.95 per hour
8. 49 hours at $3.75 per hour

6-4 D

In the table on page 268 the number of hours worked each day of a 40-hour week is shown for 8 employees. Their company pays $1\frac{1}{2}$ times regular pay for time over 40 hours per week. Assume a rate of 4.2% for Social Security tax. Find the following for each employee:

(a) Gross income (b) Social Security withholding
(c) Income tax withholding (d) Take-home pay

Exercises 6-4 D continued on page 268.

Employee Number	M	T	W	Th	F	S	Rate per Hour	Married	Number of Exemptions
1	8	8	8	8	6	0	$1.50	No	1
2	8	8	9	$9\frac{1}{2}$	9	4	$1.50	Yes	2
3	8	$6\frac{1}{2}$	6	8	8	0	$2.00	No	1
4	9	9	9	10	$9\frac{1}{2}$	6	$1.80	Yes	3
5	8	8	$8\frac{1}{2}$	9	9	8	$2.20	Yes	2
6	8	9	8	6	6	4	$2.40	No	2
7	8	8	$9\frac{1}{2}$	$9\frac{1}{2}$	$8\frac{1}{2}$	6	$1.90	No	3
8	$8\frac{1}{2}$	8	$7\frac{1}{2}$	8	$9\frac{1}{2}$	0	$3.00	Yes	4

6-4 E

1. The Brown Company had a total payroll of $18,750 for the first quarter of the year. The company paid 4.2% of this figure for Social Security tax. Find the amount of this tax. (*Note:* It is assumed that no employee earned more than $6600 during this particular quarter.)

2. A certain worker receives $1.90 per hour for a regular 40-hour week with time and a half for overtime. In a busy week he worked 10 hours a day from Monday through Saturday. Find his gross income for the week.

3. The worker in Exercise 2 had $19.80 withheld for income tax and 4.2% of his total wages withheld for Social Security. Find his take-home pay for the week.

4. A secretary works 5 days a week from 8:00 A.M. to 5:00 P.M. with 1 hour off for lunch. She is paid $2.45 per hour.
   (a) Find her total wages for a week.
   (b) Find her weekly take-home pay if 4.2% is withheld for Social Security and $12.65 is withheld for income tax.

In Exercises 5–7 use the tax table on page 266 to calculate withholding for income tax.

5. A salesman is paid $50 per week plus a commission of $4\frac{1}{2}\%$ of his week's sales.
   (a) Find his total pay for a week if he made sales of $1075 during that time.
   (b) Find his Social Security tax at a rate of 4.2%.
   (c) Find his income tax if he is married and has 2 exemptions.
   (d) Find his take-home pay.
6. A student who earns $62.50 a week claims 1 exemption. Find his take-home pay. Deduct 4.2% for Social Security.
7. A married man earns $220 per week. He claims 3 exemptions and pays a rate of 4.2% for Social Security tax. Find his weekly take-home pay in January.

■ 6-5 FAMILY EXPENSES

All families must consider maintaining a home. For the home owner this expense will usually include: a loan payment with interest, taxes, insurance, and maintenance costs. Operating costs for utilities, such as electricity, gas, water, and telephone, must also be included. For the home renter the costs cover the rental charge plus the above operating costs.

Most families must also consider the expense of owning and operating an automobile. Other items for which families must spend money include: deductions for income tax and Social Security tax, food, clothing, health and recreation, education, savings, and miscellaneous.

The exercises suggest ways of planning for family expenses.

Exercises for Section 6-5

6-5 A

1. One guide for a home buyer is, "Spend no more than $2\frac{1}{2}$ times your annual income for a home." That is, $C \leq 2\frac{1}{2}i$, where C represents the cost of a home; i, annual income. Use this guide to find the maximum cost of a home for a family under each given condition.
   (a) Income is $524 per month.

Exercises 6-5 A continued on page 270.

(b) The father works 44 hours per week, 48 weeks per year. He receives time and a half for all hours over 40 hours per week, and his regular rate of pay is $2.50 per hour. His earnings represent the family income.

(c) The father, the only earner, makes sales of about $120,000 a year. His income is $5\frac{1}{2}\%$ of his sales.

2. Another guide for home payments is, "The monthly payment P for a loan, interest, taxes, and insurance premiums should not exceed a week's income." That is, $P \leq w$, where w represents the number of dollars of weekly income. Find P in each case listed.

(a) Family income is based on a 40-hour week at a wage of $2.84 per hour.

(b) The annual family income is $5720. Use 52 weeks for 1 year.

(c) The annual family income is $11,440. Use 52 weeks for 1 year.

3. A man insures his home for $14,750. The yearly rate for insurance is $0.48 per $100 of insurance. Find the cost of 1 year's insurance.

4. In Exercise 3 find the cost of a 3-year policy if this cost is $2\frac{1}{2}$ times the yearly rate.

5. In Exercises 3 and 4 find the amount saved by the purchase of one 3-year policy instead of three 1-year policies.

6. The assessed value of a certain home is 74% of its cost. The tax rate is $3.43 per $100 of assessed value. Find the tax if the home cost $18,500.

7. One family planned for these monthly operating costs on their home: electricity, $5.50; gas, $6.25; water, $2.45; telephone, $4.15. Find the monthly total.

8. In Exercise 7 find the percent of income devoted to operating costs. Use $600 as monthly income.

6–5 B

1. A family wishes to build a fence around the back yard. The yard is rectangular. Its dimensions are 75 feet by 109 feet. No fence is needed along the house, a distance of 60 feet. The fence the family wants will cost $1.05 per linear foot. Find the total cost.

2. The family in Exercise 1 planned to plant $\frac{3}{4}$ of the area of the back yard in grass. If it costs about $0.15 per square foot to prepare and plant the lawn, find the total cost.

3. A family wishes to panel 3 walls of their living room with knotty pine plywood. A sheet of this plywood is 4 feet by 8 feet and costs $6.35. The walls are each 8 feet high and have lengths of 16 feet, 20 feet, and 24 feet. One sheet of plywood may be saved because of openings such as windows, doors, and a fireplace. Find the cost of the plywood.

4. A home owner plans to insulate the ceiling and walls of his shop. The shop has the shape of a rectangular solid 10 feet wide, 18 feet long, and 9 feet high. It has 2 windows 3 feet by 4 feet and 1 door 3 feet by 7 feet. Insulation materials will cost $7\frac{3}{4}$ cents per square foot. Find the total cost of insulating the shop.

5. Composition roofing shingles are sold by the "square." A "square" is an amount of shingles which will cover 100 square feet of roof. How many squares are needed to cover 1795 square feet of roof?

6. A family plans to build a wooden deck in the patio, having the shape shown in Figure 6–1. The deck will cost 58¢ per square foot. Find the total cost.

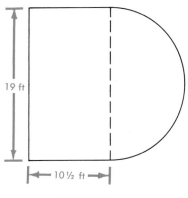

19 ft

10½ ft

FIGURE 6-1

7. Find the cost of laying a sidewalk 175 feet by $4\frac{1}{2}$ feet at $2.25 per square yard.

8. The roof of a building has two sections each 75 feet by 30 feet. Find the cost of composition shingles at $10.15 a "square" for this roof. (*Note:* See Exercise 5 for "square.")

9. Find the cost of wall-to-wall carpeting for a rectangular room 13 feet by 18 feet if carpet costs $9.75 per square yard.

Exercises 6–5 B continued on page 272.

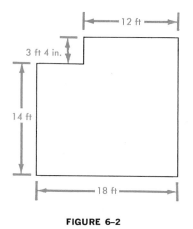

FIGURE 6–2

10. Find the number of asphalt tiles 8 inches by 8 inches that would be needed to cover the floor of the family room shown in the drawing.

11. One family deposits $11.50 per month in a savings account to be used for home maintenance. Find the amount of these savings for 1 year if interest is 2% of total deposits. (*Note:* Amount $A = 12 (11.50) + 2\%$ of 12 (11.50))

12. A landlord figured these costs on a house which he leased for income: interest on the $16,000 value of the house at 6%; taxes and insurance, $420 per year; maintenance costs, $120 per year. Does a monthly rent of $125 seem to be a fair charge for the house? Explain.

6–5 C

1. A family figured the following as the costs of operating an automobile for 1 year:

Interest on loan	$140.00
Depreciation in value	$500.00
Gasoline and oil	$364.00
Maintenance (tires, repair, and so on)	$205.00
Insurance and taxes	$135.00

Find the total cost for the year.

2. In Exercise 1 find the cost per mile if the car was driven 16,000 miles during the course of the year. Give your answer to the nearest 0.1¢.
3. Use your answer in Exercise 2 to find the cost of driving:
   (a) A 50-mile round trip to work
   (b) 200 miles on a weekend for pleasure
   (c) 1000 miles on a vacation
4. Suppose that annual family income in Exercise 1 was $6720. What percent of this was automobile costs?
5. From Exercises 1 and 2 find the cost per mile for depreciation. Give your answer to the nearest 0.1¢.

6–5 D

1. One year the total income of a factory worker was $8400. He paid these amounts for taxes: state and Federal income tax, 15.6% of $6000; Social Security tax, 4.9% of $6600. Find the amount of these taxes.
2. In Exercise 1 find the worker's income after taxes.
3. In Exercise 1 find the ratio of the amount of these taxes to the factory worker's total income for the year. Give your answer to the nearest 0.1%.
4. Consider a person who works 40 years and then retires under Social Security. Suppose that he pays 4.9% of $6600 as Social Security tax each year, and that his employer pays an equal amount. Find the total tax paid by the employee and the employer.
5. Consider the factory worker in Exercise 1 who had a total income of $8400. Find the total T of these expenses:
   Income tax, Social Security tax (total, Exercise 1)
   Home costs, including utilities, 25% of $8400
   Automobile costs (total, 6–5C, Exercise 1)
6. In Exercise 5 find the ratio $T/8400$ to the nearest 1%.
7. In Exercises 5 and 6 the worker and his family have left a certain number N of dollars for costs of food, clothing, health and recreation, education, savings, and miscellaneous. Is $T > N$? By how much?
8. From your answers for Exercises 5, 6, and 7, make a circle graph of costs T and N.

6–5 E

1. A family of 4 with annual income of $8400 has these annual expenses:

Tax, home costs, automobile costs	56% of income
Food	20% of income
Clothing	6% of income
Health and recreation	5% of income
Education	3% of income
Savings	8% of income
Miscellaneous	2% of income

Find the annual amount for each item.

2. From Exercise 1 make a circle graph of the expenses.

3. In Exercise 1 find the ratio of costs for education to costs for clothing.

4. In Exercise 1 find the ratio of costs for clothing to costs for savings.

6–5 F

In these exercises consider the expenses of a family with annual income of i dollars. The items in Exercise 1, 6–5 E, are grouped as follows:

x dollars for income taxes, Social Security, home, and automobile costs;

y dollars for food and clothing costs;

z dollars for health and recreation, education, savings, and miscellaneous costs.

1. Write an equation for each statement:
(a) x is 56% of i.   (b) y is 26% of i.
(c) z is 18% of i.   (d) i is the sum of x, y, and z.

2. Refer to Exercise 1 and mark each statement true or false:
(a) $x > y$ (b) $x > z$ (c) $y > z$ (d) $i < x + y$

3. Consider the equation $x = 0.56i$, where $6000 < i < 9000$. Mark each statement true or false:
(a) The domain is the set of numbers, in dollars and cents, from 6000 to 9000 inclusive.
(b) The range is the resulting set of values for x.

4. Make a line graph of the equation $x = 0.56i$, $6000 < i < 9000$.
5. In Exercise 4 suppose that the equation is approximately correct for $i = 9000$. Does $0.56i$ seem either too large or too small for x when $i = 6000$? Explain.
6. From Exercise 1 does $y = 0.26i$? Does y seem large enough for expenses of food and clothing where $6000 < i < 9000$?
7. In Exercise 1 let i represent the whole. Make a circle graph relating x, y, and z.

6-6 COMPOUND INTEREST

Money placed in a savings account for a period of time earns interest. If, at the end of each such period, the interest is deposited in the account, then an increased principal results. When interest is figured on this increasing principal, it is called compound interest.

Example 1. Suppose $100 is placed in a savings account at 5% interest, compounded annually. Find the amount A at the end of:
(a) 1 year   (b) 2 years   (c) 3 years

First Method

(a) $I = p \times r \times t$

$I = 100 \times 0.05 \times 1 = 5.00$

The interest is $5.

$A_1 = p + I$

$A_1 = 100 + 5 = 105$

During the second year the principal is $105.

(b) $I = p \times r \times t$

$I = 105 \times 0.05 \times 1 = 5.25$

$A_2 = p + I$

$A_2 = 105.00 + 5.25 = 110.25$

During the third year the principal is $110.25.

(c) $I = 110.25 \times 0.05 \times 1 = 5.51$

$A_3 = 110.25 + 5.51 = 115.76$

During the fourth year the principal is $115.76.

Second Method

We may reduce the work of the First Method, using the distributive law in this way.

(a) Note that at the end of the first year,

$$A_1 = p + 0.05p$$
$$= p(1 + 0.05)$$
$$= p \times 1.05;$$

that is, $100 \times 1.05 = 105.00$.

(b) At the end of the second year,

$$A_2 = (p \times 1.05) + 0.05(p \times 1.05)$$
$$= (p \times 1.05)(1 + 0.05)$$
$$= p \times 1.05^2;$$

that is, $100 \times 1.05^2 = 110.25$.

(c) At the end of the third year,

$$A_3 = (p \times 1.05^2) + 0.05(p \times 1.05^2)$$
$$= (p \times 1.05^2)(1 + 0.05)$$
$$= p \times 1.05^3;$$

that is, $100 \times 1.05^3 = 115.76$.

The principal for the fourth year is $115.76.

From the Second Method, it appears that for p dollars compounded at rate r for n periods of time, we find the amount A by formula VI.

VI. $\qquad A = p(1 + r)^n$

The formula is true. Thus for $p = 100$, $r = 5\%$, and $t = 4$ (years),

$$A = 100(1 + 0.05)^4.$$

Also, if a principal of $200 is deposited at an annual rate of 6%, compounded each half year for 10 years, then

$$A = 200(1 + 0.03)^{20}.$$

Compound Amount of $1

End of Period	1%	2%	$2\frac{1}{2}$%	3%	4%	5%	6%
1	1.0100	1.0200	1.0250	1.0300	1.0400	1.0500	1.0600
2	1.0201	1.0404	1.0506	1.0609	1.0816	1.1025	1.1236
3	1.0303	1.0612	1.0769	1.0927	1.1249	1.1576	1.1910
4	1.0406	1.0824	1.1038	1.1255	1.1699	1.2155	1.2625
5	1.0510	1.1041	1.1314	1.1593	1.2167	1.2763	1.3382
6	1.0615	1.1262	1.1597	1.1941	1.2653	1.3401	1.4185
7	1.0721	1.1487	1.1887	1.2299	1.3159	1.4071	1.5036
8	1.0829	1.1717	1.2184	1.2668	1.3686	1.4775	1.5938
9	1.0937	1.1951	1.2489	1.3048	1.4233	1.5513	1.6895
10	1.1046	1.2190	1.2801	1.3439	1.4802	1.6289	1.7908
11	1.1157	1.2434	1.3121	1.3842	1.5395	1.7103	1.8983
12	1.1268	1.2682	1.3449	1.4258	1.6010	1.7959	2.0122
13	1.1381	1.2936	1.3785	1.4685	1.6651	1.8856	2.1329
14	1.1495	1.3195	1.4130	1.5126	1.7317	1.9799	2.2609
15	1.1610	1.3459	1.4483	1.5580	1.8009	2.0789	2.3966

Example 2. Find the amount of $200 at an annual rate of 6% compounded semiannually for 2 years.

First Method

$$A = p(1 + r)^n$$

$A = 200(1 + 0.03)^4$ Note, $r = 3\%$ per half year

$A = 225.10$ By multiplication

Second Method

The first method involves much multiplication, which can be avoided by using a table of interest. The table on the previous page shows the amount of $1 compounded at various rates. For 4 periods of time at 3%, this amount is 1.1255. Thus

$$A = 200 \times 1.1255$$
$$= 225.10.$$

The amount is $225.10.

We call the amount A in Examples 1 and 2 the **compound amount.**

Example 3. Find the amount and the interest on $20 at 8% compounded quarterly for 3 years.

Since 3 years is 12 quarters, we use the figure opposite 12 in the 2% column of the table.

$$A = (20)(1.2682)$$
$$A = 25.3640$$

Thus the amount is $25.36; the interest is $5.36.

Exercises for Section 6-6

6-6 A

Use formula VI to find the amount of:
1. $1000 at 8% for 1 year
2. $1000 at 8% for 2 years compounded annually
3. $1000 at 8% for 3 years compounded annually
4. $500 at $\frac{1}{2}$% for 2 years compounded annually
5. $500 at 1% for 4 years compounded annually
6. $1500 at $3\frac{1}{2}$% for 2 years compounded annually

6-6 B

Use the table in this section to find the compound amount and the compound interest for:
1. $100 at 5% for 12 years compounded annually
2. $400 at 4% for 7 years compounded annually
3. $400 at 4% for 7 years compounded semiannually   (*Note:* $n = 2 \times 7 = 14$)

4. $400 at 4% for 3 years compounded quarterly
5. $1000 at $2\frac{1}{2}$% for 10 years compounded annually
6. $1200 at 5% for 15 years compounded annually
7. $1000 at 2% for 7 years compounded semiannually
8. $750 at 8% for 3 years compounded quarterly
9. $100 at 4% for 3 years compounded quarterly
10. $2000 at 5% for 6 years compounded semiannually

6–6 C

1. One dollar is invested at 3% compounded annually. When, approximately, will the amount be $1.30? Use the table on page 277.
2. How long will it take $100 to double at 12% compounded semi-annually? (*Note:* For use of the table, $r = 6\%$; n will be found in half years.)
3. A man wishes to have $3000 5 years from now for his daughter's education. How much must he invest at 6% compounded semi-annually? (*Note:* $3000 = p(1 + 0.03)^{10}$, so $3000 = p \times 1.3439$)
4. Determine the amount of $1000 invested at 4% compounded annually for 10 years. Find the amount of $1000 at 4% simple interest for 10 years. Find the difference in these amounts.
5. Find the difference in the amounts between $1000 at 6% compounded annually for 3 years and $1000 at 6% compounded semiannually for 3 years.
6. A man invested $300 at a certain rate of interest compounded annually. After 15 years his amount was $623.67. Find the rate of interest. (*Note:* Find the amount on $1 for this plan. Then use the table.)
7. A veterinary student estimates that he will need $5000 to start his practice 4 years from now. If he invests $4000 at 6% compounded annually, will he have enough?
8. The parents of a 14-year-old girl place $1000 in a savings account in her name at 5% interest compounded semiannually. Find the amount in this girl's account when she becomes 21.
9. A man deposited $100 in a bank at 5% interest compounded semiannually. At the end of the first 6 months he deposited another $100 in the same account. Find his amount at the end of 1 year.
10. The man in Exercise 9 deposited another $100 at the end of 18 months. Find the amount at the end of 2 years.

6-6 D

Figure 6–3 shows a graph of the amounts given in a compound interest table for certain rates. In Exercises 1–4 refer to the graph (answers will be approximate).

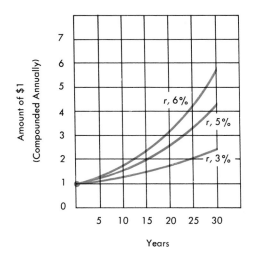

FIGURE 6–3

1. Find the amount of:
   (a) $1 at 3% for 15 years
   (b) $1 at 5% for 25 years
   (c) $1 at 6% for 28 years
2. Find the length of time it will take $1 to double at 3% compounded annually.
3. Find the length of time for $1 to double at 5% compounded annually.
4. Find the length of time for $1 to double at 6% compounded annually.
5. Find the amount of $1 at 5% compounded annually for 30 years. Consider an extended curve and make an estimate of the amount after 40 years.
6. Consider an extended curve and make an estimate of the amount on $1 at 6% compounded annually for 40 years.
7. Make a graph similar to Figure 6–3, showing the 2% and the 4% curves.

▨ 6–7 SAVINGS AND INVESTMENTS

People invest their savings in many ways. For example, savings may be invested in: a savings account in a bank, a savings and loan company, or a credit union; various kinds of life insurance; stocks and bonds.

Bank savings accounts are usually insured through Federal Deposit Insurance. The amount of such insurance is $15,000 per account. Similarly, Federal insurance is provided for savings and loan accounts. Thus investments in an insured bank or savings and loan company are quite safe.

Investment in an established credit union or in a life insurance company also does not involve much risk to the investor. However investment in stocks and bonds is more speculative. Of course, the safety of such investment depends upon the stability of the company issuing the stocks or bonds.

The exercises suggest ways in which these kinds of investments produce income on savings.

Exercises for Section 6–7

6–7 A

1. The Bank of the West computes interest on savings from the date of deposit to the date of withdrawal; the rate is 1% per quarter. Interest is paid quarterly on January 1, April 1, July 1, and October 1. Find the interest on this account, payable on April 1.

Entry	Balance
January 1, balance on deposit	$500.00
February 10, deposit, $100.00	$600.00
March 1, deposit, $50.00	$650.00
March 12, deposit, $100.00	$750.00

No withdrawal was made, so interest is calculated for the time deposits were in the account. (*Note:* $I = (500 \times 0.01 \times 1) + (100 \times 0.01 \times \frac{49}{90}) + (50 \times 0.01 \times \frac{31}{90}) + (100 \times 0.01 \times \frac{19}{90})$)

Exercises 6–7 A continued on page 282.

2. As in Exercise 1, find the interest on this savings account for the second quarter of 1 year:

Entry	Balance
April 1	$450.00
May 1, deposit, $150.00	$600.00
June 1, deposit, $100.00	$700.00
June 15, deposit, $100.00	$800.00

3. As in Exercise 1, find the interest on this savings account for the third quarter of 1 year. (*Note:* Interest will be paid on these amounts: $800 for the first month; $1100 for the second month; and $1000 for the third month.)

Entry	Balance
July 1	$800.00
August 1, deposit, $200.00	$1000.00
August 16, deposit, $100.00	$1100.00
September 1, withdrawal, $100.00	$1000.00

4. As in Exercise 1, complete this record of a savings account for two quarters. (*Note:* The deposit of interest on April 1 earns interest for the second quarter.)

Entry	Balance
January 1	$1000.00
February 1, deposit, $100.00	$1100.00
March 1, deposit, $100.00	$1200.00
April 1, deposit, $100.00	$1300.00
April 1, deposit, interest for quarter	
May 1, deposit, $100.00	
June 1, deposit, $100.00	
June 10, withdrawal, $100.00	
July 1, deposit, $100.00	
July 1, deposit, interest for quarter	

6-7 B

The table shows the compound amount for a number of periods of time where $1 is deposited at the beginning of each period.

Periods, n	$\frac{1}{2}\%$	1%	$1\frac{1}{2}\%$	2%	$2\frac{1}{2}\%$	3%	5%
1	1.0000	1.0000	1.0000	1.0000	1.0000	1.0000	1.0000
2	2.0050	2.0100	2.0150	2.0200	2.0250	2.0300	2.0500
3	3.0150	3.0301	3.0452	3.0604	3.0756	3.0909	3.1525
4	4.0301	4.0604	4.0909	4.1216	4.1525	4.1836	4.3101
5	5.0503	5.1010	5.1523	5.2040	5.2563	5.3091	5.5256
6	6.0755	6.1520	6.2296	6.3081	6.3877	6.4684	6.8019
7	7.1059	7.2135	7.3230	7.4343	7.5474	7.6625	8.1420
8	8.1414	8.2857	8.4328	8.5830	8.7361	8.8923	9.5491
9	9.1821	9.3685	9.5593	9.7546	9.9545	10.1591	11.0266
10	10.2280	10.4622	10.7027	10.9497	11.2034	11.4639	12.5779
11	11.2792	11.5668	11.8633	12.1687	12.4835	12.8078	14.2068
12	12.3356	12.6825	13.0412	13.4121	13.7956	14.1920	15.9171
13	13.3972	13.8093	14.2368	14.6803	15.1404	15.6178	17.7130
14	14.4642	14.9474	15.4504	15.9739	16.5190	17.0863	19.5986
15	15.5365	16.0969	16.6821	17.2934	17.9319	18.5989	21.5786
16	16.6142	17.2579	17.9324	18.6393	19.3802	20.1569	23.6575
17	17.6973	18.4304	19.2014	20.0121	20.8647	21.7616	25.8404
18	18.7858	19.6147	20.4894	21.4123	22.3863	23.4144	28.1324
19	19.8797	20.8109	21.7967	22.8406	23.9460	25.1169	30.5390
20	20.9791	22.0190	23.1237	24.2974	25.5447	26.8704	33.0660

Exercises 6–7 B continued on page 284.

(*Note:* We read the table: At the beginning of period 1, the amount is the deposit, $1. Suppose that a deposit of $1 is made on January 1; that another deposit of $1 is made on April 1. Interest is paid for the quarter at 1% per quarter on April 1. The amount on April 1 is (1.00 + 1.00 + 0.01) dollars, that is, $2.01. The table reads 2.0100; that is, $2.01 is the amount at the beginning of period 2.)

Use the table to solve each exercise:

1. A secretary started an account in a savings and loan company on January 1 and made deposits as shown:

> January 1, $100
> April 1, $100
> July 1, $100
> October 1, $100
> January 1 (the next year), $100

Find the amount of her account on January 1 (second year) if the interest rate is 4% compounded quarterly. (*Note:* The rate is 1% per quarter. Look in the column headed 1% across from $n = 5$. Remember, this is the amount of $1 for $n = 5$.)

2. A worker started an account in a credit union on January 1 with deposits as shown:

> January 1, $50
> April 1, $50
> July 1, $50
> October 1, $50

Find the amount of the account on October 1 if the interest rate is 4% compounded quarterly.

3. A merchant started an account in a savings and loan company on April 1 with deposits as shown:

> April 1, $500
> July 1, $500
> October 1, $500
> January 1, $500

Find the amount of the account on January 1 if the interest rate is 6% compounded quarterly. (*Note:* The rate per quarter is $\frac{1}{4}$ of 6%, that is, $1\frac{1}{2}$%.)

4. A housewife started an account in a savings bank on January 1 (first year) with deposits as shown:

> January 1, $300
> July 1, $300
> January 1 (second year), $300
> July 1, $300
> January 1 (third year), $300
> July 1, $300

Find the amount of the account on July 1 (third year) if the interest rate is 5% compounded semiannually. (*Note:* $r = 2\frac{1}{2}\%$, $n = 6$)

5. A lawyer started an account in a savings and loan company on January 1 (first year) with deposits as shown:

> January 1, $700
> July 1, $700
> January 1 (second year), $700
> July 1, $700

Find the amount of the account on July 1 (second year) if the interest rate is 6% compounded semiannually.

6. Find the amount of a savings account in which $40 is deposited on the first day of each month with $n = 20$ and $r = 6\%$. The interest on the account is compounded monthly. (*Note:* The rate per month is $\frac{1}{12}$ of 6%.)

7. Find the amount of a savings account in which $40 is deposited on the first day of each quarter with $n = 20$ and $r = 6\%$. Interest on the account is compounded quarterly. (*Note:* The rate is $\frac{1}{4}$ of 6%.)

8. Find the amount of a savings account in which $40 is deposited on January 1 and July 1 of each year with $n = 20$ and $r = 6\%$. Interest is compounded semiannually.

9. Find the amount of a savings account in which $40 is deposited on January 1 of each year with $n = 20$ and $r = 5\%$. Interest is compounded annually.

10. Find the amount of the savings account described in Exercise 9 if $r = 3\%$.

6-7 C

In Exercises 1-3 refer to the following table for age 20.

Ordinary Life Table, $10,000 Policy

Age at Purchase	*Annual Premium	Guaranteed Cash Value at Age				
		25	30	35	40	65
		$420	$1070	$1700	$2390	$6260
		Anticipated Total Dividends at Age				
		25	30	35	40	65
20	$165.60	$74	$268	$633	$1228	$8670

*A premium is the cost of insurance per period of time, and is paid by the insured. Thus the annual premium is the cost per year.

1. Find the total of premiums paid on an ordinary life policy for $10,000 after the:
   (a) tenth annual payment
   (b) twentieth annual payment
   (c) forty-fifth annual payment
2. Find the total anticipated value (guaranteed cash value plus anticipated total dividends) at:
   (a) age 30   (b) age 35   (c) age 40   (d) age 65
3. In case of the death of the insured at any time, the policy pays $10,000 to the family. Discuss the protection thus provided.

In Exercises 4-6 refer to the following table for age 25.

Ordinary Life Table, $10,000 Policy

Age at Purchase	Annual Premium	Guaranteed Cash Value at Age				
		25	30	35	40	65
		$510	$1260	$1990	$2770	$6060
		Anticipated Total Dividends at Age				
		25	30	35	40	65
25	$186.90	$80	$290	$677	$1305	$7050

4. Find the total of premiums paid on an ordinary life policy for
$10,000 after the:
   (a) tenth annual payment
   (b) twentieth annual payment
   (c) forty-fifth annual payment
5. Find the total anticipated value (guaranteed cash value plus
anticipated total dividends) at:
   (a) age 30   (b) age 35
   (c) age 40   (d) age 65
6. Compare your answers in Exercise 4 with those in Exercise 1.
Compare your answers in Exercise 5 with those in Exercise 2.

In Exercises 7–9 refer to the Endowment Table for age 20.

Endowment Table, $10,000 Policy

Age at Purchase	Annual Premium	Guaranteed Cash Value at Age			
		25	30	35	40
		$1890	$4350	$6990	$10,000
		Anticipated Total Dividends at Age			
		25	30	35	40
20	$489.20	$138	$522	$1368	$2966

7. Find the total of premiums paid on an endowment policy for
$10,000 after the:
   (a) fifth annual payment
   (b) tenth annual payment
   (c) fifteenth annual payment
   (d) twentieth annual payment
8. Find the total anticipated value at:
   (a) age 25   (b) age 30
   (c) age 35   (d) age 40
9. At age 20 a father bought a $10,000 endowment insurance policy
to pay for his daughter's education. Find the anticipated worth
of the policy 20 years later. How much would this be, per month,
for 36 months of college?

Exercises 6–7 C continued on page 288.

In Exercises 10 and 11, refer to the following table for age 25.

Endowment Table, $10,000 Policy

Age at Purchase	Annual Premium	Guaranteed Cash Value at Age			
		30	35	40	45
		$1900	$4350	$6990	$10,000
		Anticipated Total Dividends at Age			
		30	35	40	45
25	$492.50	$142	$538	$1402	$2962

(*Note:* This policy guarantees payment of $10,000 after 20 years.)

10. Find the total of premiums paid on an endowment policy for $10,000 after the:
  (a) fifth annual payment
  (b) tenth annual payment
  (c) fifteenth annual payment
  (d) twentieth annual payment
11. Find the total anticipated value at:
  (a) age 30   (b) age 35
  (c) age 40   (d) age 45

6-7 D

In Exercises 1–10 use the table below.

Stock Sales on a Certain Day

For the year High	Low		Sales in 100's	Open	High	Low	Close
$63\frac{1}{2}$	$49\frac{3}{4}$	Am T & T 2.20	972	51	$51\frac{5}{8}$	$50\frac{3}{4}$	$51\frac{1}{2}$
$61\frac{3}{8}$	$33\frac{1}{2}$	Chrysler 2	1432	39	$39\frac{5}{8}$	$38\frac{3}{8}$	$38\frac{1}{2}$
$64\frac{7}{8}$	$37\frac{1}{8}$	Comsat	123	$45\frac{1}{4}$	$45\frac{3}{4}$	$43\frac{1}{8}$	$43\frac{1}{8}$
$56\frac{3}{4}$	$42\frac{1}{4}$	Magnavox .80	1311	$54\frac{1}{8}$	$55\frac{1}{2}$	$52\frac{3}{8}$	54
$27\frac{1}{2}$	$15\frac{7}{8}$	Petrolane .70	13	$16\frac{1}{4}$	$16\frac{1}{2}$	$16\frac{1}{4}$	$16\frac{1}{2}$

(*Note:* We read the table in this way: "The high for the year for Am T & T (American Telephone and Telegraph) was $63½; low for the year, $49¾. Total of sales for the day was 97,200 shares. The opening price (beginning of the day) was $51; the high price for the day, $51⅝; the low price for the day, $50¾; the closing price for the day, $51½." Am T & T 2.20 means that the dividend for the past year was $2.20.)

1. Find these values for Comsat:
   (a) High for the year
   (b) Low for the year
   (c) Range for the year
   (d) High for the day
   (e) Number of shares sold for the day
2. Suppose that a buyer bought some Chrysler stock at $33½ a share and received a dividend of $2. Find the rate. (*Note:* $I = prt$, so $2 = 33\frac{1}{2} \times r \times 1$.)
3. Find the rate on a share of Magnavox purchased at $45 if the dividend is $0.80. (*Note:* The reason for the high price and low rate of return on this stock is probably that investors expect a growing prosperity for the company and thus an increase in price for the stock.)
4. Find the cost of 100 shares of Comsat stock bought at the closing price of the day.
5. Find the range in price for the day of:
   (a) Am T & T   (b) Comsat
   (c) Chrysler   (d) Magnavox
6. Find the loss on 100 shares of Petrolane purchased at the high for the year and sold at the opening of the day as shown in the table.
7. Assume that the average price of Magnavox for the day was $54. Find the total cost of Magnavox shares sold that day.
8. Find the difference between the opening price and the closing price for Comsat.
9. Estimate the total sales of Chrysler stock for the day. (Find $1.4 \times 10^5 \times 40$.)
10. Find the ratio of the low price for the year to the high price for the year of Am T & T. Give your answer to the nearest 0.1 percent.

Vocabulary

The section in which each word appears is indicated in parentheses.

amount (6–1)	gross income (6–4)
annual premium (Exercises 6–7 C)	interest (6–1)
arithmetic sequence (6–2)	premium (Exercises 6–7 C)
common difference (6–2)	principal (6–1)
compound amount (6–6)	rate (6–1)
compound interest (6–6)	sequence (6–2)
exact interest (6–1)	series (6–2)
Federal Deposit Insurance (6–7)	take-home pay (6–4)
Federal Income Tax (6–4)	term (6–2)
Federal Social Security (6–4)	

Chapter Review

A

1. Find the interest to be paid on a loan of $500 for 60 days at 6% per year.
2. Find the interest to be paid on a loan of $1200 for 1 month at $\frac{1}{2}$% per month.
3. Find the sum of the terms of the sequence 1, 6, 11, . . . , 101.
4. The cash price for a used car is $1000. The installment price is $200 down and 12 monthly payments of $80 each. Find the interest rate r.
5. An employee earned $6500 one year. Find his Social Security tax at a rate of 4.2%.
6. In Exercise 5 the deduction for income tax from the employee's salary was $21.30 per week. Find the deduction for income tax (use 52 weeks for 1 year).
7. In Exercises 5 and 6 find the amount of earnings after the deductions for taxes.
8. Find the amount of a savings account for $200 at 4% compounded annually for 3 years. Use the formula $A = p(1 + 0.04)^3$. Multiply to find the answer.
9. In Exercise 8 check your work by using the table in Section 6–6.
10. Make a graph of the formula $I = 0.07p$. Show values of p from 0 to 500. From your graph find I when $p = 350$.

B

1. Solve for S: $S = 1 + 8 + 15 + \cdots + 50$.
2. Solve for S: $S = 50 + 100 + 150 + \cdots + 750$.
3. In the formula

$$r = \frac{24C}{B(n + 1)},$$

find r if: $C = 50$, $B = 2000$, and $n = 5$.
4. Find the Social Security tax on an income of $5000 for one year if $r = 4.2\%$.
5. A family with income i dollars per year spends x dollars for automobile costs, where $x = 0.25i$. Make a line graph of this formula for i from 0 dollars to 8000 dollars.
6. From your graph in Exercise 5 find x when i is:
    (a) 4000   (b) 6000   (c) 7000
7. In Exercise 5 is the formula realistic for a family with $i = 3000$? For a family with $i = 4000$? For a family with $i = 5000$? Explain.
8. Use the table in Section 6–7 to find the amount of a deposit of $35 per period for 20 periods if the rate is $1\frac{1}{2}\%$ per period.
9. As in Exercise 8, find the amount of a deposit of $60 per period for 20 periods if the rate is 1% per period.
10. Find the interest on a savings account of $650 for 1 month at an annual rate of $6\frac{1}{2}\%$.

REVIEW OF CHAPTERS 1–6

A

Find the sums:

1. 218.75	2. $4\frac{1}{2}$	3. $n = 2\frac{3}{4} + 1.75 + 0.62$
109.32	$3\frac{1}{3}$	
90.09	$4\frac{3}{4}$	4. $n = 16.73 + 29\frac{1}{2} + 101 + 47\frac{3}{4}$

Find the quotients (give the answers to the nearest tenth):
  5. $35\overline{)7595}$ 6. $8.75\overline{)8767.5}$ 7. $8\frac{1}{2} \div 2\frac{3}{8}$

Review of Chapters 1–6 continued on page 292.

Find the products:

8. 21,703
   × 49

9. 40.075
   × 3.24

10. $4\frac{3}{8} \times 6\frac{2}{5}$

In Exercises 11–13 subtract:

11. 2623
    1982

12. $37\frac{2}{3}$
    $24\frac{7}{8}$

13. 12,360.205
    9,295.119

14. Find 29% of $10,500.
15. Find the number of centimeters in $1\frac{1}{2}$ yards.
16. A square plot of land has sides 12,300 feet long. Find the area. Write the answer in scientific notation.
17. The interest on a loan of $650 at 4% was $65. What was the length of time for which this loan was held? Use $I = prt$.
18. A man worked 55 hours 1 week at a regular rate of $3.50 per hour. Find his gross earnings for that week. Use $1\frac{1}{2}$ times the regular rate for all time over 40 hours.
19. Make a list of four ordered pairs for the formula $y = 2x + 3$. On a set of axes plot these ordered pairs and sketch the graph.
20. A certain type of rug material costs $9.95 per square yard installed. Find the total cost to cover the floor shown in Figure 6–4.

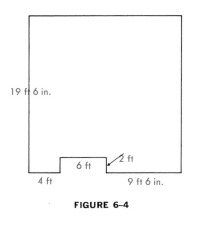

19 ft 6 in.

6 ft

2 ft

4 ft

9 ft 6 in.

FIGURE 6-4

B

1. Find the mean for these test scores: 65, 72, 88, 72, 62, 91, 85, 72, 90, and 65. Give your answer to the nearest tenth.
2. For the scores in Exercise 1 find:
   (a) the mode   (b) the range   (c) the median

3. If you select 1 of the scores from Exercise 1 at random, what is the probability that it will be 72?

4. Find the speed in feet per minute of a ship traveling at 15 knots. (*Note:* 1 nautical mile is about 6080 feet)

5. Use the formula $A = p(1 + r)^n$ to find the amount on \$500 at $5\frac{1}{2}\%$ compounded annually for 2 years.

6. Use a table to determine the interest and the amount of \$300 at 5% for 3 years compounded quarterly.

7. A certain ship had facilities to carry 1086 passengers. If it left port with only 905 passengers aboard, what percent of its total capacity was it carrying?

8. Find the interest on a loan of \$1200 for $2\frac{1}{2}$ years at $3\frac{1}{2}\%$. Use the formula $I = prt$.

9. Find the circumference of a circular wheel which has a diameter of $2\frac{1}{4}$ feet. Use 3.14 for π.

10. Use the formula $d = 16t^2$ to find t when $d = 144$.

c

In Exercises 1-6 solve for x:

1. $x = 12.06 + 2\frac{3}{8}$

2. $3x + 5 = 32$

3. $2x - 7 = 17$

4. $x = 16(48\frac{1}{4} - 13\frac{2}{3})$

5. $x = \dfrac{3\frac{1}{2}}{2\frac{1}{2} - 1}$

6. $x = \dfrac{12,264}{24}$

7. Arrange these numbers in order of size from largest to smallest: 29, $30\frac{1}{4}$, $28\frac{7}{8}$, 27.99, and 30.24.

8. Perform the indicated operations and round off each answer:

   (a) $\dfrac{21,290}{50}$, nearest ten   (b) $\dfrac{1727 + 49 + 805}{9.5}$, nearest tenth

9. Give the number of significant digits in each number:

   (a) 21,700   (b) 0.0605

   (c) 12.0   (d) 40.08

10. What fraction of a square yard is 18 square inches?

11. Find the difference in price per ounce between 6 ounces of tea selling at 95¢ per pound and 8 ounces of tea selling at \$1.25 per pound.

12. Give the height of a building in meters if it has 6 stories each one of which is 12 feet high.

D

In this book you have studied many of the properties of numbers. Among these are:

The commutative property for addition: $a + b = b + a$
The commutative property for multiplication: $ab = ba$
The associative property for addition: $a + (b + c) = (a + b) + c$
The associative property for multiplication: $a(bc) = (ab)c$
The distributive property: $a(b + c) = ab + ac$

Name the property illustrated in each problem in Exercises 1–8:

1. $3 \times 5 = 5 \times 3$
2. $a(b + c) = (b + c)a$
3. $x + y = y + x$
4. $2(x + y) = 2x + 2y$
5. $2(1\frac{1}{2} + \frac{3}{4}) = 3 + \frac{3}{2}$
6. $3 + (7 + d) = (3 + 7) + d$
7. $5(6c) = (5 \times 6)c$
8. $6y + 3n = 3(2y + n)$
9. State whether or not each number is prime.
   (a) 47
   (b) 231
   (c) 27,312
   (d) 91
10. State the axiom used in each step:

$$3x + 7 = 25,$$
$$3x = 18,$$
$$x = 6.$$

11. Find the set of prime factors of 150.
12. How many whole numbers are there in the interval $13 < x \leq 29$?

7 Indirect Measurement

■ **7-1 PROPORTION**

An equality of ratios is called a **proportion.** For example, the equations in (1) and (2) are proportions.

$$\tfrac{3}{4} = \tfrac{6}{8} \tag{1}$$

$$\tfrac{5}{10} = \tfrac{1}{2} \tag{2}$$

When purchasing a number n of items at a fixed price p per item, we say that the total cost C is proportional to the number of items purchased. That is, $C = p \times n$, or $C/n = p$.

Example 1. (a) Use the formula $C = p \times n$ to find the price p of one item if $n = 10$ and $C = 5$ (dollars). (b) Use the formula to find p if $n = 16$ and $C = 8$ (dollars). (c) Use the answers to (a) and (b) to write a proportion.

(a) $C = p \times n$

$\quad$ $500 = p \times 10$ $\qquad$ Substitute.

$\quad$ $\tfrac{500}{10} = p$ $\qquad$ That is, p is 50 (cents).

(b) $C = p \times n$

$\quad$ $800 = p \times 16$ $\qquad$ Substitute.

$\quad$ $\tfrac{800}{16} = p$ $\qquad$ That is, p is 50 (cents).

(c) $\tfrac{500}{10} = \tfrac{800}{16}$ $\qquad$ Substitution axiom, since each fraction equals p; that is, 50.

295

Example 2. A customer paid C_1 cents for n_1 items at p cents each. A second customer paid C_2 cents for n_2 of the same item. Find a proportion.

$$C_1 = p \times n_1$$

$$\frac{C_1}{n_1} = p$$

Also,

$$C_2 = p \times n_2,$$

or

$$\frac{C_2}{n_2} = p.$$

Since each ratio equals p, the ratios are equal by substitution. Therefore

$$\frac{C_1}{n_1} = \frac{C_2}{n_2}.$$

Example 3. If 23 items cost \$9.20, find the cost of 31 such items. Use the proportion in Example 2.

$$\frac{C_1}{n_1} = \frac{C_2}{n_2}$$

$$\frac{920}{23} = \frac{C_2}{31} \qquad \text{Substitute.}$$

$$40 = \frac{C_2}{31} \qquad \text{Divide by 23.}$$

$$40 \times 31 = C_2 \qquad \text{Multiply by 31.}$$

$$1240 = C_2 \qquad \text{The cost is \$12.40.}$$

From the examples we may observe that two variables, such as C and n, are proportional only if $C = kn$, where k is a constant. Thus I is true.

I. If $y = kx$, then $\dfrac{y_1}{x_1} = \dfrac{y_2}{x_2}$.

In I we say that y **varies directly** as x.

Exercises for Section 7–1

7–1 A

In Exercises 1–6 tell whether or not the statement is a proportion:

1. $\dfrac{7}{8} = \dfrac{3\frac{1}{2}}{4}$ 2. $\dfrac{10}{12} = \dfrac{5}{6}$ 3. $\dfrac{15}{20} = \dfrac{3}{4}$

4. $\dfrac{6}{8} = \dfrac{7}{10}$ 5. $\dfrac{5}{9} = \dfrac{20}{40}$ 6. $\dfrac{5}{8} = \dfrac{60}{104}$

7. If $y_1 = 3$, $x_1 = 4$, $y_n = 3k$, and $x_n = 4k$, does it appear that y and x are proportional? $\left(Note:\ \text{Does}\ \dfrac{y_1}{x_1} = \dfrac{3}{4}\ ?\quad \text{Does}\ \dfrac{y_n}{x_n} = \dfrac{3k}{4k} = \dfrac{3}{4}\ ?\right)$

In Exercises 8–12 does it appear that the two variables are proportional?

8. $A_1 = 20$, $W_1 = 5$; $A_n = 20k$, $W_n = 5k$
9. $r_1 = 20$, $d_1 = 40$; $r_n = 20k$, $d_n = 40k$
10. $C_1 = 100$, $n_1 = 10$; $C_n = 100k$, $n_n = 10k$
11. $x_1 = 20$, $y_1 = 8$; $x_n = 20k$, $y_n = 10k$
12. $x_1 = 9$, $y_1 = 12$; $x_n = 3k$, $y_n = 4k$

7–1 B

In Exercises 1–6 tell whether or not the variables are proportional:

1. $c = 5n$ 2. $p = 4s$ 3. $y = 7x$
4. $p = 4s + 2$ 5. $y = 4x - 1$ 6. $y = \frac{1}{2}x$

In Exercises 7–12 tell whether or not y and x are proportional:

	x_1	y_1	x_n	y_n
7.	4	5	8	10
8.	3	6	15	30
9.	9	12	27	36
10.	4	5	8	11
11.	21	30	42	60
12.	25	35	75	120

7-1 C

1. Does the cost c of a number n of 5¢ postage stamps vary directly as the number n? (*Note:* It does if $c = 5n$.)
2. In Exercise 1 find c_2 if $n_1 = 1$, $c_1 = 5$, and $n_2 = 13$. Use the proportion

$$\frac{c_1}{n_1} = \frac{c_2}{n_2}.$$

3. Does the distance d vary as the time t for a car going 40 miles per hour? (Does $d = 40t$?)
4. In Exercise 3 find d_2 if $d_1 = 80$, $t_1 = 2$, and $t_2 = 4$. Use

$$\frac{d_1}{t_1} = \frac{d_2}{t_2}.$$

5. Does a wage W vary as the rate r per hour for 8 hours? Does $W = 8r$?
6. In Exercise 5 find W_2 if $W_1 = 8$, $r_1 = 2$, and $r_2 = 4$. Use

$$\frac{W_1}{r_1} = \frac{W_2}{r_2}.$$

7. The formula for the circumference of a circle is $C = \pi d$.
   (a) Does C vary directly as d?
   (b) Does $\dfrac{C_1}{d_1} = \dfrac{C_2}{d_2}$?
   (c) If $C_1 \approx 22$, $d_1 = 7$, and $d_2 = 20$, approximate C_2. Use

$$\frac{C_1}{d_1} = \frac{C_2}{d_2}.$$

7-1 D

In Exercises 1–5 does $\dfrac{x_1}{y_1} = \dfrac{x_n}{y_n}$?

	x_1	y_1	x_n	y_n
1.	4	8	6	12
2.	3	4	12	16
3.	5	6	10	12
4.	7	8	14	16
5.	9	10	27	30

6. In Exercise 1 does $\dfrac{x_1}{x_n} = \dfrac{y_1}{y_n}$?

7. In Exercise 2 does $\dfrac{x_1}{x_n} = \dfrac{y_1}{y_n}$?

8. In Exercise 3 does $\dfrac{x_1}{x_n} = \dfrac{y_1}{y_n}$?

9. In Exercise 4 does $\dfrac{x_1}{x_n} = \dfrac{y_1}{y_n}$?

10. In Exercise 5 does $\dfrac{x_1}{x_n} = \dfrac{y_1}{y_n}$?

11. (a) Does $\dfrac{4}{6} = \dfrac{8}{12}$? Does $\dfrac{4}{6} \times \dfrac{2}{2} = \dfrac{8}{12}$? If $\dfrac{4}{6} \times \dfrac{k}{k} = \dfrac{8}{12}$, does $k = 2$?

  (b) Does $\dfrac{1}{2} = \dfrac{5}{10}$? Does $\dfrac{1}{2} \times \dfrac{5}{5} = \dfrac{5}{10}$? If $\dfrac{1}{2} \times \dfrac{k}{k} = \dfrac{5}{10}$, does $k = 5$?

  (c) If $\dfrac{a}{b} = \dfrac{c}{d}$, does it seem that $\dfrac{a}{b} \times \dfrac{k}{k} = \dfrac{c}{d}$? If so, does $a \times k = c$ and $b \times k = d$? Is a proportional to c? Is b proportional to d? $\left(\textit{Note:} \text{ For } \dfrac{k}{k} = 1, k \text{ cannot be zero.}\right)$

7–1 E

1. On a scale drawing, lengths are proportional to those of the figure represented. We can find measures represented in Figure 7–1 as follows: (*Note: x, y,* and *z* are in feet.)

(a) $\dfrac{2\frac{1}{2}}{1} = \dfrac{x}{16}$. Solve for x.

(b) $\dfrac{2}{1} = \dfrac{y}{16}$. Solve for y.

(c) $\dfrac{1\frac{1}{2}}{1} = \dfrac{z}{16}$. Solve for z.

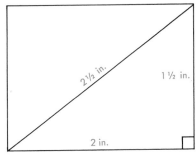

scale 1 in. = 16 ft

FIGURE 7–1

Exercises 7–1 E continued on *page 300.*

2. Consider a length of d inches on the scale drawing in Figure 7-1, as shown on page 299. Is $16d$ feet the length l represented in the figure? That is, does $l = 16d$, in feet? Also, is l proportional to d?

In Exercises 3–12, let x represent a measure in inches on a scale drawing where y is the length represented. The scale being used is 1 inch = 32 feet. Solve for y.

3. $x = 3$ **4.** $x = 5$
5. $x = 2$ **6.** $x = 1\frac{1}{2}$
7. $x = 2\frac{1}{4}$ **8.** $x = 1\frac{1}{4}$
9. $x = 1\frac{7}{8}$ **10.** $x = 2\frac{1}{16}$
11. $x = 3\frac{7}{8}$ **12.** $x = 4\frac{3}{4}$

7-1 F

1. In Section 2–7 we noted that

$$\text{if } ad = bc, \text{ then } \frac{a}{b} = \frac{c}{d}.$$

Now consider the proportion $a/b = c/d$.

$$bd\left(\frac{a}{b}\right) = bd\left(\frac{c}{d}\right) \qquad \text{Give reason.}$$

$$\frac{b}{b}(ad) = \frac{d}{d}(bc) \qquad \text{Give reason.}$$

$$ad = bc \qquad \text{Give reason.}$$

Thus we have proved theorem II.

II.   If $\dfrac{a}{b} = \dfrac{c}{d}$, then $ad = bc$.

We call ad and bc the **cross products** of the proportion.

2. Use cross products to show that $\frac{3}{4} = \frac{6}{8}$. That is, does

$$3 \times 8 = 4 \times 6?$$

3. Solve for x: $\dfrac{5}{8} = \dfrac{x}{16}$. (*Note:* $5 \times 16 = 8x$ and $8x = 80$)

In Exercises 4–7 solve for x:

4. $\dfrac{x}{10} = \dfrac{4}{5}$

5. $\dfrac{10}{x} = \dfrac{5}{6}$

6. $\dfrac{3}{4} = \dfrac{x}{16}$

7. $\dfrac{8}{9} = \dfrac{x}{18}$

8. $\dfrac{10}{11} = \dfrac{30}{x}$

9. $\dfrac{2}{5} = \dfrac{12}{x}$

7-2 SIMILAR TRIANGLES

Man has always had a need to measure such distances as the height of a tree, the width of a stream, and the distance between two stars. Since some of these measures are difficult (if not impossible) to obtain directly, he has devised means of finding them indirectly. The concept of similar triangles has been widely used in making indirect measurements.

Consider the triangles in Figure 7–2. We say that the following angles are pairs of **corresponding angles**: A and A', B and B', C and C'. The following sides are pairs of **corresponding sides**: $\overline{AB}$ and $\overline{A'B'}$, $\overline{BC}$ and $\overline{B'C'}$, $\overline{AC}$ and $\overline{A'C'}$.

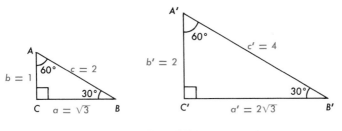

FIGURE 7-2

In Figure 7–2 observe that corresponding angles are congruent:

$$\angle A \cong \angle A', \quad \angle B \cong \angle B', \quad \angle C \cong \angle C'.$$

Also, note that corresponding sides are proportional:

$$\frac{a}{a'} = \frac{1}{2}, \quad \frac{b}{b'} = \frac{1}{2}, \quad \frac{c}{c'} = \frac{1}{2}.$$

That is,

$$\frac{a}{a'} = \frac{b}{b'} = \frac{c}{c'}.$$

The triangles have the same shape, but *not* the same size, since corresponding sides are *not congruent*. The word *congruent*, as described in Section 4–1, means "equal in measure." We may observe that one triangle is a scale drawing of the other. Such triangles are said to be similar. More precisely, we define similar triangles in this way: If, in two triangles, corresponding angles are congruent and corresponding sides are proportional, then the triangles are similar.

In geometry theorems III, IV, and V are proved.

III.   **Two triangles are similar if two pairs of corresponding angles are congruent.**

IV.   **Two triangles are similar if corresponding sides are proportional.**

V.   **Two triangles are similar if two pairs of corresponding sides are proportional and the angles included by these sides are congruent.**

From Figure 7–2, by definition $\triangle ABC \sim \triangle A'B'C'$ (read, "triangle ABC is similar to triangle $A'B'C'$"). Theorems III, IV, and V provide simplified rules for our work. Consider Figure 7–3:

In (a), $\triangle ABC \sim \triangle A'B'C'$ by theorem III.

In (b), $\triangle ABC \sim \triangle A'B'C'$ by theorem IV.

In (c), $\triangle ABC \sim \triangle A'B'C'$ by theorem V.

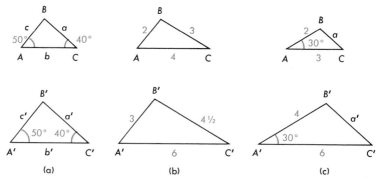

FIGURE 7–3

We have another theorem from geometry.

VI.   **If two triangles are similar, then corresponding angles are congruent and corresponding sides are proportional.**

We know that the pairs of triangles in Figure 7–3 are *similar*. Hence, applying theorem VI, we have the following.

From (a), $\dfrac{a}{a'} = \dfrac{b}{b'} = \dfrac{c}{c'}$ and $\angle B \cong \angle B'$.

From (b), $\angle A \cong \angle A'$; $\angle B \cong \angle B'$; $\angle C \cong \angle C'$.

From (c), $\dfrac{a}{a'} = \dfrac{2}{4} = \dfrac{3}{6}$; that is, $\dfrac{a}{a'} = \dfrac{1}{2}$. Also, $\angle B \cong \angle B'$ and $\angle C \cong \angle C'$.

In labeling the parts of a triangle, we use capital letters to name the vertices; we label the side opposite a vertex with the lower case letter corresponding to the capital letter at the vertex. This lower case letter will be used to represent the measure of the side. For example, in Figure 7–4 the side opposite R is marked r; it is also r units long.

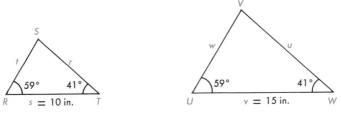

FIGURE 7–4

Example 1. Is $\triangle RST \sim \triangle UVW$? Explain. Find the ratio $\dfrac{r}{u}$. The triangles are similar by theorem III.

$$\frac{r}{u} = \frac{10}{15}$$

That is,

$$\frac{r}{u} = \frac{2}{3}.$$

Example 2. Suppose that a vertical pole casts a shadow 32 feet long on level ground. At the same time a yardstick standing vertically by the pole casts a shadow 4 feet long. Find the height of the pole.

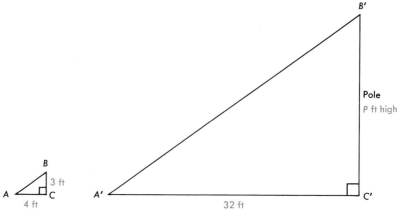

FIGURE 7-5

The sun's rays make congruent angles at the ground. Thus

$$\angle A \cong \angle A'.$$

$\triangle ABC \sim \triangle A'B'C'$	Theorem III
$\dfrac{p}{3} = \dfrac{32}{4}$	Theorem VI
$4p = 96$	Multiplication axiom
$p = 24$	Division axiom

The height of the pole is 24 feet.

Exercises for Section 7-2

7-2 A

In Exercises 1–5 measurements are given for the triangles in Figure 7–6. In each, state whether or not the triangles are similar. If the triangles are similar, give the reason.

1. A, 50°; B, 70°; D, 50°; E, 70°
2. a, 5 in.; b, 7 in.; C, 43°; d, 10 in.; e, 14 in.; F, 43°
3. a, 7 in.; b, 10 in.; c, 8 in.; d, 14 in.; e, 20 in.; f, 16 in.

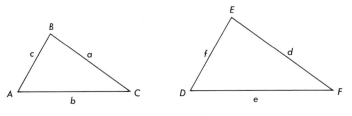

FIGURE 7-6

4. A, 50°; C, 69°; D, 50°; F, 68°
5. a, 2 in.; b, 3 in.; c, 4 in.; d, 3 in.; e, $4\frac{1}{2}$ in.; f, 6 in.

7-2 B

Solve for n:

1. $\dfrac{n}{3} = \dfrac{8}{4}$

2. $\dfrac{n}{5} = \dfrac{21}{7}$

3. $\dfrac{n}{6} = \dfrac{18}{5}$

4. $\dfrac{n}{21} = \dfrac{84}{125}$

5. $\dfrac{3}{n} = \dfrac{6}{8}$

6. $\dfrac{15}{n} = \dfrac{20}{38}$

7. $\dfrac{5}{12} = \dfrac{n}{24}$

8. $\dfrac{1.5}{20} = \dfrac{n}{36.2}$

9. $\dfrac{5}{9} = \dfrac{20}{n}$

10. $\dfrac{18}{25} = \dfrac{16.5}{n}$

11. $\dfrac{125}{144} = \dfrac{60.5}{n}$

12. $\dfrac{2}{5} = \dfrac{167.5}{n}$

7-2 C

1. Triangle ABC has angles whose measures are 35, 78, and 67. Triangle DEF has two angles whose measures are 67 and 78. Are the triangles similar? Explain.
2. The sides of one triangle are 16 inches, 15 inches, and 8 inches long. The sides of another triangle are 36 inches, $33\frac{3}{4}$ inches, and 26 inches long. Are they similar triangles? Explain.
3. Triangle I is similar to triangle II; the ratio of corresponding sides is 3 to 1. Triangle I has a side 36 inches long. Find the length of the corresponding side in triangle II.

Exercises 7-2 C continued on page 306.

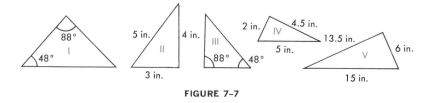

FIGURE 7-7

4. Name the pairs of similar triangles in Figure 7–7.
5. The sides of one triangle are 5 inches, 12 inches, and 13 inches long. The sides of a second triangle are $2\frac{1}{2}$ rods, 6 rods, and $6\frac{1}{2}$ rods long. Are they similar? Explain.
6. In Figure 7–8, AI and AE are line segments. Name the pairs of similar triangles in Figure 7–8. (*Note:* $\angle A$ is an angle of right triangles AFB, AHD, and AIE.)

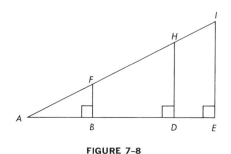

FIGURE 7-8

7. In Figure 7–9 name the side in triangle ABC which corresponds to $\overline{DE}$ in triangle DEF. To $\overline{DF}$. To $\overline{EF}$.

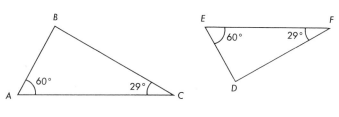

FIGURE 7-9

8. Name the pairs of corresponding sides in Figure 7–10.
9. Are the triangles in Figure 7–11 similar? Explain.
10. In Figure 7–11 name the side in triangle ABC which corresponds to $\overline{DF}$ in triangle DEF.

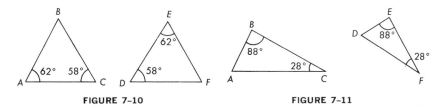

FIGURE 7-10   FIGURE 7-11

7-2 D

1. Figure 7–12 shows two similar triangles with lengths of sides as marked. Find:
   (a) The length of $\overline{BC}$ (b) the length of $\overline{AC}$

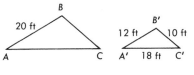

FIGURE 7-12

2. A flagpole casts a shadow 36 feet long on level ground. At the same time a man 6 feet tall casts a shadow 8 feet long. Find the height of the flagpole.

3. A man 6 feet tall casts a 7-foot shadow on level ground. At the same time and place a building casts a shadow 120 feet long. Find the height of the building.

4. Find the length of $\overline{AC}$ in Figure 7–13.

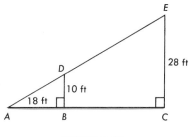

FIGURE 7-13

5. In Exercise 4 could you find the length of $\overline{AD}$ if you were given the length of $\overline{AE}$? (*Note:* Suppose $\overline{AE}$ is x feet long. How long is $\overline{AD}$?)

Exercises 7–2 D continued on page 308.

6. At the same time and on level ground a steeple casts a shadow 100 feet long and an 8-foot vertical pole casts a shadow 10 feet long. Find the height of the steeple.

7. In Figure 7-14, $\overline{AC}$ and $\overline{AD}$ are line segments. Find the length of $\overline{AC}$.

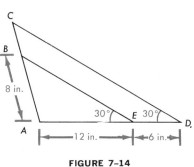

8. If an acute angle of one right triangle is congruent to an acute angle of another right triangle, would the triangles be similar? Explain your answer.

9. Triangle ABC is similar to triangle DEF. Triangle HIK is similar to triangle DEF. Do you believe that triangle ABC is similar to triangle HIK? Explain your answer.

FIGURE 7-14

10. In Figure 7-15, $\overline{CD}$ is perpendicular to $\overline{AB}$, $m(\angle ABC) = 90$, $m(\angle BCD) = 60$, and $m(\angle CAD) = 60$. Name three pairs of similar triangles. Also, give the reason why each pair of triangles is similar.

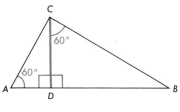

FIGURE 7-15

7-3 THE TRIGONOMETRIC RATIOS

Indirect measurements can often be determined by making use of the ratios of pairs of sides in a right triangle. These are called **trigonometric ratios.**

A triangle which contains a right angle is referred to as a **right triangle.** The side opposite the right angle is referred to as the **hypotenuse,** and the other two sides are referred to as the **legs of a right triangle.**

Consider the right triangle ABC in Figure 7-16. The measure of the side opposite a vertex is represented by the lower case letter which corresponds to the capital letter at that vertex. For example, the measure of the side opposite right angle C is c units. We also name this measure with the symbol AB; that is, the measure of $\overline{AB}$ is AB units.

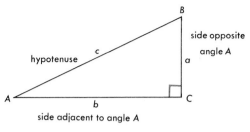

FIGURE 7–16

We refer to the legs of a right triangle as the side opposite a given acute angle or the side adjacent to that angle. In Figure 7–16

$\overline{BC}$ is the side opposite angle A;
$\overline{AC}$ is the side adjacent to angle A.

Similarly, with respect to angle B in the figure,

$\overline{AC}$ is the side opposite angle B;
$\overline{BC}$ is the side adjacent to angle B.

In a right triangle, the sine ratio of an angle is the ratio of the measure of the side opposite the angle to the measure of the hypotenuse. We state this briefly in VII.

VII. $\quad$ sine ratio $= \dfrac{\text{side opposite}}{\text{hypotenuse}}$

In the same manner we define two other ratios in VIII and IX.

VIII. $\quad$ cosine ratio $= \dfrac{\text{side adjacent}}{\text{hypotenuse}}$

IX. $\quad$ tangent ratio $= \dfrac{\text{side opposite}}{\text{side adjacent}}$

Then, from Figure 7–16, we have the following ratios. (*Note:* sin $\angle A$ means "sine of angle A"; cos $\angle A$, "cosine of angle A"; tan $\angle A$, "tangent of angle A.")

$$\sin \angle A = \frac{a}{c} \qquad \sin \angle B = \frac{b}{c}$$

$$\cos \angle A = \frac{b}{c} \qquad \cos \angle B = \frac{a}{c}$$

$$\tan \angle A = \frac{a}{b} \qquad \tan \angle B = \frac{b}{a}$$

Example 1. In Figure 7–17, ABC and ADE are right triangles. (a) Refer to triangle ABC and determine $\sin \angle A$, $\cos \angle A$, and $\tan \angle A$. (b) Refer to triangle ADE and determine $\sin \angle A$, $\cos \angle A$, and $\tan \angle A$.

(a) $\sin \angle A = \frac{3}{5}$

$\cos \angle A = \frac{4}{5}$

$\tan \angle A = \frac{3}{4}$

(b) $\sin \angle A = \frac{6}{10} = \frac{3}{5}$

$\cos \angle A = \frac{8}{10} = \frac{4}{5}$

$\tan \angle A = \frac{6}{8} = \frac{3}{4}$

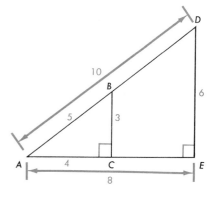

FIGURE 7–17

In Example 1 you may wonder why corresponding answers for (a) and (b) are equal. For the two right triangles of Figure 7–17 observe that

$\angle C \cong \angle E$ since each is a 90° angle;

$\angle A$ is an angle of each triangle.

Hence the two triangles are similar and corresponding sides are proportional. That is, if AD is equal to twice AB, then DE must equal twice BC, and AE must equal twice AC. We illustrate this fact in Example 2.

Example 2. Consider the two right triangles in Figure 7–18. Show that $x = ka$, $d = kb$, and $e = kc$ where $k \neq 0$.

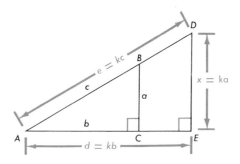

FIGURE 7–18

It is obvious that the two triangles, *ACB* and *AED*, are similar. Hence,

$$\frac{x}{a} = \frac{d}{b} = \frac{e}{c} = k,$$

where k is some number not zero. That is,

$$\frac{x}{a} = k \quad \text{and} \quad x = ka;$$

$$\frac{d}{b} = k \quad \text{and} \quad d = kb;$$

$$\frac{e}{c} = k \quad \text{and} \quad e = kc.$$

Thus from triangle *ADE*

$$\sin \angle A = \frac{ka}{kc} = \frac{a}{c}, \text{ as in triangle } ABC;$$

$$\cos \angle A = \frac{kb}{kc} = \frac{b}{c}, \text{ as in triangle } ABC;$$

$$\tan \angle A = \frac{ka}{kb} = \frac{a}{b}, \text{ as in triangle } ABC.$$

In other words, these ratios are constants which do not depend on the size of the right triangle.

Exercises for Section 7–3

7–3 A

1. From Figure 7–19 determine the following ratios to the nearest hundredth:
   (a) sin $\angle H$
   (b) cos $\angle H$
   (c) tan $\angle H$
2. As in Exercise 1, find the three ratios for angle *I*.

Exercises 7–3 A continued on page 312.

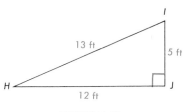

FIGURE 7–19

3. In Figure 7–20 each small angle at A is $15°$; $\overline{BF}$ is one line segment. By counting squares, find approximations of:
   (a) $\tan 15°$
   (b) $\tan 30°$
   (c) $\tan 45°$
   (d) $\tan 60°$
4. Refer to Exercise 3. Mark each statement true or false:
   (a) $\tan 15° < \tan 30°$
   (b) $\tan 30° < \tan 45°$
   (c) $\tan 45° < \tan 60°$
   (d) $\tan 60° < \tan 70°$
   (e) As the measure of $\angle A$ increases, its tangent ratio increases.
5. For a right triangle ABC, $m(\angle A) > m(\angle B)$. Then is
   $$\tan \angle A > \tan \angle B?$$
   Explain.
6. In Figure 7–21 we show a part of a circle with center at A and radius 10 spaces. Each small angle at A is $15°$. By counting squares, find approximations of:
   (a) $\sin 15°$
   (b) $\sin 30°$
   (c) $\sin 45°$
   (d) $\sin 60°$
   Note: In (a), $\sin 15° \approx \dfrac{2.6}{10}$; that is, 0.26.

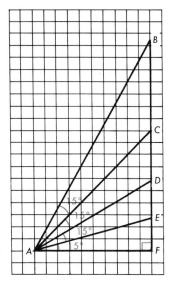

FIGURE 7-20

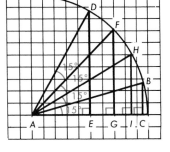

FIGURE 7-21

7. Refer to Exercise 6. Mark each statement true or false:
   (a) $\sin 15° < \sin 30°$
   (b) $\sin 30° < \sin 45°$
   (c) $\sin 45° < \sin 60°$
   (d) $\sin 60° < \sin 70°$
   (e) As the measure of angle A increases, its sine ratio increases.
8. By counting squares in Figure 7–21 find approximately:
   (a) $\cos 15°$ (b) $\cos 30°$ (c) $\cos 45°$ (d) $\cos 60°$

9. Refer to Exercise 8. Mark each statement true or false:
   (a) $\cos 15° < \cos 30°$
   (b) $\cos 30° < \cos 45°$
   (c) $\cos 45° < \cos 60°$
   (d) $\cos 60° < \cos 70°$
   (e) As the measure of angle A increases, its cosine ratio decreases.
10. Draw a right triangle ABC with C the right angle.

   (a) Does $\tan A = \dfrac{a}{b}$?

   (b) Does $\sin A = \dfrac{a}{c}$?

   (c) Is $\tan A > \sin A$? That is, is $\dfrac{a}{b} > \dfrac{a}{c}$? Explain.

7-3 B

1. (a) Is $\frac{10}{12} < \frac{10}{11}$?   (b) Is $\frac{10}{11} < \frac{10}{10}$?   (c) Is $\frac{10}{10} < \frac{10}{9}$?

   (d) If $x > y$, $y > 0$, and $a > 0$, then is $\dfrac{a}{x} < \dfrac{a}{y}$? Explain.

2. Consider Figure 7–22 in which BC is a line segment.
   (a) Is $\tan \angle B < \tan \angle B'$?
   (b) Is $\tan \angle B' < \tan \angle B''$?
   (c) Is $\tan \angle B'' < \tan \angle B'''$?
   (*Note:* In (a), is $b/BC < b/B'C$?)

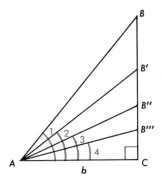

FIGURE 7–22

3. The measurements of two acute angles are $x°$ and $y°$; also, $x > y$. Is $\tan x° > \tan y°$? Explain. (*Note:* Consider Exercise 1.)

Exercises 7–3 B continued on page 314.

4. Refer to Figure 7–22.
   (a) Is cos ∠4 > cos ∠3?
   (b) Is cos ∠3 > cos ∠2?
   (c) Is cos ∠2 > cos ∠1?
   (*Note:* In (a), is $AB''' < AB''$? Is $b/AB''' > b/AB''$?)
5. In Figure 7–23 we have an arc of a circle with center A and radius 10 units.
   (a) Is sin ∠3 > sin ∠2?
   (b) Is sin ∠2 > sin ∠1? Explain.

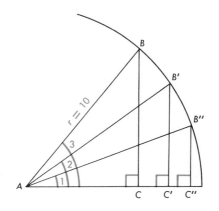

FIGURE 7–23

6. The measurements of two acute angles are $x°$ and $y°$; also, $x > y$.
   (a) Is cos $x° <$ cos $y°$?
   (b) Is sin $x° >$ sin $y°$? Explain.

■ 7–4 THE TANGENT RATIO AND ITS APPLICATIONS

The following examples illustrate some of the applications of the tangent ratio.

Example 1. At a point 100 feet from the base of a tower on level ground, the measure of the angle between the ground and the line of sight to the top of the tower is 42°. Find the height h of the tower.

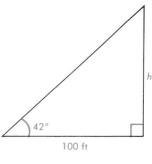

100 ft

FIGURE 7–24

We use a trigonometric ratio:

$$\tan 42° = \frac{h}{100}.$$

Now, if we know the value of tan 42°, we can easily solve the equation for h. We can use a protractor to draw a right triangle and then find tan 42°. However, such work is too tedious to make the use of trigonometric ratios practical or accurate. For this reason tables of trigonometric ratios have been developed. The Table of Trigonometric Ratios in the Appendix is such a table.

From the table, we find tan 42° = 0.900 (approximately). Now we can solve Example 1.

$$\tan 42° = 0.900 = \frac{h}{100}$$

$$90 = h \qquad \text{Axiom I (Section 4–3)}$$

The tower is about 90 feet tall.

The **angle of elevation** of an object is the angle between a horizontal line from the eye of the observer and his line of sight as he looks upward. In Figure 7–25 below, $\angle CAB$ is the angle of elevation of B from A.

The **angle of depression** of an object is the angle between a horizontal line from the eye of the observer and his line of sight as he looks downward. In Figure 7–25, $\angle DBA$ is the angle of depression of A from B.

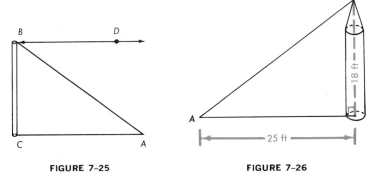

FIGURE 7–25   FIGURE 7–26

Example 2. The tower shown in Figure 7–26 is 18 feet tall. Find the angle of elevation of the top of the tower from point A on level ground 25 feet from its base.

To find $\angle A$ we use the tangent ratio.

$$\tan \angle A = \tfrac{18}{25} = 0.72$$

We look down the tangent column in the tables to find the tangent ratio nearest to 0.72. We find 0.727 opposite 36° in the table. Hence

$$m(\angle A) \approx 36 \text{ (degrees)}.$$

Most of the trigonometric ratios are irrational numbers. That is, nearly all values in the table are approximate. Examples of ratios which are rational numbers are

$$\tan 45° = 1 \quad \text{and} \quad \sin 30° = \tfrac{1}{2}.$$

Note that we use the tangent ratio to find:

(a) one leg of a right triangle where an acute angle and the other leg are known;

(b) an acute angle of a right triangle when the two legs are known.

Exercises for Section 7-4

7-4 A

Use the Table of Trigonometric Ratios in the Appendix to find the value of:

1. $\tan 5°$	**2.** $\tan 15°$	**3.** $\tan 25°$
4. $\tan 35°$	**5.** $\tan 45°$	**6.** $\tan 55°$
7. $\tan 65°$	**8.** $\tan 75°$	**9.** $\tan 85°$

7-4 B

Use the table to find the measurement of $\angle A$, to the nearest degree:

1. $\tan \angle A = 0.035$	**2.** $\tan \angle A = 0.213$	**3.** $\tan \angle A = 0.532$
4. $\tan \angle A = 0.839$	**5.** $\tan \angle A = 0.966$	**6.** $\tan \angle A = 1.111$
7. $\tan \angle A = 1.881$	**8.** $\tan \angle A = 9.514$	**9.** $\tan \angle A = 19.081$

7-4 C

Use the table to find the measurement of $\angle B$, to the nearest degree:

1. $\tan \angle B = 0.250$	**2.** $\tan \angle B = 0.065$	**3.** $\tan \angle B = 0.379$
4. $\tan \angle B = 0.862$	**5.** $\tan \angle B = 3.280$	**6.** $\tan \angle B = 1.431$
7. $\tan \angle B = 1.669$	**8.** $\tan \angle B = 8.555$	**9.** $\tan \angle B = 0.580$

7-4 D

Solve:

1. $\tan 27° = \dfrac{y}{5}$ 　　　　　　　**2.** $\tan 43° = \dfrac{y}{20}$

3. $\tan 19° = \dfrac{y}{100}$ 　　　　　**4.** $\tan 48° = \dfrac{150}{x}$

5. $\tan 45° = \dfrac{71.2}{x}$ 　　　　　**6.** $\tan 70° = \dfrac{27.47}{x}$

7. $\tan \angle A = \dfrac{137.6}{100}$ 　　　　**8.** $\tan \angle A = \dfrac{159}{75}$

Consider the equation $\tan A = y/x$. It contains three variables: A, y, and x. If any two of these three variables are given, we can solve for the third.

In 7–4 D, Exercises 1–3, A and x are given. We solve for y.

In 7–4 D, Exercises 4–6, A and y are given. We solve for x.

In 7–4 D, Exercises 7 and 8, y and x are given. We solve for A.

7-4 E

Read each exercise carefully; then draw a diagram and label the known parts. Solve as directed.

1. The angle of elevation of the top of a tree from a point 150 feet away is 30°. The tree is on level ground. Find its height.

2. A ladder is leaning against a building, as in Figure 7–27. Use the dimensions given to find the measure of the angle between the ladder and the ground.

3. At a distance of 120 feet from the base of a television tower, the angle of elevation of the tower's top is 38°. The tower is on level ground. Find its height.

Exercises 7–4 E continued on *page 318.*

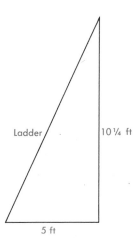

5 ft

FIGURE 7–27

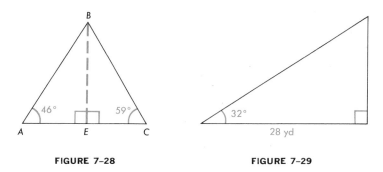

FIGURE 7–28   FIGURE 7–29

4. Figure 7–28 shows part of a construction diagram. A technician knows that the perpendicular distance from B to $\overline{AC}$ is $18\frac{1}{2}$ feet. He needs to find AE. Show how he can solve the problem.

5. The area of a right triangle can be found by taking $\frac{1}{2}$ the product of its legs. Find the area of the right triangle shown in Figure 7–29. (*Note:* Use the tangent ratio first.)

6. On level ground a woman casts a shadow 9 feet long when the angle of elevation of the sun is 30°. Determine the height of this woman.

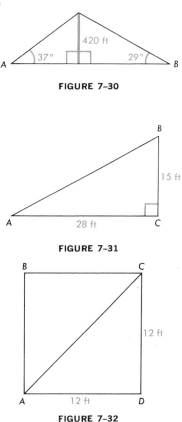

FIGURE 7–30

7. From the top of a cliff the angle of depression of a boat which is 90 yards from the base of the cliff is 20°. Find the height of the cliff.

8. A television tower that is 420 feet high is anchored by two cables in the same vertical plane at points A and B, as shown in Figure 7–30. If $m(\angle A) = 37$ and $m(\angle B) = 29$, find the distance from point A to point B.

FIGURE 7–31

9. Find the measure of $\angle A$ in Figure 7–31.

10. Figure 7–32 shows square $ABCD$, which has a diagonal extending from A to C. Use the tangent ratio to show that $\overline{AC}$ divides $\angle BAD$ in half.

FIGURE 7–32

◼ 7–5   THE SINE RATIO AND ITS APPLICATIONS

The sine ratio is used in solving the following examples.

Example 1. A guy wire runs from point A on the ground to B on the top of a 30-foot tower, as shown in Figure 7–33. Find the length AB of the wire if $m(\angle CAB) = 32$.

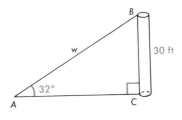

FIGURE 7–33

$$\sin 32° = \frac{30}{w}$$

$$0.530 = \frac{30}{w}$$

From the table, $\sin 32° = 0.530$.

$$0.530w = 30$$

$$w = \frac{30}{0.530} = 56.6$$

The wire is 56.6 feet long, to the nearest 0.1 foot.

In Example 1 observe that in the equation $\sin 32° = 30/w$, two numbers are known; only w is unknown, so we can solve. Furthermore, note that the tangent ratio does not lead to a solution, since

$$\tan 32° = \frac{30}{AC},$$

and AC is not the measure sought.

Example 2. A steel brace 30 feet long is shown by $\overline{AB}$ in Figure 7–34. The length of $\overline{BC}$ is 12 feet. Find $m(\angle BAC)$.

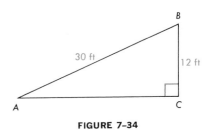

FIGURE 7–34

$\sin \angle A = \frac{12}{30}$

$\sin \angle A = 0.400$

$m(\angle A) \approx 24$ (degrees)

Note that we can use the sine ratio to find:

(a) the hypotenuse of a right triangle when an acute angle and the side opposite it are known;

(b) a leg of a right triangle when the acute angle opposite it and the hypotenuse are known;

(c) an acute angle of a right triangle when the leg opposite it and the hypotenuse are known.

Exercises for Section 7-5

7-5 A

Use the Table of Trigonometric Ratios in the Appendix to find the value of:

1. sin 5°	**2.** sin 17°	**3.** sin 30°
4. sin 41°	**5.** sin 45°	**6.** sin 60°
7. sin 71°	**8.** sin 84°	**9.** sin 89°

7-5 B

Use the table to solve for $m(\angle B)$:

1. sin $\angle B$ = 0.438	**2.** sin $\angle B$ = 0.695
3. sin $\angle B$ = 0.755	**4.** sin $\angle B$ = 0.743
5. sin $\angle B$ = 0.883	**6.** sin $\angle B$ = 0.985
7. sin $\angle B$ = 0.500	**8.** sin $\angle B$ = 0.906

7-5 C

Use the table to solve for $m(\angle A)$, to the nearest whole number.

1. sin $\angle A$ = 0.020	**2.** sin $\angle A$ = 0.313
3. sin $\angle A$ = 0.498	**4.** sin $\angle A$ = 0.702
5. sin $\angle A$ = 0.986	**6.** sin $\angle A$ = 0.898
7. sin $\angle A$ = 0.729	**8.** sin $\angle A$ = 0.944

7-5 D

Solve:

1. $\sin 30° = \dfrac{y}{12}$ **2.** $\sin 40° = \dfrac{y}{420}$

3. $\sin 75° = \dfrac{y}{251}$ **4.** $\sin 45° = \dfrac{70.7}{r}$

5. $\sin 70° = \dfrac{18.8}{r}$

6. $\sin \angle A = \dfrac{19.64}{20.0}$

7. $\sin \angle A = \dfrac{103}{200}$

8. $\sin \angle A = \dfrac{17.8}{40.2}$

Consider the equation $\sin A = y/r$. It contains three variables: A, y, and r. If any two of these are given, we can solve for the third.

In 7–5 D, Exercises 1–3, A and r are given. We solve for y.

In 7–5 D, Exercises 4 and 5, A and y are given. We solve for r.

In 7–5 D, Exercises 6–8, y and r are given. We solve for A.

7–5 E

Read the problem carefully; then draw a diagram and label the known parts. Solve as directed.

1. Suppose that the hypotenuse $\overline{DE}$ of right triangle DEF is 100 feet long and $m(\angle D) = 33$. Find EF.

2. In right triangle ABC, $BC = 60$ and $m(\angle A) = 19$. Find AB (Figure 7–36).

3. In a certain right triangle EFG, $m(\angle G) = 90$, $EF = 26$, and $FG = 24$. Find $m(\angle E)$, to the nearest whole number.

4. A road is inclined at 6° to the horizontal. Find the distance a man traveled on the road if his elevation increased by 10½ feet.

5. A radio tower 420 feet high is anchored by two cables in the same vertical plane at points A and B, as in Figure 7–37. If $m(\angle A) = 40$ and $m(\angle B) = 33$,

Exercises 7–5 E continued on page 322.

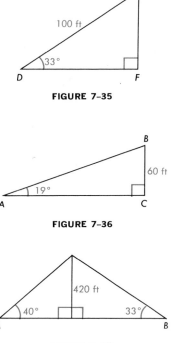

FIGURE 7–35

FIGURE 7–36

FIGURE 7–37

find the length of each cable. Assume that a total of 3 feet of cable is added for tying.

6. In triangle ABC, find AC and BC if $m(\angle C) = 90$, $AB = 20$ (yards), and $m(\angle A) = 30$.

7. The measure of one acute angle of a right triangle is 52. The leg opposite this angle is 15 meters long. Find the length of the hypotenuse.

8. A pilot (see Figure 7–38) observes that he is flying at an altitude of 20,000 feet. He finds that his angle of depression with a point on an airport runway is 7°. Find his distance d from that point.

FIGURE 7–38

9. A satellite is at point B, 100 miles above point P on the earth. The space pilot sees the horizon at point C. He knows that if the center of the earth is at A, then $m(\angle C) = 90$. Use 4000 miles as the radius of the earth and find the measure of angle B. (*Note:* $\sin B = \frac{4000}{4100}$.)

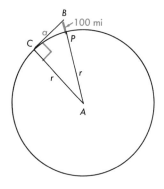

FIGURE 7–39

10. From Exercise 9, we have

$$m(\angle A) = 180 - 90 - m(\angle B).$$

Now we can write $\sin \angle A = \dfrac{a}{4100}$. Solve for A.

■ 7–6 THE COSINE RATIO AND ITS APPLICATIONS

The cosine ratio is useful in solving a right triangle when two of these parts are known and we wish to solve for the third part: an acute angle of the triangle, the side adjacent to the angle, and the hypotenuse of the right triangle.

Example 1. A car climbed 200 feet along a ramp which formed an angle of 10° with the level ground. What horizontal distance did it travel?

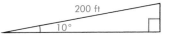

FIGURE 7–40

$$\cos 10° = \frac{d}{200}$$

$$(200)(\cos 10°) = d \qquad \text{We multiply by 200.}$$

$$(200)(0.985) = d \qquad \cos 10° = 0.985$$

$$197.0 = d$$

The horizontal distance which the car traveled is equal to approximately 197 feet.

Example 2. Consider 7–5 D, Exercise 9. Solve, this time using the cosine ratio.

$$\cos \angle A = \tfrac{4000}{4100} \approx 0.976$$

$$m(\angle A) \approx 12 \text{ (degrees)}$$

$$\sin 12° = \frac{a}{4100}$$

$$0.208 = \frac{a}{4100}$$

$$a = 4100 \times 0.208$$

$$a = 852.8$$

The distance to the horizon is about 853 miles.

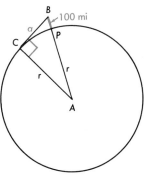

FIGURE 7–41

Exercises for Section 7-6

7-6 A

Use the Table of Trigonometric Ratios in the Appendix to find the value of:

1. $\cos 2°$ **2.** $\cos 9°$ **3.** $\cos 18°$
4. $\cos 30°$ **5.** $\cos 45°$ **6.** $\cos 52°$
7. $\cos 60°$ **8.** $\cos 75°$ **9.** $\cos 88°$

7-6 B

Use the Table of Trigonometric Ratios in the Appendix to find $m(\angle A)$:

1. $\cos \angle A = 0.995$ **2.** $\cos \angle A = 0.891$
3. $\cos \angle A = 0.731$ **4.** $\cos \angle A = 0.616$
5. $\cos \angle A = 0.500$ **6.** $\cos \angle A = 0.342$
7. $\cos \angle A = 0.191$ **8.** $\cos \angle A = 0.052$

7-6 C

Use the Table of Trigonometric Ratios in the Appendix to solve for $m(\angle B)$ to the nearest whole number:

1. $\cos \angle B = 0.031$ **2.** $\cos \angle B = 0.195$
3. $\cos \angle B = 0.499$ **4.** $\cos \angle B = 0.650$
5. $\cos \angle B = 0.785$ **6.** $\cos \angle B = 0.900$
7. $\cos \angle B = 0.938$ **8.** $\cos \angle B = 0.992$

7-6 D

Solve:

1. $\cos 30° = \dfrac{x}{15}$ **2.** $\cos 45° = \dfrac{x}{40.5}$

3. $\cos 60° = \dfrac{x}{200}$ **4.** $\cos 19° = \dfrac{110}{r}$

5. $\cos 70° = \dfrac{3.42}{r}$ **6.** $\cos \angle B = \dfrac{24.2}{100}$

7. $\cos \angle B = \dfrac{235}{250}$ **8.** $\cos \angle B = \dfrac{19.6}{33.3}$

> Consider the equation $\cos B = x/r$. It contains three variables: B, x, and r. If any two of these are given, we can solve for the third.
>
> In 7–6 D, Exercises 1–3, B and r are given. We solve for x.
>
> In 7–6 D, Exercises 4 and 5, B and x are given. We solve for r.
>
> In 7–6 D, Exercises 6–8, x and r are given. We solve for B.

7–6 E

In Exercises 1–12, if a statement is true, mark it true. If it is false, write a replacement for the symbol ($>$, $=$, $<$) to make it true.

1. $\sin 10° < \sin 20°$

2. $\sin 40° < \sin 60°$

3. $\sin 48° < \cos 80°$

4. $\sin 31° = \cos 59°$

5. $\cos 9° > \sin 80°$

6. $\sin 9° > \cos 81°$

7. $(\sin 30°)^2 = 1 - (\cos 30°)^2$

8. $\cos 15° < \tan 15°$

9. $\tan 75° < \tan 5°$

10. $\sin 70° < \cos 20°$

11. $\sin 45° < \cos 45°$

12. $\sin 33° = \cos 57°$

13. $\tan 45° > 1$

14. $\cos 12° > \sin 78°$

15. In Figure 7–42 $\sin \angle A = \cos \angle B$. (*Note:* $\sin \angle A = a/c$; $\cos \angle B = $?)

16. If $0° < x < 90°$, then $\sin x = \cos(90° - x)$. (*Note:* In Figure 7–42 below, $m(\angle A) + m(\angle B) = 90$. Therefore we see that $m(\angle B) = 90 - x$.)

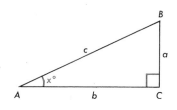

FIGURE 7–42

17. If $0° < x < 90°$, then $\cos x = \sin(90° - x)$.

18. If $0° < x < 45°$, then $\cos(45° + x) = \sin(45° - x)$.

7-6 F

Read the problem carefully; then draw a diagram and label the known parts. Solve as directed.

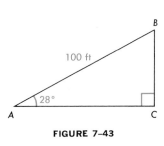

1. The hypotenuse of right triangle *ABC* is 100 feet long and $m(\angle A) = 28$ (see Figure 7-43). Find *AC*.

2. In a given right triangle *EFG*, $m(\angle G) = 90$, $EG = 44$, and $m(\angle E) = 40$. Find *EF*.

3. In right triangle *HKE*, $m(\angle E) = 90°$, $HE = 30$, and $HK = 34$. Find $m(\angle H)$.

FIGURE 7-43

4. A road is inclined at 8° to the horizontal. Find the horizontal distance a man has traveled after he has walked 100 feet along the road.

5. In rectangle *DEFG* the diagonal $\overline{DF}$ is 26 inches long and the side $\overline{DG}$ is 24 inches long. Find $m(\angle FDG)$.

6. In right triangle *ABC*, $\sin \angle A = \frac{3}{5}$. The hypotenuse is 25 centimeters long. Find the lengths of the legs.

7. The hypotenuse of a right triangle is 2.5 inches long. One of its acute angles has a measure of 39°. Find the measure of the other acute angle and the lengths of the legs.

8. A 25-foot ladder rests against the side of a building. Its foot is $12\frac{1}{2}$ feet from the base of the building, which is on level ground. Find the measure of the angle between the ladder and the ground.

9. A balloon is tied to the ground with a taut rope (see $\overline{AB}$, Figure 7-44) which is 200 feet long. From point *A* the angle of elevation of the balloon is 49°. Determine the distance *d* from point *A* to point *C*, directly under the balloon.

10. An airplane takes off from a level runway, climbing at an angle of 15°. The speed of the plane in the direction of flight is 225 miles per hour. Find its speed over the ground.

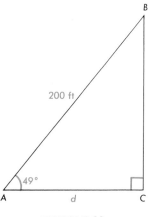

FIGURE 7-44

7-6 G

1. The sum of the measures of the angles of a triangle is $180°$.
   Hence, in Figure 7–45, $m(\angle B) = 180° - 90° - 45° = 45°$. That
   is, $m(\angle A) = m(\angle B) = 45°$.

   (a) Does $\sin \angle A = \sin 45° = \dfrac{a}{c}$?

   (b) Does $\sin \angle B = \sin 45° = \dfrac{b}{c}$?

   (c) Does $\sin 45° = \dfrac{a}{c} = \dfrac{b}{c}$?

   (d) Does $a = b$?

2. From Exercise 1 note that $a = b$. Hence $\tan 45°$ is an exact
   number. What is $\tan 45°$?

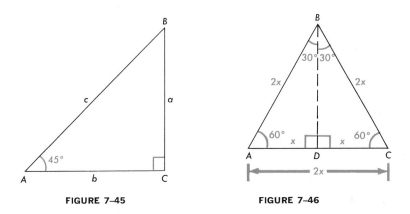

FIGURE 7–45   FIGURE 7–46

In Figure 7–46 triangle ABC is equilateral (the three sides are congruent), and $\overline{BD}$ forms right angles with $\overline{AC}$. Such a triangle has
these properties:

$$m(\angle A) = m(\angle B) = m(\angle C) = 60,$$
$$m(\angle ABD) = m(\angle CBD) = 30,$$
$$AD = DC = x.$$

Refer to Figure 7–46 in the following exercises:

3. Does $AD = \frac{1}{2}AB$? Does $DC = \frac{1}{2}AB$?
4. In right triangle ABD does the measure of the hypotenuse equal
   twice AD?
5. Find $\sin 30°$. Is this value exact or approximate?
6. Find $\cos 60°$. Is this value exact or approximate?

■ **7-7 IRRATIONAL NUMBERS AND FINDING SQUARE ROOTS**

In Section 2–1 we defined a rational number as a number which can be expressed as a/b, where a and b are whole numbers with $b \neq 0$. It was pointed out that there is a one-to-one correspondence between the rational numbers and certain points on the number line. There are other points on the number line and other numbers which are associated in a one-to-one correspondence with these other points. They are called **irrational numbers.** An irrational number cannot be expressed in the form a/b, as can a rational number.

If $n^2 = K$, we can say that K is the square of n. For example, $5^2 = 25$; thus we say that 25 is the square of 5. From this statement we see that 5 is one of the two equal factors of 25. In mathematics we say that 5 is a square root of 25, which is written symbolically as

$$\sqrt{25} = 5.$$

That is, if $n^2 = K$, then n is a **square root** of K.

Example 1. Find $\sqrt{5}$.

Try 2.3:
$$2.3^2 = 5.29.$$

Hence
$$\sqrt{5} < 2.3.$$

Try 2.2:
$$2.2^2 = 4.84.$$

Hence
$$\sqrt{5} > 2.2.$$

Thus
$$2.2 < \sqrt{5} < 2.3.$$

By further trials we find
$$2.23 < \sqrt{5} < 2.24.$$

Also,
$$2.236 < \sqrt{5} < 2.237.$$

From Example 1, we find that $\sqrt{5} = 2.24$, correct to the nearest hundredth. However, we can never find a terminating or repeating decimal n such that $n^2 = 5$. This kind of a number is called *irrational*. It can be proved that irrational numbers such as $\sqrt{2}$, $\sqrt{3}$, $\sqrt{5}$, $\sqrt{19}$, and so on, cannot be expressed in the form a/b as were the rationals. The number π which was introduced in Chapter 4 is irrational, and there are many others. In fact the irrational numbers form an infinite set.

Despite their strange characteristics, irrational numbers appear often in man's problems (for example, in square roots and many problems of higher mathematics). For this reason we will study a method for finding the approximate square root of a number.

Example 2. Find $\sqrt{240}$.

Suppose we guess that $\sqrt{240}$ is 15. Then we find that $240 \div 15 = 16$. We find the mean m of 15 and 16:

$$m = \frac{15 + 16}{2} = 15.5.$$

Now we use 15.5 as a new guess and find

$$240 \div 15.5 = 15.48+.$$

We find the mean m of 15.5 and 15.48:

$$m = \frac{15.5 + 15.48}{2} = 15.49$$

By multiplication you will find that

$$15.49 < \sqrt{240} < 15.50.$$

In fact

$$\sqrt{240} = 15.492, \text{ to the nearest thousandth.}$$

To find the square root of a number N:

1. *Guess at the square root.*
2. *Divide N by the guess.*
3. *Take the mean of the divisor and the quotient.*
4. *Use this mean as a new divisor.*
5. *Repeat this process, keeping more places to the right of the decimal each time.*

Example 3. Find $\sqrt{56.49}$.

The first guess is 7:

$$\frac{56.49}{7} \approx 8.0,$$

$$\frac{8 + 7}{2} = 7.5.$$

The second guess is 7.5:

$$\frac{56.49}{7.5} = 7.53,$$

$$\frac{7.5 + 7.53}{2} = 7.51.$$

The third guess is 7.51:

$$\frac{56.49}{7.51} = 7.52.$$

Continuing in this manner, we find

$$\sqrt{56.49} = 7.52, \text{ to the nearest hundredth.}$$

In the Appendix is a Table of Square Roots, given to the nearest thousandth.

Example 4. From the table find $\sqrt{79}$.

We look down the n-column until we come to 79; then we read the square root in the column headed $\sqrt{n}$. Thus

$$\sqrt{79} = 8.888, \text{ to the nearest thousandth.}$$

The table also lists the squares of the numbers from 1 to 150. We can use this list to find the square roots of some numbers larger than 150 (see Exercises 7–7 F and 7–7 G). For example,

$$\sqrt{7900} = \sqrt{100} \times \sqrt{79}$$
$$= 10\sqrt{79}$$
$$= 88.88, \text{ to the nearest hundredth.}$$

We say that an irrational number cannot be expressed in the form a/b *as can a rational number.* Remember, a rational number can be expressed in the form a/b where a and b are *whole numbers.* Note that the irrational numbers

$$\frac{\pi}{1}, \frac{\pi}{2}, \frac{\sqrt{2}}{1}, \frac{\sqrt{2}}{2}$$

are in the form a/b, but π and $\sqrt{2}$ are *not whole numbers.*

Exercises for Section 7–7

7–7 A

The following are perfect squares, so they will have rational numbers as their square roots. Find the square root of each number:

1. 16	**2.** 49	**3.** 121	**4.** 169
5. 1	**6.** 64	**7.** 36	**8.** 121
9. 256	**10.** 400	**11.** 100	**12.** 900

7–7 B

The following are perfect squares. Solve for n:

1. $\sqrt{4} = n$ **2.** $\sqrt{0} = n$ **3.** $\sqrt{25} = n$

*4. $\sqrt{\frac{1}{4}} = n$ **5.** $\sqrt{289} = n$ ***6.** $\sqrt{\frac{1}{9}} = n$

7. $\sqrt{100} = n$ **8.** $\sqrt{324} = n$ ***9.** $\sqrt{\frac{9}{4}} = n$

*10. $\sqrt{\frac{4}{9}} = n$ ***11.** $\sqrt{\frac{25}{4}} = n$ ***12.** $\sqrt{\frac{9}{16}} = n$

*Note: When $a > 0$ and $b > 0$, then $\sqrt{\dfrac{a}{b}} = \dfrac{\sqrt{a}}{\sqrt{b}}$.

7–7 C

The following are not perfect squares. Hence they are irrational. Locate each square root between two consecutive whole numbers. For example, $8 < \sqrt{75} < 9$ since $8^2 < 75 < 9^2$.

1. $\sqrt{5}$	**2.** $\sqrt{17}$	**3.** $\sqrt{19}$	**4.** $\sqrt{30}$
5. $\sqrt{35}$	**6.** $\sqrt{70}$	**7.** $\sqrt{55}$	**8.** $\sqrt{105}$
9. $\sqrt{88}$	**10.** $\sqrt{395}$	**11.** $\sqrt{157}$	**12.** $\sqrt{200}$

7-7 D

Use the method shown in Example 1 to find x, to the nearest hundredth:

1. $\sqrt{21} = x$ 2. $\sqrt{5} = x$ 3. $\sqrt{3} = x$

4. $\sqrt{11} = x$ 5. $\sqrt{30} = x$ 6. $\sqrt{55} = x$

7. $\sqrt{35} = x$ 8. $\sqrt{17} = x$ 9. $\sqrt{105} = x$

10. $\sqrt{220} = x$ 11. $\sqrt{375} = x$ 12. $\sqrt{552} = x$

7-7 E

Find n, to the nearest hundredth:

1. $\sqrt{7.4} = n$ 2. $\sqrt{5.5} = n$ 3. $\sqrt{12.5} = n$

4. $\sqrt{21.9} = n$ 5. $\sqrt{7.85} = n$ 6. $\sqrt{9.96} = n$

7. $\sqrt{18.03} = n$ 8. $\sqrt{58.75} = n$ 9. $\sqrt{109.3} = n$

10. $\sqrt{94.77} = n$ 11. $\sqrt{40.72} = n$ 12. $\sqrt{475.68} = n$

7-7 F

Consider using the Table of Square Roots in the Appendix to find $\sqrt{2670}$. We do not find $n = 2670$ in the table. However, we find

$$n^2 = 2601 \quad \text{for} \quad n = 51,$$

and

$$n^2 = 2704 \quad \text{for} \quad n = 52.$$

Hence

$$51 < \sqrt{2670} < 52.$$

Now we consider the two number lines in Figure 7–47 and, by the process of interpolation, we approximate n.

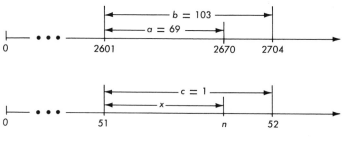

FIGURE 7-47

We assume that
$$\frac{x}{c} = \frac{a}{b}.$$

Then
$$\frac{x}{1} = \frac{69}{103} \quad \text{and} \quad x \approx 0.7.$$

That is, $n \approx 51 + 0.7$. Thus $\sqrt{2670} \approx 51.7$.

In these exercises use interpolation, where needed, to find the approximate value of n. Give answers correct to the nearest hundredth. Check your work with the answers in the table.

1. $n = \sqrt{8}$ **2.** $n = \sqrt{21}$ **3.** $n = \sqrt{33}$

4. $n = \sqrt{90}$ **5.** $n = \sqrt{110}$ **6.** $n = \sqrt{160}$

7. $n = \sqrt{200}$ **8.** $n = \sqrt{3060}$ **9.** $n = \sqrt{5800}$

10. $n = \sqrt{8900}$ **11.** $n = \sqrt{5200}$ **12.** $n = \sqrt{11,900}$

7-7 G

It is known that the following law holds where $a \geq 0$ and $b \geq 0$:
$$\sqrt{ab} = \sqrt{a} \times \sqrt{b}.$$

Thus
$$\sqrt{20} = \sqrt{5} \times \sqrt{4},$$
$$\sqrt{18} = \sqrt{2} \times \sqrt{9}.$$

This law is used to find the square roots of many numbers not in the table. Note that in the example we find a number b which is a perfect square; then if $\sqrt{a}$ can be found in the table, we can solve by multiplying.

Here we use the Table of Square Roots to find:

(a) $\sqrt{1600}$ (b) $\sqrt{15,000}$ (c) $\sqrt{750}$ (d) $\sqrt{657}$ (e) $\sqrt{2,000,000}$

$$\text{(a)} \ \sqrt{1600} = \sqrt{16} \times \sqrt{100} = 4 \times 10$$
$$= 40$$
$$\text{(b)} \ \sqrt{15,000} = \sqrt{150} \times \sqrt{100} = 12.247 \times 10$$
$$= 122.47$$

Exercises 7–7 G continued on page 334.

(c) $\sqrt{750} = \sqrt{30} \times \sqrt{25} = 5.477 \times 5$
$$= 27.385$$

(d) $\sqrt{657} = \sqrt{73} \times \sqrt{9} = 8.544 \times 3$
$$= 25.632$$

(e) $\sqrt{2,000,000} = \sqrt{2} \times \sqrt{1,000,000} = 1.414 \times 1000$
$$= 1414$$

Use the method shown in (a) through (e) to find:

1. $\sqrt{500}$. Use $\sqrt{5} \times \sqrt{100}$.

2. $\sqrt{160}$. · Use $\sqrt{10} \times \sqrt{16}$.

3. $\sqrt{250}$. Use $\sqrt{10} \times \sqrt{25}$.

4. $\sqrt{360}$. Use $\sqrt{10} \times \sqrt{36}$.

5. $\sqrt{490}$. Use $\sqrt{10} \times \sqrt{49}$.

6. $\sqrt{4100}$. Use $\sqrt{41} \times \sqrt{100}$.

7. $\sqrt{700}$. Use $\sqrt{7} \times \sqrt{100}$.

8. $\sqrt{600}$. Use $\sqrt{6} \times \sqrt{100}$.

9. $\sqrt{640}$. Use $\sqrt{10} \times \sqrt{64}$.

10. $\sqrt{810}$. Use $\sqrt{10} \times \sqrt{81}$.

11. $\sqrt{240}$. Use $\sqrt{60} \times \sqrt{4}$.

12. $\sqrt{999}$. Use $\sqrt{111} \times \sqrt{9}$.

13. $\sqrt{5200}$

14. $\sqrt{5500}$

15. $\sqrt{5800}$

16. $\sqrt{8900}$

17. $\sqrt{572}$

18. $\sqrt{1026}$

19. $\sqrt{352}$

20. $\sqrt{396}$

▪ 7-8 THE PYTHAGOREAN THEOREM

Many problems of indirect measurement can be solved by use of a certain relationship among the sides of a right triangle. This theorem has been named after the famous Greek mathematician Pythagoras.

X.   **The square of the measure of the hypotenuse of a right triangle is equal to the sum of the squares of the measures of the legs.**

From Figure 7–48 the theorem can be written as

$$c^2 = a^2 + b^2.$$

If any two sides of a right triangle are known, the third side can be found by using this property.

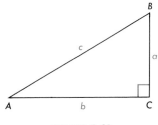

FIGURE 7–48

Example 1. If $a = 3$ and $b = 4$, find c.

$$c^2 = a^2 + b^2$$
$$c^2 = 3^2 + 4^2$$
$$c^2 = 9 + 16$$
$$c^2 = 25$$
$$c = 5$$

Example 2. If $a = 5$ and $c = 13$, find b.

$$c^2 = a^2 + b^2$$
$$13^2 = 5^2 + b^2$$
$$169 - 25 = b^2 \qquad \text{Axiom II}$$
$$144 = b^2$$
$$\sqrt{144} = b$$
$$12 = b$$

When the measures of the sides of a right triangle are integers, as in Examples 1 and 2, they are called **Pythagorean numbers.** In general not all sides will be integers.

Example 3. From Figure 7–49 find c.

$$c^2 = a^2 + b^2$$
$$c^2 = 10^2 + 18^2 = 100 + 324$$
$$c^2 = 424$$
$$c = \sqrt{424}$$
$$c \approx 20.6, \text{ to the nearest tenth}$$

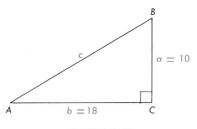

FIGURE 7–49

Exercises for Section 7-8

7-8 A

Solve, expressing answers to the nearest tenth:

1. $3^2 + 4^2 = c^2$
2. $9^2 + 12^2 = c^2$
3. $18^2 + 24^2 = c^2$
4. $5^2 + 7^2 = c^2$
5. $4^2 + 9^2 = c^2$
6. $10^2 + 24^2 = c^2$
7. $7^2 + 24^2 = c^2$
8. $(6.5)^2 + 8^2 = c^2$
9. $9^2 + 3^2 = c^2$
10. $8^2 + 15^2 = c^2$

7-8 B

Solve, expressing answers to the nearest tenth:

1. $8^2 + b^2 = 10^2$
2. $15^2 + b^2 = 17^2$
3. $9^2 + b^2 = 41^2$
4. $a^2 + 11^2 = 15^2$
5. $a^2 + 6^2 = 12^2$
6. $5^2 + b^2 = 9^2$
7. $a^2 + 24^2 = 25^2$
8. $(2.7)^2 + b^2 = 7^2$
9. $10^2 + b^2 = 26^2$
10. $a^2 + 40^2 = 41^2$

7-8 C

In right triangle ABC, c is the measure of the hypotenuse, and the legs have measures a and b. Find the measure of the side not given. Express answers to the nearest tenth:

1. $a = 9, b = 81$
2. $a = 6, b = 8$
3. $a = 10, b = 24$
4. $a = 6, b = 10$
5. $a = 12, b = 15$
6. $a = 9, c = 15$
7. $a = 18, c = 26$
8. $b = 24, c = 26$
9. $b = 16, c = 23$
10. $b = 20, c = 48$

7-8 D

Read the problem carefully; then draw a diagram and label the known parts. Express answers to the nearest tenth.

1. A wooden beam 15 feet long is leaning against the side of a building on level ground. Its bottom end is 9 feet from the wall. Find the height that the beam will reach on the building.

2. Find the length of the diagonal $\overline{DF}$ in the rectangle in Figure 7-50.

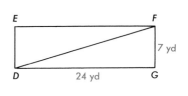

FIGURE 7-50

3. An empty field in the shape of a rectangle has dimensions 60 yards by 32 yards. How much distance is saved by crossing the field diagonally rather than walking along the length and then along the width?

4. The length of the hypotenuse of a right triangle is 41 centimeters. One of the other sides has a length of 9 centimeters. Find the length of the third side.

5. A guy line from the top of a flagpole 48 feet high reaches the ground 14 feet from the pole. How long is the guy line?

6. A baseball diamond has the shape of a square whose sides are 90 feet long. Find the direct distance from home plate to second base.

7. Two poles are erected in a flat parking lot. Their lengths are 29 feet and 38 feet, and they are 40 feet apart. Find the distance from the top of one pole to the top of the other.

8. Figure 7-51 shows an *equilateral triangle* (all sides are equal in length) with each side 15 inches long. The line drawn from any vertex perpendicular to the opposite side divides the opposite side into two equal parts. Find *BE*.

9. In Figure 7-51 of Exercise 7, $\overline{BE}$ is the altitude and $\overline{AC}$ is the base of the triangle. Find the area of the triangle.

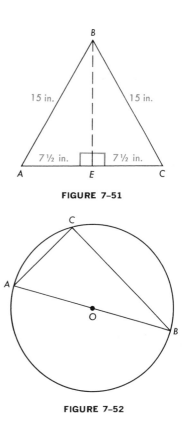

FIGURE 7-51

10. Use the method developed in Exercises 7 and 8 to find the area of an equilateral triangle with each side 20 inches long.

11. In Figure 7-52 triangle *ABC* has its vertices on the circle; side $\overline{AB}$ is a diameter of the circle. Therefore, by a rule of geometry, triangle *ABC* is a right triangle. The radius of the circle is $7\frac{1}{2}$ feet; $\overline{AC}$ is 7 feet long. Find *BC*.

FIGURE 7-52

7-8 E

The drawing in Figure 7–53 represents a rectangular solid. Find:

1. AC 2. AD
3. $m(\angle BAC)$ 4. $m(\angle CAD)$
5. BD 6. AG

7. The total surface area
8. The volume of the solid

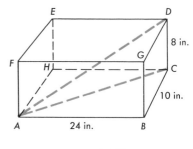

FIGURE 7–53

■ 7-9 SPECIAL TRIANGLES

Some right triangles have special properties which make them useful in solving many problems. In Exercises 7–6 G some relations were pointed out for two such triangles.

XI.   In a 45°-45°-90° triangle the legs have equal measures. Thus the triangle is isosceles.

XII.   In a 30°-60°-90° triangle the measure of the side opposite the 30° angle is exactly one-half the measure of the hypotenuse.

Example 1. Refer to Figures 7–54 and 7–55 and find: (a) tan 45° (b) sin 30° (c) cos 60°.

$$\tan 45° = \frac{x}{x} = 1$$

$$\sin 30° = \frac{x}{2x} = \frac{1}{2}$$

$$\cos 60° = \frac{x}{2x} = \frac{1}{2}$$

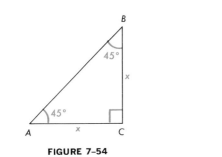

FIGURE 7–54

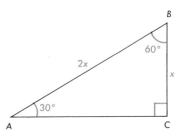

FIGURE 7–55

Example 2. Find the measure of one leg of an isosceles right triangle if the hypotenuse is 10 inches long.

$$x^2 + x^2 = 10^2$$ The Pythagorean theorem
$$2x^2 = 100$$ Add; square 10.
$$x^2 = 50$$ Divide both sides by 2.
$$x = \sqrt{50} \approx 7.071$$

The 30°-60°-90° triangle and the 45°-45°-90° triangle are common tools in a drawing course.

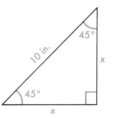

FIGURE 7–56

Exercises for Section 7–9

7–9 A

In isosceles right triangle ABC, $m(\angle C) = 90°$. Find BC if:

1. $AC = 10$ (feet)   **2.** $AC = 12$ (feet)
3. $AB = 15$ (feet)   **4.** $AB = 18$ (feet)

In a 30°-60°-90° triangle, find the measure of the hypotenuse if the measure of the side opposite the 30° angle is:

5. 10 (inches)   **6.** 15 (inches)
7. 20 (inches)   **8.** 25 (inches)

9. The measure of the hypotenuse of a 45°-45°-90° triangle is 20 feet. Find the measure of a leg.

10. In Figure 7–57, $\overline{AB}$ shows the slope of a mountainside. Find the height of the mountain above $\overline{AC}$.

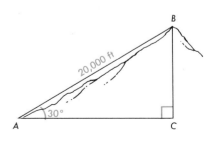

FIGURE 7–57

Exercises 7–9 A continued on page 340.

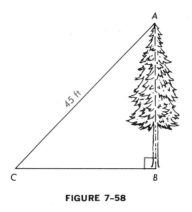

FIGURE 7-58

11. From point A on level ground, the angle of elevation of a tree-top is 45° (Figure 7–58). If $\overline{AC}$ is 45 feet long, find the height of the tree.

12. The shorter leg of a 30°-60°-90° triangle is 6 feet long. Find the lengths of the other sides.

7-9 B

In finding square roots we simplify in this manner. Consider $\sqrt{98}$:

$$\sqrt{98} = \sqrt{49 \times 2}$$
$$= \sqrt{49} \times \sqrt{2}$$
$$= 7 \times \sqrt{2}.$$

That is, we look for a factor which is a perfect square. Then we write the answer as a product of a whole number and the square root of a number. (See Exercises 7–7 G, pages 333 and 334.)

In Exercises 1–7 simplify:

1. $\sqrt{12}$. (*Note:* $\sqrt{12} = \sqrt{4 \times 3}$)

2. $\sqrt{50}$. (*Note:* $\sqrt{50} = \sqrt{25 \times 2}$)

3. $\sqrt{1200}$. (*Note:* $\sqrt{1200} = \sqrt{400 \times 3}$)

4. $\sqrt{98}$ **5.** $\sqrt{200}$ **6.** $\sqrt{300}$ **7.** $\sqrt{500}$

8. Use the Table of Square Roots in the Appendix to find $\sqrt{700}$. (*Note:* $\sqrt{700} = \sqrt{100 \times 7} = 10 \times \sqrt{7} = 10 \times 2.646$)

9. Use the Table of Square Roots to find $\sqrt{1700}$.

10. Use the Table of Square Roots to find $\sqrt{2100}$.

7-9 C

1. In Figure 7–59, $a = 1$ (foot). Find b and c. (*Note:* $a = b = 1$; $c = \sqrt{1^2 + 1^2}$)
2. In Figure 7–59, $a = 2$ (feet). Find b and c. (*Note:* $a = b = 2$; $c = \sqrt{2^2 + 2^2}$. Thus $c = \sqrt{4 \times 2}$.)
3. In Exercise 1 does $c = 1 \times \sqrt{2}$?
4. In Exercise 2 does $c = 2 \times \sqrt{2}$?

In Exercises 5–8 refer to Figure 7–59 and find the missing measures:

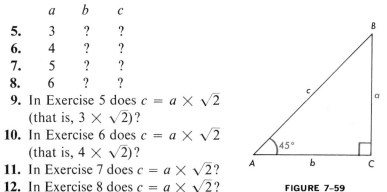

	a	b	c
5.	3	?	?
6.	4	?	?
7.	5	?	?
8.	6	?	?

9. In Exercise 5 does $c = a \times \sqrt{2}$ (that is, $3 \times \sqrt{2}$)?
10. In Exercise 6 does $c = a \times \sqrt{2}$ (that is, $4 \times \sqrt{2}$)?
11. In Exercise 7 does $c = a \times \sqrt{2}$?
12. In Exercise 8 does $c = a \times \sqrt{2}$?

FIGURE 7–59

From Exercises 1–12 it should be observed that, in a 45°-45°-90° triangle with hypotenuse c and legs a units long, $c = a \times \sqrt{2}$.

7-9 D

1. In Figure 7–60, $b = 1$ (foot). Find a and c. (*Note:* $c = 2b = 2$; $a^2 + b^2 = c^2$, so $a^2 + 1^2 = 2^2$. Then $a^2 = 3$.)
2. In Figure 7–60 find a and c if $b = 2$ (feet). (*Note:* $c = 2b = 4$; $a^2 + 2^2 = 4^2$. Then $a^2 = 12$.)
3. In Exercise 1 does $a = b \times \sqrt{3}$ (that is, $1 \times \sqrt{3}$)?
4. In Exercise 2 does $a = b \times \sqrt{3}$ (that is, $2 \times \sqrt{3}$)?

In Exercises 5–8 refer to Figure 7–60 to find the missing measures:

5. $a = ?$ $b = 3$ $c = ?$
6. $a = ?$ $b = 4$ $c = ?$
7. $a = ?$ $b = 5$ $c = ?$
8. $a = ?$ $b = 6$ $c = ?$

Exercises 7–9 D continued on page 342. Exercises 7–9 D continued on page 342.

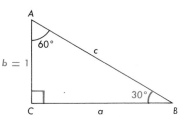

FIGURE 7–60

9. In Exercise 5 does $a = b \times \sqrt{3}$ (that is, $3 \times \sqrt{3}$)?
10. In Exercise 6 does $a = b \times \sqrt{3}$ (that is, $4 \times \sqrt{3}$)?
11. In Exercise 7 does $a = b \times \sqrt{3}$?
12. In Exercise 8 does $a = b \times \sqrt{3}$?

From Exercises 1–12 it should be observed that in a 30°-60°-90° triangle with hypotenuse c and the shorter leg b, then $c = 2b$ and $a = b \times \sqrt{3}$.

7–9 E

1. One side of a right triangle is 20 feet long; the measure of the angle opposite this side is 30. Determine the length of the hypotenuse of this triangle.
2. In a right triangle ABC, $m(\angle A) = 60$. The leg adjacent to angle A is 4 inches long. Find the lengths of the hypotenuse and the other leg.
3. In Figure 7–61, the diagonal $\overline{AC}$ of the rectangle $ABCD$ is 80 feet long; $m(\angle CAD) = 30$. Find CD and AD.
4. Find the area of the rectangle in Exercise 3.

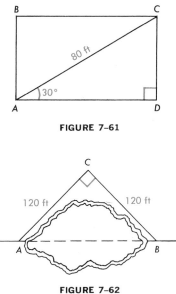

FIGURE 7–61

5. A television technician plans to erect a tower 30 feet tall on the flat roof of a building. He will stabilize the tower by attaching 4 guy wires to it. Each one is to be tied to the roof at a point 30 feet from the base of the tower. Determine the total length of wire the technician will need for all 4 guy wires. Add 3 feet to each guy wire for purposes of tying.

FIGURE 7–62

6. A survey line will cross a small lake. In order to determine the distance across the lake, offset lines are run around it as shown in Figure 7–62. Find the shortest distance from point A to point B on the opposite shore.

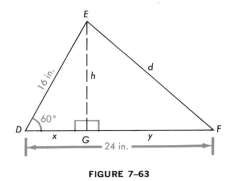

FIGURE 7-63

7. A student wished to solve the triangle shown in Figure 7–63 above. This means that he had to find the lengths of all the sides and the measures of all the angles in the triangle. Since it is not a right triangle, he drew $\overline{EG}$ perpendicular to $\overline{DF}$ to form two right triangles. Solve the given triangle by finding these parts, in order:

(a) $m(\angle DEG)$ (b) x and y

(c) h (d) $m(\angle F)$ $\left(\textit{Note:} \ \tan F = \dfrac{h}{y} \right)$

(e) $m(\angle FEG)$ (f) d

■ **7-10 HYPOTHESIS, CONCLUSION, AND CONVERSE**

Often, we make a statement which contains an *if* clause and a *then* clause. Consider the following examples:

If the animal is a bear, *then* it is a mammal.   (1)

If the triangle has a right angle, *then* it is a right triangle.   (2)

If I get wet, *then* I catch a cold.   (3)

If it is a square, *then* it is a rectangle.   (4)

The *if* part of the statement is called the **hypothesis.** The *then* part is called the **conclusion.** Thus in (1) we have

Hypothesis: The animal is a bear.
Conclusion: It is a mammal.

When we interchange the hypothesis and the conclusion, we form a new statement called the converse of the original statement. The converses of (1), (2), (3), and (4) are the following.

If it is a mammal, then the animal is a bear.   (1′)

If it is a right triangle, then the triangle has a right angle.   (2′)

If I catch a cold, then I get wet.   (3′)

If it is a rectangle, then it is a square.   (4′)

Suppose we use T for "true"; F for "false." Then we observe that for statements (1) through (4):

(1) T   (2) T   (3) T   (4) T

Now, we observe that for statements (1′) through (4′):

(1′) F   (2′) T   (3′) F   (4′) F

Thus we see that the converse of a statement may be false.

Note that the truth or falsity of the original statement has no bearing on the truth of the converse. For example, (1), (2), (3), and (4) are true; (1′), (3′), and (4′) are false and (2′) is true. Now consider (1′) as an original statement:

If it is a mammal, then the animal is a bear.

The statement is false. Its converse is statement (1) and is true:

If the animal is a bear, then it is a mammal.

The following are statements XIII, XIV, and XV of this chapter, written in short form and followed by their converses. Each statement is true; each converse is true.

XIII.   If it is a right triangle ABC with C a right angle, then $c^2 = a^2 + b^2$ (see Figure 7–64).
Converse: If $c^2 = a^2 + b^2$, then it (triangle ABC) is a right triangle.

XIV.   If it is a 45°-45°-90° triangle, then the legs have equal measures (see Figure 7–65).
Converse: If the legs of a right triangle have equal measures, then it is a 45°-45°-90° triangle.

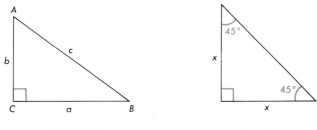

FIGURE 7–64   FIGURE 7–65

XV. If a triangle is a 30°-60°-90° triangle, then the measure of the side opposite the 30° angle is exactly one-half the measure of the hypotenuse (see Figure 7–66).

Converse: If the measure of one leg of a right triangle is exactly one-half the measure of the hypotenuse, then the angle opposite this leg is a 30° angle.

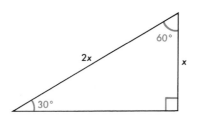

FIGURE 7–66

Exercises for Section 7–10

7–10 A

Write: (a) the hypothesis; (b) the conclusion of each statement.

1. If it rains, then the streets will be wet.
2. If I study hard, then I will pass the course.
3. If two angles of a triangle are congruent, the sides opposite these angles have the same measure.
4. An empty stomach causes hunger pangs in man. (*Note:* First write the statement in *if-then* form: If a man has an empty stomach, then . . .)
5. If the number is 16, then it is divisible by 8.
6. If an animal is a dog, it has four legs.

Exercises 7–10 A continued on page 346.

7. All even numbers are divisible by 2. (*Note:* If it is an even number, then . . .)

8. A person who exercises daily is healthy.

9. A rectangle with sides of length 8 feet and 6 feet has an area of 48 square feet.

10. If the sum of the digits of a number is divisible by 9, then the number is divisible by 9.

11. When the airline strike is settled, the flight schedules will at last be met.

7-10 B

Write the converse for each exercise in set 7–10 A. State whether you believe each converse to be true or false.

7-10 C

Each of the following ordered triples represents the dimensions of a triangle. Which ones are right triangles?

1. (3, 4, 5)	**2.** (5, 12, 14)
3. (10, 24, 26)	**4.** (40, 9, 41)
5. (7.2, 4, 6)	**6.** (0.8, 1.5, 1.7)
7. (5, 5, 7)	***8.** $(1, 1, \sqrt{2})$
9. (8, 6, 10)	**10.** (4, 5.657, 4)
11. (0.9, 1.2, 1.5)	**12.** (7, 25, 24)

*(*Note:* In this exercise $(\sqrt{a})^2 = a$ when $a \geq 0$.)

7-10 D

1. Centuries ago people used a rope to lay out right angles. The rope was 12 units long. It had a mark on it at the end of the first 3 units and another mark 4 units farther along. Tell how they may have used this rope to construct a right angle? (*Note:* Consider the converse of XIII.)

FIGURE 7-67

2. A certain triangle has sides whose lengths are 9 yards, 12 yards, and 15 yards. Is this a right triangle?

3. A certain triangle has sides whose lengths are 5 inches, 10 inches, and 8.66 inches. Determine the angles of this triangle. (*Note:* Does $5^2 + 8.66^2 \approx 10^2$?)

4. In a certain triangle ABC, $BC = 10$, $AB = 20$, and $m(\angle C) = 90$. Determine the measure of side AC. Give your answer to the nearest 0.1 unit.

5. In Exercise 4 find $m(\angle A)$.

6. In Figure 7–68 find the area of right triangle ABC.

7. In triangle ABC, $c > a$ and $c > b$. Consider this statement: If $c^2 \neq a^2 + b^2$, then triangle ABC is not a right triangle. Is the statement true?

8. Write the converse of the statement in Exercise 7. Is the converse true?

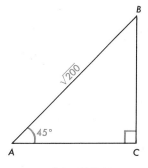

FIGURE 7–68

9. Consider the following statement: If N is a whole number, then it is a rational number as well. Do you think that this statement is true?

10. Write the converse of the statement in Exercise 9. Is the converse statement true?

Vocabulary

The section in which each word appears is indicated in parentheses.

angle of depression (7–4)
angle of elevation (7–4)
conclusion (7–10)
converse (7–10)
corresponding angles (7–2)
corresponding sides (7–2)
cosine ratio (7–3)
cross products (7–1)
hypotenuse (7–3)
hypothesis (7–10)
irrational numbers (7–7)
legs of a right triangle (7–3)

proportion (7–1)
Pythagorean numbers (7–8)
Pythagorean theorem (7–8)
right triangle (7–3)
side adjacent (7–3)
side opposite (7–3)
similar triangles (7–2)
sine ratio (7–3)
square root (7–7)
tangent ratio (7–3)
trigonometric ratios (7–3)
varies directly (7–1)

Chapter Review

A

1. Solve for x:

   (a) $\dfrac{x}{17} = \dfrac{50}{12.5}$ (b) $\dfrac{32}{55} = \dfrac{128}{x}$ (c) $\dfrac{2\frac{2}{3}}{x} = \dfrac{15}{5\frac{5}{8}}$

2. Write a proportion using the 4 numbers in each case:
   (a) 2, 27, 3, 18   (b) 15, 3, 2, 22.5
   (c) 6, 42, 56, 8   (d) 7, 21, 6, 18

3. To do a certain job 24 men work 18 days. Use a proportion to determine how long it would take 16 men to do this job. Assume that each man works at the same rate.

4. An experimental airplane is to be built with a wingspan of 48 feet. Find the wingspan of a model which is to be built on a scale of 1 to 72.

5. A certain pump can empty a tank containing 960 gallons of water in $6\frac{1}{2}$ minutes. How long will it take this pump to empty a tank containing 7200 gallons of water?

6. In Figure 7–69 angles B and C are right angles; AED is a line segment. Find AC.

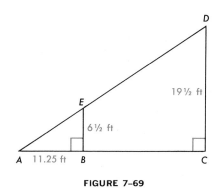

FIGURE 7–69

7. Use the trigonometric tables to find:
   (a) $\sin 17°$ (b) $\cos 17°$ (c) $\tan 17°$

8. Use the tables to solve:
   (a) $\sin A = 0.559$ (b) $\cos B = 0.500$ (c) $\tan C = 1.00$

B

In Exercises 1–3 solve:

1. $a^2 + 5^2 = 13^2$ **2.** $9^2 + 40^2 = c^2$ **3.** $8^2 + b^2 = 17^2$

4. Find the measure of the hypotenuse of a right triangle whose legs have measures of 17 and 24. State your answer to the nearest tenth.

5. Find the area of a right triangle with a hypotenuse 25 feet long and one leg 7 feet long. (*Note:* Use the Pythagorean theorem to find the other leg.)

6. Find the measure of a diagonal of a rectangle which is 40 yards long and 9 yards wide.

7. In Exercise 6 find the measure of the angle which the diagonal forms with the longer side.

8. In a 30°-60°-90° triangle the side opposite the 30° angle is 6 feet long. Find the measure of the other leg and of the hypotenuse.

9. Write the converse of this statement: Two lines which intersect and form congruent angles are perpendicular lines.

10. Write the converse of the converse of this statement: All right angles are congruent.

C

In Exercises 1–6 find n, to the nearest hundredth:

1. $n = \sqrt{1024}$ **2.** $n = \sqrt{19.8}$ **3.** $n = \sqrt{97.1}$

4. $n = (3)(\sqrt{289})$ **5.** $n = (\sqrt{75}) \div 3$ **6.** $n = (\sqrt{64})^2$

7. Find the hypotenuse of a right triangle whose legs are 36 feet and 15 feet long.

8. A triangle has sides whose lengths are 16 inches, 30 inches, and 34 inches. Is it a right triangle? Explain.

9. The area of a square is 100 square meters. Find the length of one side and of a diagonal.

10. Find $n = \sqrt{5 \cdot 9 \cdot 36}$. (*Note:* $\sqrt{5 \cdot 9 \cdot 36} = \sqrt{5} \cdot \sqrt{9} \cdot \sqrt{36}$)

D

1. State the definition of the sine ratio.
2. List some facts needed in order to determine whether two triangles are similar.

Chapter Review continued on page 350.

3. State the definition of the tangent ratio.
4. List three ways of determining distance indirectly.
5. Give sin 30° without using tables.
6. What special triangle is formed by the diagonal and two sides of a square?
7. Give three examples of rational numbers and three examples of irrational numbers.
8. If $ab = ef$, write a proportion with terms a, b, e, and f. Use the cross product rule to check.
9. State the definition of the cosine ratio.
10. Write a statement and underline the hypothesis.

E

If a statement is true, mark it true. If it is false, write a replacement for the symbol $(<, =, >)$ to make it true.

1. $\sqrt{80} < 9$ 2. $\sqrt{146} < 12$
3. $\sqrt{225} < 15$ 4. $\sqrt{0.09} > 0.3$
5. $\sqrt{\frac{1}{4}} = \frac{1}{2}$ 6. $\sqrt{27^2} = 27$
7. $\sin 45° < \cos 45°$ 8. $\tan 45° = \sin 45°$
9. $\cos 63° < \cos 3°$ 10. $\cos 87° < \cos 86°$
11. $\cos 13° > 1$ 12. $\tan 0° = 0$

8 Negative Numbers and Operations

8-1 NEGATIVE NUMBERS

We have studied the numbers which we associate with the points to the right of the origin on the number line. We refer to these as **positive numbers.** **Negative numbers** are associated with the points to the left of the origin. We use the same unit and mark off the points as we did for positive numbers; we symbolize the negative numbers as $-1, -2, -3, \ldots$, as in Figure 8-1.

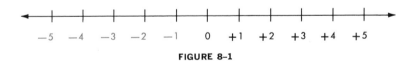

FIGURE 8-1

Like the positive numbers, the negative numbers form an infinite set. The union of the set of all negative whole numbers N, the set of all positive whole numbers P, and $\{0\}$ is called the set of integers I. That is,

$$I = N \cup P \cup \{0\}.$$

Numbers expressed with a $+$ or $-$ sign are sometimes called signed numbers. Since zero is neither positive nor negative we do not express it with a sign.

351

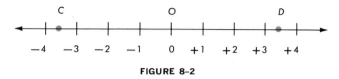

FIGURE 8–2

Consider points C and D in Figure 8–2. Point C is $3\frac{1}{2}$ units to the left of the origin; Point D is $3\frac{1}{2}$ units to the right of the origin. The numbers $+3\frac{1}{2}$ and $-3\frac{1}{2}$ have in common this property: they are associated with points which are the same distance from the origin. The length of $\overline{OC}$ is $3\frac{1}{2}$ units; of $\overline{OD}$, $3\frac{1}{2}$ units.

The numbers $+3\frac{1}{2}$ and $-3\frac{1}{2}$ are called **opposites.** In fact for every number b there is an opposite number $-b$ such that their sum is zero.

$$\textbf{I.} \qquad (+b) + (-b) = 0$$

Mathematicians say that b is the **additive inverse** of $-b$; $-b$ is the additive inverse of b.

In Chapter 5 we established a one-to-one correspondence between ordered pairs of positive rational numbers and zero and certain points in a plane. We now expand this concept to include all ordered pairs of real numbers. To do this we must extend the axes to make each axis a real number line. The axes divide the plane into four regions called **quadrants.** The quadrants are numbered as shown in Figure 8–3.

We have located points in quadrant I. The expression $P(2, 3)$ means "the point with coordinates

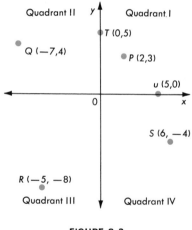

FIGURE 8–3

(2, 3)." To locate $P(2, 3)$ move 2 units to the right from the origin on the horizontal axis; then move 3 units up and parallel to the vertical axis.

Example. Locate the points: (a) point $Q(-7, 4)$ (b) $R(-5, -8)$
(c) $S(6, -4)$ (d) $T(0, 5)$ (e) $U(5, 0)$.

(a) Move 7 units to the left from the origin along the horizontal axis; then move 4 units up and parallel to the vertical axis.

(b) Move 5 units to the left from the origin along the horizontal axis; then move 8 units down and parallel to the vertical axis.

(c) Move 6 units to the right from the origin along the horizontal axis; then move 4 units down and parallel to the vertical axis.

(d) As before, move zero units right; move 5 units up.

(e) Move 5 units right; move zero units up.

Observe that for a point in quadrant I the coordinates are (positive, positive); for a point in quadrant II, (negative, positive); for a point in quadrant III, (negative, negative); for a point in quadrant IV, (positive, negative).

Generally we label these axes as the *y*-axis (vertical) and the *x*-axis (horizontal), as shown in Figure 8–3. The general point then has the coordinates (x, y).

The coordinate plane is established in the following way. We divide a plane into four regions with two perpendicular lines and establish a unit so that we can associate an ordered pair of real numbers with every point in the plane. Remember, our real number system includes the rational numbers and numbers such as π, $-\pi$, $\sqrt{2}$, and $-\sqrt{2}$, which are called irrational numbers.

Special Meanings of $+$ and $-$

The $+$ and $-$ signs are used two different ways. In the problem

$$x = (+7) + (-11),$$

the $+$ by the 7 and the $-$ by the 11 refer to the locations of their associated points on the number line. The $+$ between the $(+7)$ and (-11) indicates the operation of addition. Similarly, in

$$x = (+7) - (-3),$$

the first $-$ indicates subtraction; -3 expresses the negative of 3. We call a number *positive* or *negative* according to its sign. The operation symbols are called *plus* for $+$ and *minus* for $-$.

When a number is expressed without a sign, it is understood to be positive.

Exercises for Section 8-1

8-1 A

1. Express the opposites of 5, -3, $2\frac{1}{2}$, -7.3, -16, and 1.
2. Express the opposite of the opposite of -5. Of 5.
3. Draw a number line and locate the points with these coordinates:
   3, -3, $2\frac{1}{4}$, -1, 5, and $-2\frac{3}{4}$.

We write $P(+3)$ and read, "The point P on the number line with coordinate $+3$." Thus $P(b)$ is the point P on the number line with coordinate b. In Exercises 4–10 state whether point P is to the right or to the left of the origin:

4. $P(-7)$ 5. $P(+8)$
6. $P(-4\frac{1}{4})$ 7. $P(30\frac{1}{2})$
8. $P(b)$ if b is positive   9. $P(b)$ if b is negative

10. $P(-b)$ if b is positive; $P(b)$ if b is negative

We say that the coordinates are ordered on the number line; that is, if a point P is to the right of a point Q, then the coordinate of P is greater than the coordinate of point Q. Thus in Figure 8–4, $+2 > 0$. In Figure 8–5, $0 > -3$.

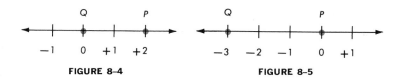

FIGURE 8–4   FIGURE 8–5

11. Mark each statement true or false:
    (a) $-2 > -5$ (b) $-7 > -19$
    (c) $0 > -800$ (d) $+1 > -500$
12. Rearrange the following numbers in order as they appear on the number line: 6, -5, 0, 2, -1, -4.9, and $+5$.
13. Draw a number line and plot the points for all integers b such that $-3 < b < +4$. How many integers are included?
14. On a number line plot the points for all integers b such that $-3 \leq b \leq +4$. How many integers are included?
15. Express the following, using signed numbers:
    (a) A gain of 5 yards   (b) A penalty of 15 yards
    (c) Ten degrees above zero   (d) Five feet below sea level
    (e) Four degrees below zero   (f) A loss of $12

8–1 B

We recall that $a < b$ when a is to the left of b on the number line. If a statement is true, mark it true. If it is false, write a replacement for the symbol $(<, =, >)$ to make it true.

1. $6 < 7$
2. $6 > -7$
3. $-6 > -4$
4. $-1 > -8$
5. $0 > -2$
6. $-5 < 5$
7. $+1 = -1$
8. $0 = 105$
9. $-8 < 0$
10. $-6 < 0$
11. $-7 < +7$
12. $-4 > 0$
13. $2^3 > -4$
14. $2^4 > 16$
15. $-6 < -5 < 0$

8–1 C

Draw a coordinate plane on squared graph paper. Locate and label these points:

1. $A(2, 5)$
2. $B(-2, 5)$
3. $C(-2, -5)$
4. $D(2, -5)$
5. $E(3\frac{1}{2}, -3)$
6. $F(0,3)$
7. $G(0, -5)$
8. $H(4, 0)$
9. $I(-6, 0)$

8–1 D

1. On a set of axes locate and label the following points: $A(1, 2)$; $B(-2, -4)$; $C(2\frac{1}{2}, 5)$; $D(-4, -8)$. Draw line segments from D to B; then from B to C; then from C to A. Name the figure formed by the line segments.
2. On a set of axes locate and label the following points: $A(2, 2)$; $B(-2, 2)$; $C(-2, -2)$; $D(2, -2)$. Connect these points with line segments in the order A, B, C, D. Name the figure formed by the line segments.
3. Find the area of the figure formed in Exercise 2.
4. Locate points $A(3, 0)$, $B(0, 4)$, and $C(0, 0)$ in a coordinate plane. Find the area of the triangle formed.
5. Find the distance from A to B in Exercise 4. (*Note:* Use the Pythagorean theorem.)
6. Use the ideas of Exercises 4 and 5 to find the distance from $A(-5, 0)$ to $B(0, -12)$.
7. Suppose that a and b are positive numbers. In which quadrant will each of the following points lie?
   (a) $(a, -6)$ (b) $(0, -6)$
   (c) $(0, a + b)$ (d) $(-b, -a)$
8. Locate $A(2, -6)$, $B(0, 0)$, $C(-1, 3)$, and $D(-2, 6)$. Do they seem to lie on the same line?

8-1 E

On a number line graph $P(b)$ and $Q(-b)$ if:

1. $b = 2$ **2.** $b = -4$ **3.** $b = 1\frac{1}{2}$ **4.** $b = -3$

5. $b = -5$ **6.** $b = 6$ **7.** $b = -10$ **8.** $b = 8$

9. In a coordinate plane plot these points: $A(1, 2)$, $B(2, 4)$, $C(4, 8)$, $D(5, 10)$. Do these points seem to lie on a straight line?

10. On your graph for Exercise 9 plot these points: $E(-1, -2)$, $F(-2, -4)$, $G(-4, -8)$, $H(-5, -10)$. Do these points seem to lie on a straight line with A, B, C, and D?

8-2 ADDITION OF POSITIVE AND NEGATIVE NUMBERS

Consider Figure 8–6. The length of $\overline{OC}$ is $3\frac{1}{2}$ units; of $\overline{OD}$, $3\frac{1}{2}$ units. This length is the number of units from the origin, without regard to direction, and is called the **absolute value** of the coordinate at C or D. The absolute value of a positive number is the number itself; the absolute value of a negative number is the number without the sign. We read $|b|$ as "the absolute value of b." Thus

$$|+3\tfrac{1}{2}| = |-3\tfrac{1}{2}| = 3\tfrac{1}{2},$$
$$|-5| = |+5| = 5,$$
$$|-b| = |+b|.$$

Since 0 is neither positive nor negative, $|0| = 0$.

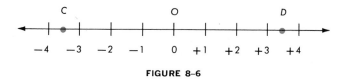

FIGURE 8-6

In adding positive and negative numbers we consider: (1) distance, that is, absolute value; (2) direction. On the number line, direction to the right is positive; to the left, negative. Thus in Figure 8–7 direction

from A to B is negative.

from B to C is negative.

from C to B is positive.

from B to A is positive.

FIGURE 8-7

To find the sum $(+3) + (+4)$ on the number line, as in Figure 8–8, move 3 units to the right, starting from the origin; then 4 more units to the right. Stop at the point with coordinate $+7$. The sum is $+7$.

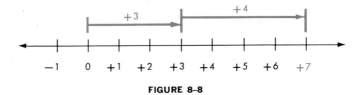

FIGURE 8-8

To find the sum $(-3) + (-4)$ on the number line, move 3 units to the left starting from the origin; then move 4 more units to the left. You stop at the point with coordinate -7. The sum is -7.

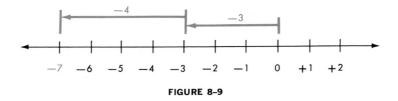

FIGURE 8-9

These two cases help to illustrate the following law.

II. **To add numbers having the same sign, add the absolute values of the numbers and affix the common sign.**

Consider finding the sum $(+5) + (-3)$ on the number line, as shown in Figure 8–10. Move 5 units to the right from the origin; then move 3 units to the left. You stop at the point with coordinate $+2$. The sum is $+2$.

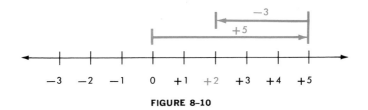

FIGURE 8-10

To find $(+3) + (-5)$ on the number line (Figure 8–10, page 357), move 3 units to the right of the origin; then move 5 units to the left. You stop at the point with coordinate -2. The sum is -2.

In each of these cases we have added two numbers with opposite signs. Notice that the sign of the answer in each case is the same as that of the number with the larger absolute value; that is, in Figure 8–10, $|+5| > |-3|$ and in Figure 8–11, $|-5| > |+3|$.

III.   To add two numbers having unlike signs, subtract their absolute values and affix to the answer the sign of the number having the greater absolute value.

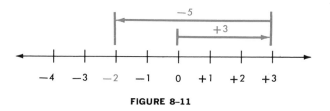

FIGURE 8–11

Example 1. Solve: $x = (-27) + (+13)$.

$$|-27| - |+13| = 14.$$

Since

$$|-27| > |+13|,$$

the answer must be negative: $x = -14$.

To add more than two signed numbers we apply laws II and III to find:

1. The sum of the positive addends
2. The sum of the negative addends
3. The sum of the results in steps 1 and 2

Example 2. Solve $x = (-5) + (+3) + (-2) + (-4) + (+7)$.

$$x = [(-5) + (-2) + (-4)] + [(+3) + (+7)]$$
$$x = (-11) + (+10)$$
$$x = -1$$

Exercises for Section 8–2

8–2 A

1. Solve for x:

(a) $x = |-9|$ (b) $x = |+15|$ (c) $x = |-15|$

(d) $x = |-14|$ (e) $x = |+12|$ (f) $x = |-105|$

2. Express without absolute value signs: (a) $|-12|$, (b) $|16 - 5|$, (c) $|3^2 - 15|$, (d) $|\sqrt{16} - 4.5|$.

If a statement is true, mark it true. If it is false, write a replacement for the symbol ($>$, $=$, $<$) to make it true.

3. $|-6| > 6$ **4.** $-3 = |3|$

5. $|-5| < 5$ **6.** $|-1| = -1$

7. $|-105| = 105$ **8.** $|-6| < 0$

9. $|-6| < +6$ **10.** $-7 < |7|$

11. $|-7| < 7$ **12.** $2^3 < |-9|$

13. $|21 - 17| < \sqrt{36} - 4$ **14.** $|(-8) + 5| < 3$

8–2 B

Solve for n:

1. $n = (+6) + (+8)$ **2.** $n = (-6) + (+8)$

3. $n = (-6) + (-8)$ **4.** $n = (+6) + (-8)$

5. $n = (+75) + (-75)$ **6.** $n = (+260) + (-195)$

7. $n = (-395) + (-208)$ **8.** $n = (-67.5) + (19.8)$

9. $n = (+18) + (-109)$ **10.** $n = (-64) + (-64)$

11. $n = (-7\frac{1}{2}) + (-14\frac{2}{3})$ **12.** $n = (2\frac{3}{8}) + (-5\frac{3}{4})$

8–2 C

Solve for x:

1. $x = (+4) + (+8) + (+16)$

2. $x = (-4) + (-8) + (-16)$

3. $x = (-4) + (+8) + (+16)$

4. $x = (-4) + (-6) + (+16)$

5. $x = (+4) + (+6) + (-16)$

6. $x = (+17) + (-6) + (-17)$

7. $x = (+21) + (-9) + (-13) + (-7)$

8. $x = (-12) + (-17) + (+98) + (-42)$

9. $x = (-75) + (-82) + (-139) + (+500)$

10. $x = (-16) + (+75) + (-19) + (-8)$

8-2 D

1. (a) Does $|+5| = +5$, that is, 5?
   (b) Does $|+16| = +16$, that is, 16?
   (c) Does $|+9| = +9$, that is, 9?
   (d) Does $|+8| = +8$, that is, 8?
2. For $N \geq 0$, does $|N| = N$? Consider Exercise 1.
3. Remember, the negative of a number is its opposite. Therefore, $-(+3) = -3$, and $-(-3) = +3$.
   (a) Does $|-5| = -(-5)$, that is, 5?
   (b) Does $|-16| = -(-16)$, that is, 16?
   (c) Does $|-9| = -(-9)$, that is, 9?
   (d) Does $|-8| = -(-8)$, that is, 8?
4. For $N < 0$, does $|N| = -N$? Consider Exercise 3.

A Definition

From Exercises 2 and 4, we define

$$|N| = N \text{ if } N \geq 0,$$
$$|N| = -N \text{ if } N < 0.$$

8-2 E

1. Suppose a student has $10 and owes $5. We may think of his wealth in dollars as $(+10) + (-5)$. Find his wealth.
2. Suppose a student is $5 in debt. He then earns $10. Find his wealth by adding.
3. In football a team has these results in four plays: a loss of 5 yards, a gain of 8 yards, a loss of 2 yards, and a gain of 14 yards. Find the total: $(-5) + (+8) + (-2) + (+14)$.
4. On a certain beach the low tides each day for a week were: -1.1 feet, -0.7 foot, -0.1 foot, -0.6 foot, 1.4 feet, 2.1 feet, and 2.8 feet. Find the mean low tide (the average) for the week.
5. In one town the temperature was recorded at 2:00 P.M. each day during the first 10 days of January. The temperatures were: 10°, 13°, 6°, 1° below zero, 3° below zero, 3°, 4°, 1°, 5° below zero, and 8° below zero. Find the mean daily temperature.
6. A small business establishment had the following record of profit and loss for 12 months of a certain year. Profits were $675, $1025, $275, $985, $605.75, $1109.50, $875.05, $195.27,

and $205.37. The losses were: $60.33, $72.48, and $275.38. Find the mean profit.

7. Is the set of all integers closed over addition? (*Note:* Is the sum of any two integers an integer?)

8-3 SUBTRACTION OF POSITIVE AND NEGATIVE NUMBERS

Consider this problem in subtraction: $9 - 4$. You know that the answer is 5. We may think of the problem in this way: "How much must we *add* to 4 to get 9?" We must add 5. That is, since $4 + 5 = 9$, then $9 - 4 = 5$.

On the number line in Figure 8–12, we think, "How far is it from point *A* to point *B*?" The *direction* from *A* to *B* is positive; the *distance* is 5 units. Hence $9 - 4 = 5$.

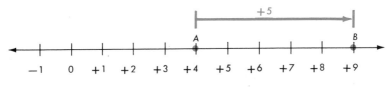

FIGURE 8–12

Example 1. Solve: (a) $x = (-6) - (+2)$; (b) $x = (-6) - (-2)$; (c) $x = (-2) - (-6)$; (d) $x = (+2) - (-6)$.

(a) In Figure 8–13(a) the direction is negative; the distance is 8. So, $x = -8$.

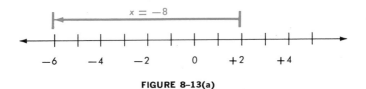

FIGURE 8–13(a)

(b) In Figure 8–13(b) the direction is negative; the distance is 4. So, $x = -4$.

FIGURE 8–13(b)

(c) In Figure 8–13(c) the direction is positive; the distance is 4. So, $x = +4$.

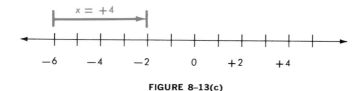

FIGURE 8–13(c)

(d) In Figure 8–13(d) the direction is positive; the distance is 8. So, $x = +8$.

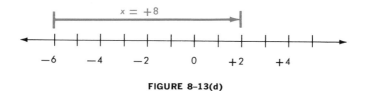

FIGURE 8–13(d)

The law of subtraction is presented in IV.

IV.   **To subtract a number *b* from a number *a*, we add the negative of *b* to *a*. That is,**

$$a - b = a + (-b).$$

Example 2. Use the law of subtraction to solve each part of Example 1.

(a) If $x = (-6) - (+2)$, then

$$x = (-6) + (-2),$$

and

$$x = -8. \quad \text{By II, Section 8–2}$$

(b) If $x = (-6) - (-2)$, then

$$x = (-6) + (+2),$$

and

$$x = -4. \quad \text{By III, Section 8–2}$$

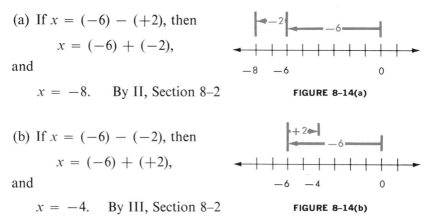

FIGURE 8–14(a)

FIGURE 8–14(b)

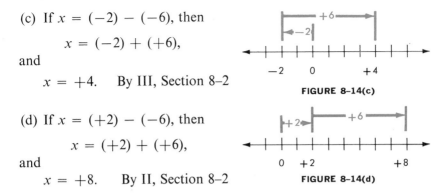

(c) If $x = (-2) - (-6)$, then

$$x = (-2) + (+6),$$

and

$$x = +4. \quad \text{By III, Section 8-2}$$

FIGURE 8-14(c)

(d) If $x = (+2) - (-6)$, then

$$x = (+2) + (+6),$$

and

$$x = +8. \quad \text{By II, Section 8-2}$$

FIGURE 8-14(d)

Observe that the answers in Examples 1 and 2 are the same.

Exercises for Section 8-3

8-3 A

Solve for y:

1. $y = (+18) - (+12)$
2. $y = (-18) - (+12)$
3. $y = (+18) - (-12)$
4. $y = (-18) - (-12)$
5. $y = (17\frac{1}{8}) - (-7\frac{1}{8})$
6. $y = (+6\frac{1}{2}) - (2\frac{3}{4})$
7. $y = (+19.7) - (9.8)$
8. $y = (43.7) - (29.8)$
9. $y = (+19.3) - (+71.6)$
10. $y = (18.25) - (+48.36)$
11. $y = (+12.75) - (-12.75)$
12. $y = (-12.75) - (-12.75)$

8-3 B

Solve for x:

1. $x = (-10) - (-12)$
2. $x = (-20) - (-20)$
3. $x = (-40) - (-40)$
4. $x = (-70) - (-70)$
5. $x = (-70) - (-100)$
6. $x = (-70) - (-200)$
7. $x = (+20.4) - (-20.4)$
8. $x = (+16.1) - (-16.1)$
9. $x = (+200) - (-200)$
10. $x = |-50| - (-50)$
11. $x = |-60| - (-60)$
12. $x = |-70| - (-70)$

8-3 C

1. In a certain city the low temperature for a day was $7°$ below zero; the high, $18°$ above zero. Find the difference. (*Note: How far is it* from -7 to $+18$? That is, find $(+18) - (-7)$.)

Exercises 8–3 C continued on page 364.

2. As in Exercise 1, find the difference on a day when the low was $-20°$ and the high was $+40°$.

3. A student has \$150. He needs \$275 to make a down payment on a car. *How far* is he from the down payment? That is, find $275 - 150$.

4. Consider a student who is \$150 in debt. He needs \$275 for a down payment on a car. *How far* is he from the down payment? That is, find $275 - (-150)$.

5. A student's debt last week was \$18; this week, \$7. *How far* is it from last week's debt to this week's debt? That is, find $(-7) - (-18)$.

6. At noon, the temperature was $35°$. At midnight, it was $19°$ below zero. Find the change in temperature over the course of this 12-hour interval.

7. In a card game a student was 195 points "in the hole." How many points did he need to win if the winning score was 500 points?

8. Suppose that $n + 7 = 0$. Use a signed number to represent n.

9. Solve for n:

(a) $n + 8 = 10$ (b) $n + 5 = 12$
(c) $n + 10 = 15$ (d) $n + (-10) = 15$
(e) $n + (-8) = 8$ (f) $n + (-12) = 12$
(g) $n + (-12) = 1$ (h) $n + (-98) = 80$

10. Is the set of all integers closed over subtraction?

8-4 MULTIPLICATION AND DIVISION OF POSITIVE AND NEGATIVE NUMBERS

To find 3×5, one may observe that

$$3 \times 5 = 5 + 5 + 5, \tag{1}$$

that is, the product is equal to the sum found by adding 3 fives. From long practice in arithmetic, students should observe that *the product of two positive numbers is a positive number.* In (1), for example, $(+3) \times (+5) = +15$.

As in (1), note that

$$3 \times (-5) = (-5) + (-5) + (-5) \tag{2}$$
$$= -15 \qquad \text{By II, Section 8-2}$$

The commutative law for multiplication holds for all real numbers. Thus it follows that

$$3 \times (-5) = (-5) \times 3 = -15. \qquad (3)$$

From (2) and (3) it would appear that *the product of a positive number and a negative number is a negative number.*

Now consider the products in (4), (5), (6), and (7).

$$(-5) \times 3 = -15, \qquad (4)$$
$$(-5) \times 2 = -10, \qquad (5)$$
$$(-5) \times 1 = -5, \qquad (6)$$
$$(-5) \times 0 = 0. \qquad (7)$$

Notice that as we decrease the second factor from 3 to 0, the products increase from -15 to 0. It seems logical that the pattern will continue in this way:

$$(-5) \times (-1) = +5, \qquad (8)$$
$$(-5) \times (-2) = +10, \qquad (9)$$
$$(-5) \times (-3) = +15. \qquad (10)$$

The work in (4) through (10) does not represent a proof, but should give the student some appreciation of the fact that the product of two negative numbers is a positive number.

We have these rules for multiplication of signed numbers.

V.   **The product of two numbers having the same sign is positive.** (See (1) and (8) through (10).)

VI.   **The product of two numbers having unlike signs is negative.** (See (2) and (3).)

Division is the inverse of multiplication; that is, division "undoes" multiplication. Our laws for division must be compatible with those for multiplication. Consider the following example.

Example 1. Find $(+24) \div (-3)$. That is, find a number n such that $(-3) \times n = +24$.

$$(-3) \times n = +24$$

By V, n must be negative. Does $(-3) \times (-8) = +24$? It does. Hence we have

$$(+24) \div (-3) = -8.$$

Think of Example 1 in another way. To divide by a number we multiply by its reciprocal (for example, $24 \div 3 = 24 \times \frac{1}{3}$). Then

$$(+24) \div (-3) = (+24) \times (-\tfrac{1}{3})$$
$$= -8. \qquad \text{By V}$$

VII.   **The quotient of two numbers with unlike signs is negative.** (See Example 1.)

We know that $(+24) \div (+3) = +8$. In fact in all cases the quotient of two positive numbers is a positive number. However we have the problem of the quotient of two negative numbers. Consider Example 2.

Example 2. Find $(-24) \div (-3)$. That is, find a number n such that $(-3) \times n = -24$.

$$(-3) \times n = -24.$$

By V, n must be positive. Does $(-3) \times (+8) = -24$? It does. Hence we have

$$(-24) \div (-3) = +8.$$

Think of Example 2 in another way. Use the concept of multiplying by the reciprocal:

$$(-24) \div (-3) = (-24) \times -\tfrac{1}{3}$$
$$= +8. \qquad \text{By V}$$

VIII.   **The quotient of two numbers with the same sign is positive.** (See Example 2.)

Exercises for Section 8-4

8-4 A

Perform the indicated operations:

 1. $(-8) \times (+6)$ 2. $(+6) \times (-8)$ 3. $(+8) \times (-6)$
 4. $(+8) \times (+6)$ 5. $(-8) \times (-6)$ 6. $(-12) \times (-2)$
 7. $(+12) \times (+2)$ 8. $(-12) \times (+2)$ 9. $(+12) \times (-2)$
10. $(-2) \times (+7)$ 11. $(-15) \times (-15)$ 12. $(-3) \times (-105)$
13. $(-3) \times (+120)$ 14. $(+51) \times (-16)$ 15. $(+2\tfrac{1}{2}) \times (-3\tfrac{1}{2})$

8-4 B

When more than two signed factors are involved, we first find the product of two of them. We then find the product of this answer and the next factor, and so on. That is, we apply the associative law. For example,

$$(-2) \times (+3) \times (-8) = [(-2) \times (+3)] \times (-8)$$
$$= (-6) \times (-8) = +48.$$

Evaluate:

1. $(-2) \times (-3) \times (+6)$ 2. $(-5) \times (+6) \times (+8)$
3. $(+7) \times (+5) \times (-4)$ 4. $(+12) \times (-6) \times (-3)$
5. $(-16) \times (-2) \times (-3)$ 6. $(-5) \times (+5) \times (-5)$
7. $(-2) \times (-3) \times (-6) \times (-1)$
8. $(-4) \times (+4) \times (+5) \times (-2)$
9. $(-6) \times (-6) \times (-6) \times (-1)$
10. $(+2) \times (+2) \times (-2) \times (-100)$

8-4 C

Evaluate:

1. $(-2) \times (-3)$
2. $(-2) \times (-3) \times (-1)$
3. $(-2) \times (-3) \times (-1) \times (-4)$
4. $(-2) \times (-3) \times (-1) \times (-4) \times (-5)$
5. $(-2) \times (-3) \times (-1) \times (-4) \times (-5) \times (-\frac{1}{2})$
6. $(-2) \times (-2) \times (-2)$
7. Do the answers for Exercises 1, 3, and 5 have the same sign? Do the answers for Exercises 2, 4, and 6 have the same sign?
8. Write a rule for finding the sign of a product based on the number of negative factors involved.

8-4 D

Find the quotients by inspection:

1. $(-16) \div (+2)$ 2. $(-48) \div (+6)$ 3. $(-10) \div (+2)$
4. $(+12) \div (-3)$ 5. $(+15) \div (-5)$ 6. $(-20) \div (-4)$
7. $(-36) \div (-9)$ 8. $(-40) \div (-5)$ 9. $(-24) \div (-3)$
10. $(-45) \div (-9)$ 11. $(-24) \div (+24)$ 12. $0 \div (-6)$
13. $0 \div (+6)$ 14. $(-24) \div (-24)$ 15. $(+24) \div (-24)$

8-4 E

Solve for n:

1. $n = \dfrac{(+4) \times (-5)}{(+2)}$

2. $n = \dfrac{(-6) \times (-8)}{(-4)}$

3. $n = \dfrac{(-9) \times (-15)}{(+9)}$

4. $n = \dfrac{(-6) \times (-3\frac{3}{4})}{(-1)}$

5. $n = \dfrac{(-200)}{(-4) \times (+20)}$

6. $n = \dfrac{(+140)}{(-7) \times (+15)}$

7. $n = \dfrac{(-6) \times (+24)}{(-5) \times (-40)}$

8. $n = \dfrac{(-12) \times (-50)}{(-200)}$

9. $n = \dfrac{(-6) \times (-8) \times (-4)}{(-2) \times (-12)}$

10. $n = \dfrac{(-1\frac{1}{2}) \times (+12\frac{2}{3})}{(-\frac{3}{4})}$

8-4 F

Consider

$$(-2)^2 = (-2) \times (-2) = +4$$

and

$$(-2)^3 = (-2) \times (-2) \times (-2)$$
$$= (+4) \times (-2) = -8.$$

Evaluate:

1. $(-1)^2$ 2. $(-3)^2$ 3. $(-4)^2$ 4. $(-1)^3$
5. $(-2)^3$ 6. $(-3)^3$ 7. $(-1)^4$ 8. $(-3)^4$
9. $(-5)^4$ 10. $(-1)^5$ 11. $(-2)^5$ 12. $(-5)^5$

8-4 G

1. Does $(+5) + (-5) = 0$? Explain.
2. Does $(-6) \times [(+5) + (-5)] = (-30) + (-6)(-5)$? Explain.
3. Does $(-6) \times [(+5) + (-5)] = (-6)(0) = 0$? Explain.
4. Does $(-30) + (-6)(-5) = 0$? See Exercises 2 and 3.
5. If $(-30) + n = 0$, solve for n.   That is, from Exercise 4, $n = (-6)(-5)$.   (*Note:* We have $(-30) + n = 0$ so n must equal $+30$.   Also, we have $n = (-6)(-5)$ so $(-6)(-5)$ must equal $+30$.   Hence the product of the two negative factors must be positive.)
6. Consider a student whose college expenses are \$5 per day. He pays these from a savings account. Suppose that it is the fourth day of school.

(a) Will his account be less by $15 after 3 more days of school? That is, does $3 \times (-5) = -15$?

(b) Was his account greater by $15 three days ago? That is, does $(-3) \times (-5) = +15$?

8–5 EQUATIONS

Using our knowledge of the set of real numbers and Axioms I and II, we can now solve linear equations with negative roots. For example, we know that there are numbers which will satisfy equations such as $n + 8 = 3$.

Example 1. Solve: $n + 8 = 3$.

$$n + 8 - (+8) = 3 - (+8)$$
$$n = (3) - (+8)$$
$$n = -5$$

By Axiom II, subtract $+8$ from both sides.

Check: Does $(-5) + 8 = 3$? Yes.

Example 2. Solve: $-2x - 8 = 3$.

$$-2x - 8 + (+8) = 3 + (+8)$$
$$-2x = 11$$
$$\frac{-2x}{-2} = \frac{11}{-2}$$
$$x = -\frac{11}{2}$$

By Axiom II, add $+8$ to each side.

By Axiom I, divide both sides by (-2).

Check: Does $(-2)(-\frac{11}{2}) - 8 = 3$? Does $11 - 8 = 3$? Yes.

Example 3. Solve: $\dfrac{3x}{-2} = 12$.

$$(-2)\left(\frac{3x}{-2}\right) = (-2)(12)$$
$$3x = -24$$
$$x = -8$$

Multiply both sides by (-2).

Divide both sides by 3.

Check: Does $\dfrac{3(-8)}{-2} = 12$? Does $3(4) = 12$? Yes.

Example 4. The sum of 3 times a number x and -483 is 504. Find x.

$$
\begin{aligned}
3x + (-483) &= 504 \\
3x + (-483) + 483 &= 504 + 483 \qquad \text{Add 483 to each side.} \\
3x &= 504 + 483 \\
3x &= 987 \\
x &= 329 \qquad \text{Divide each side by 3.}
\end{aligned}
$$

The number is 329.

Exercises for Section 8-5

8-5 A

Solve and check:

1. $x + 2 = 8$ 2. $x + 8 = 2$ 3. $x + 19 = 19$
4. $x + 7 = -7$ 5. $x - 7 = -7$ 6. $2x = 8$
7. $2x = -8$ 8. $-2x = 8$ 9. $-2x = -8$
10. $x - 3\frac{1}{2} = -6\frac{1}{8}$ 11. $7\frac{1}{4} + x = -7\frac{1}{2}$ 12. $15 - x = 85$

8-5 B

Solve and check:

1. $2m - 1 = 17$ 2. $2m - 1 = -17$
3. $1 - 2m = 19$ 4. $-5m - 7 = -18$
5. $-7 - 3m = -7$ 6. $-19m + 31 = -102$
7. $\dfrac{x}{-3} = -3$ 8. $\dfrac{x}{-3} = 3$
9. $\dfrac{2x}{-5} = 18$ 10. $\dfrac{-x}{5} = -5$
11. $\dfrac{-x}{-5} = -5$ 12. $\dfrac{-4x}{13} = -8$

8-5 C

Solve and check:

1. $-3x + 17 = -40$ 2. $\dfrac{-3x}{2} = 6$
3. $\dfrac{-5x}{21} = -20$ 4. $\dfrac{-3x}{-1} = -1$
5. $15x - (-2) = 10$ 6. $3 = -15 - 2x$
7. $17 - 12x = -45$ 8. $-28 - 15x = -15$
9. $-28x - 28 = 28$ 10. $375 - 205x = -650$
11. $17 = -85 - x$ 12. $-64 = -3x + 200$

8-5 D

The formula $C = \frac{5}{9}(F - 32)$ is used to determine the centigrade temperature C when the Fahrenheit temperature F is known. For example, to find C when $F = 14$ we substitute and solve.

$$C = \frac{5}{9}(F - 32)$$
$$C = \frac{5}{9}(14 - 32) = \frac{5}{9}(-18)$$
$$C = -10$$

Use the formula to find C for these Fahrenheit temperatures:

1. 48°	**2.** 60°	**3.** 212°	**4.** 32°
5. 14°	**6.** 5°	**7.** 0°	**8.** −4°
9. −23°	**10.** −31°	**11.** −68°	**12.** −88°

8-5 E

Substitute the value given in each formula; then solve for the remaining letter:

1. $S = 16t^2$, $t = 3$ **2.** $S = 16t^2$, $t = -2$

3. $y = 2x - 8$, $x = 3$ **4.** $y = +3x - 40$, $x = 12$

5. $y = 10 - 3x$, $x = -2$ **6.** $V = 32t$, $t = 2$

7. $V = 32t$, $t = -3$ **8.** $F = \frac{9}{5}C + 32$, $C = 0$

9. $F = \frac{9}{5}C + 32$, $C = -10$ **10.** $F = \frac{9}{5}C + 32$, $C = -\frac{160}{9}$

8-5 F

1. The sum of three consecutive integers is zero. Find the integers. (*Note:* Let n, $n + 1$, and $n + 2$ represent the integers. Then $n + (n + 1) + (n + 2) = 0$.)

2. The sum of a number n and -6237 is 10,103. Find n.

3. The product of a number n and -31 is 9300. Find n.

4. If a number x is divided by $-3\frac{1}{2}$, the quotient is 64. Find x.

5. If 173 is added to twice a number x, the sum is -647. Find x.

6. If twice a number x is divided by $-6\frac{1}{2}$, the quotient is 834. Find x.

7. The temperature at sunrise was $n°$ below zero; at noon, it was 53°. If the temperature was higher by 64° at noon than at sunrise, find n. (*Note:* Does $n + 64 = 53$?)

8. In January a dealer's profits were x dollars; in February, $1895. If February profits exceeded January profits by $2020, find x. (*Note:* Does $x + 2020 = 1895$?)

Exercises 8–5 F continued on page 372.

9. A ball was thrown into the air. After 3 seconds it was x feet high. After 4 seconds it was $x + (-16)$ feet, or 128 feet, high. Find x. (*Note:* $x + (-16) = 128$.)

10. A rocket was shot into the air. After 15 seconds it was x feet above the ground. After 18 seconds it was $x + (-144)$ feet, or 3456 feet, above the ground. Find x.

8-5 G

If $n^2 = K$ we say that n is a square root of K. The number 16 can be factored as $16 = (+4) \times (+4)$ or as $16 = (-4) \times (-4)$. Thus the equation $x^2 = 16$ has two solutions, $x = 4$ and $x = -4$. These answers can be written as $x = \pm 4$, read, "plus or minus 4."

In Exercises 1–9 solve for two values of x. If the number is not a perfect square, use the Table of Square Roots in the Appendix to find the answers to the nearest hundredth.

1. $x^2 = 4$ 2. $x^2 = 9$ 3. $x^2 = 75$

4. $x^2 = 5$ 5. $x^2 = 121$ 6. $x^2 = 114$

7. $x^2 = 19$ 8. $x^2 - 3 = 61$ 9. $x^2 - 1 = 15$

10. In Figure 8–15 arc ABC represents an arch to be built of steel; the arch is a part of a circle as shown. In geometry it is known that $x^2 = 12 \times 48$. Solve for x. (*Note:* The builder will need to find x precisely.)

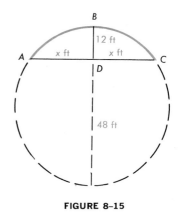

FIGURE 8–15

11. In problem 13 solve for x, correct to the nearest hundredth, if the diameter of the circle is 60 and $BD = 10$.

8-6 GRAPH OF LINEAR EQUATIONS OVER ALL QUADRANTS

In Section 5–3 we studied the graphs of linear equations in quadrant I. In an equation such as $y = 3x$, we were restricted to the set of positive numbers for the domain and for the range. Now we can expand the domain and the range to include all real numbers.

Example 1. Plot the graph of $y = 3x$.

We choose arbitrary values for x (such as -3, -1, 0, 2, and 4) and find values for y:

x	y
-3	-9
-1	-3
0	0
2	6
4	12

If $x = -3$, $y = 3 \times (-3) = -9$.
If $x = -1$, $y = 3 \times (-1) = -3$.
If $x = 0$, $y = 3 \times 0 = 0$.
If $x = 2$, $y = 3 \times 2 = 6$.
If $x = 4$, $y = 3 \times 4 = 12$.

In a coordinate plane we plot the points with coordinates given in the table; these points lie on a straight line. In fact, there is a one-to-one correspondence between the points on the line (the graph) and the pairs of numbers which satisfy the equation $y = 3x$.

Example 2. From Figure 8-16 find the coordinates of point A. Of point B. Of point C.

Point A has coordinates (5, 15). Point B has coordinates $(-2, -6)$. Point C has coordinates $(-5, -15)$.

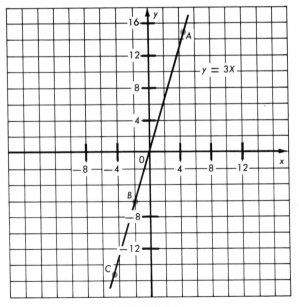

FIGURE 8-16

Exercises for Section 8-6

8-6 A

Make a list of three or four ordered pairs for each equation and graph the result:

1. $y = 5x$
2. $y = 2x - 1$
3. $y = \frac{1}{2}x + 1$
4. $y = 3 - 2x$
5. $y = 2x - 10$
6. $E = 10R - 10$
7. $V = 4t - 20$
8. $P = 2l + 10$
9. $C = \frac{5}{9}(F - 32)$

8-6 B

1. Use the formula $F = 9C/5 + 32$ to complete the table shown. Thus if $C = -40$,

$$F = \frac{9(-40)}{5} + 32,$$

that is, $C = -40$ and $F = -40$.

C	-40	-20	-5	0	5	10	40
F	-40						

2. In a coordinate plane plot the points indicated in Exercise 1. Connect them with a straight line. (*Note:* It will be helpful to use a full sheet of graph paper, marked 10 squares to the inch. Place the C-axis (horizontal axis) 3 inches from the bottom of the grid; the F-axis 2 inches from the left side of the grid. Let 1 inch represent 20 on the C-scale; let 1 inch represent 40 on the F-scale.

3. From the graph that you made in Exercise 2 find F when $C = 100$. This is the boiling point of water under normal conditions at sea level.

4. In Exercise 2 find the coordinates of the points at which the graph crosses the C-axis and the F-axis.

5. From your graph in Exercise 2 find the missing number in the pair (C, F):

(a) $(25, F)$ (b) $(-10, F)$

(c) $(-15, F)$ (d) $(-25, F)$

(e) $(30, F)$ (f) $(C, 113)$

(g) $(C, 95)$ (h) $(C, -31)$

8-6 C

1. A racing car approaches a check point C from point A at 60 meters per second, and continues at this speed through point B (Figure 8–17). Thus $d = 60t$ from A to B. Make a graph, as in Figure 8–18, for $-1 \le t \le 5$. (*Note:* $d = -60$ when $t = -1$)

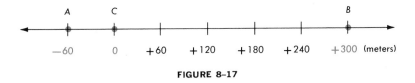

FIGURE 8-17

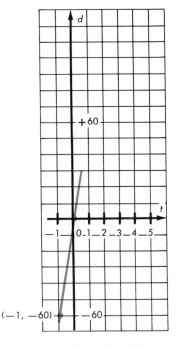

FIGURE 8-18

2. From your graph in Exercise 1 find the missing coordinate in these ordered pairs (t, d):
   - (a) $(-\frac{1}{2}, d)$
   - (b) $(0, d)$
   - (c) $(\frac{1}{2}, d)$
   - (d) $(1\frac{1}{2}, d)$
   - (e) $(2\frac{1}{2}, d)$
   - (f) $(t, 270)$
   - (g) $(t, 210)$
   - (h) $(t, 195)$
   - (i) $(t, 275)$

Exercises 8–6 C continued on page 376.

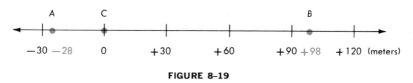

FIGURE 8–19

3. A racing car approaches a check point C from point A according to the formula $d = t^3 - 27$, where t is in seconds and d is in meters. Thus for $t = -1$, $d = (-1)^3 - 27 = -28$. Complete the table below.

t	-3	-2	-1	0	$+1$	$+2$	$+3$	$+4$	$+5$
d	-54			-27					

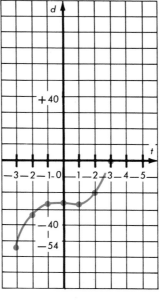

FIGURE 8–20

4. From your table in Exercise 3 make a graph of $d = t^3 - 27$ for $-3 \leq t \leq +5$.

5. Is the graph in Exercise 4 a straight line? (*Note:* The graph of a linear equation, such as $2x + 3y = 5$, is a straight line. If an equation contains a power of a variable other than the first power, as t^3 in $d = t^3 - 27$, the graph is not a straight line.)

■ 8-7 ADDITION AND SUBTRACTION OF POLYNOMIALS

In Section 1–4 polynomials in ten were used to express numbers. Later, in Section 1–10 polynomials in six were used. For example,

$$231_{\text{ten}} = (2 \times 10^2) + (3 \times 10^1) + 1, \tag{1}$$
$$231_{\text{six}} = (2 \times 6^2) + (3 \times 6^1) + 1. \tag{2}$$

Polynomials in which letters represent numbers are expressed in a similar way. For example,

$$3x^2 + 2x + 4 \text{ is a polynomial in } x; \tag{3}$$
$$4b^3 + 2b^2 + b + 3 \text{ is a polynomial in } b. \tag{4}$$

Given a value for the variable, we can evaluate a polynomial, as in equations (1) and (2).

Example 1. If $x = 5$ what number is represented by the polynomial $3x^2 + 2x + 4$?

$$\begin{aligned}
3x^2 + 2x + 4 &= (3 \times 5^2) + (2 \times 5^1) + 4 \\
&= 75 + 10 + 4 \\
&= 89
\end{aligned}$$

The polynomial represents the number 89.

Example 2. If $b = 6$ what number is represented by the polynomial $4b^3 + 2b^2 + b + 3$?

$$\begin{aligned}
4b^3 + 2b^2 + b + 3 &= (4 \times 6^3) + (2 \times 6^2) + (1 \times 6^1) + 3 \\
&= 864 + 72 + 6 + 3 \\
&= 945
\end{aligned}$$

The polynomial represents the number 945.

Addition and subtraction with polynomials relate to the distributive law. Thus

$$3 \text{ tens} + 5 \text{ tens} = (3 + 5) \text{ tens} \tag{5}$$
$$= 8 \text{ tens} = 80.$$

That is,

$$(3 \times 10) + (5 \times 10) = (3 + 5) \times 10$$
$$= 80.$$

$$3 \text{ hundreds} + 5 \text{ hundreds} = (3 + 5) \text{ hundreds} \tag{6}$$
$$= 8 \text{ hundreds} = 800.$$

That is,

$$(3 \times 10^2) + (5 \times 10^2) = (3 + 5) \times 10^2$$
$$= 800.$$

Remember, we add only like units. In (5) the like units are tens; in (6) the like units are hundreds.

Example 3. Find the sum of $7x^2$ and $8x^2$.

$$7x^2 + 8x^2 = (7 + 8)x^2$$
$$= 15x^2$$

The unit in each addend is x^2.

Example 4. Find the sum of $x^2 + 3x + 4$ and $x^2 + 3$.

$$\begin{array}{l} x^2 + 3x + 4 \\ \underline{x^2 \qquad\;\; + 3} \\ 2x^2 + 3x + 7 \end{array}$$ Align like units. Add as shown.

Note that 5 tens $+$ 3 hundreds $\neq$ 8 tens; 5 tens $+$ 3 hundreds $\neq$ 8 hundreds; and $5x + 3x^2 \neq 8x$ and $5x + 3x^2 \neq 8x^2$. The units in each case are not alike.

Example 5. Find $7x - 3x$.

$$\begin{aligned} 7x - 3x &= 7x - (+3x) \\ &= 7x + (-3x) &&\text{Definition of subtraction} \\ &= [7 + (-3)]x &&\text{Distributive property} \\ &= 4x \end{aligned}$$

Example 6. From $7x^2 - 3x + 11$ subtract $3x^2 + 5x - 6$.

$$
\begin{array}{rrrrrr}
7x^2 & - & 3x & + & 11 \\
3x^2 & + & 5x & + & -6 \\
\hline
[(7) + (-3)]x^2 & + & [(-3) + (-5)]x & + & [(+11) + (+6)] & = \\
4x^2 & + & & (-8x) & + & 17
\end{array}
$$

The difference is $4x^2 - 8x + 17$.

Example 7. Simplify $4x^3 + x^2 - 5x + 7x^3 - 6x^2 + 2x + x - 5$.

First, using the commutative and associative properties, we group in terms of like units:

$$
\begin{array}{rrrrr}
(4x^3 + 7x^3) + (x^2 - 6x^2) + (-5x + 2x + x) + (-5) & = \\
11x^3 & + & (-5x^2) & + & (-2x) & + (-5) & = \\
11x^3 & - & 5x^2 & - & 2x & - & 5.
\end{array}
$$

The answer is $11x^3 - 5x^2 - 2x - 5$.

Exercises for Section 8-7

8-7 A

Perform the indicated operations:

1. 2 tens $+$ 7 tens

2. 3 hundreds $+$ 9 hundreds

3. 5 tenths $+$ 7 tenths

4. 3 ninths $+$ 4 ninths

5. 7 ones $+$ 9 ones

6. $6x + 2x$

7. $3x + 9x$

8. $5x + 6x + (-4x)$

9. $2a + 7a + 121a$

10. $1316r + 243r + (-67r)$

8-7 B

Evaluate each polynomial when $x = 3$:

1. $x^2 + 7x + 93$

2. $2x^2 + 8x - 14$

3. $3x^2 + 11x - 12$

4. $x^3 - 5$

5. $7x^3 + x + 121$

6. $-x^3 + 125x + 10$

7. $-3x^2 + 15x - 11$

8. $-7x^2 + 70x + 7$

9. $15x^3 - 200x + 100$

10. $9x^3 + 9x^2 + 9x + 1$

8-7 C

Add:

1. $x^3 + x^2 + x + 5$
   $2x^3 + 3x^2 + 3x - 10$

2. $3x^3 - 7x^2 - 8x - 6$
   $-5x^3 + 2x^2 + 2x + 4$

3. $7a^3 + 6a^2 + 2a - 5$
   $3a^3 + 5a^2 - 3a + 12$

4. $7c^3 - 8c^2 + 9c - 10$
   $6c^3 + c^2 + c - 1$

5. $10c^4 + 5c^3 + 6c - 2$
   $-2c^4 - 4c^3 + c^2 + 2c - 3$

6. $8h^4 + 3h^3 + 7h - 21$
   $5h^4 - 12h^3 + 8h^2 - 83$

8-7 D

Subtract:

1. $7x^2 + x + 5$
   $2x^2 - 5x - 10$

2. $3r^2 + 7r - 16$
   $4r^2 - 2r + 9$

3. $6s^2 + 3s - 2$
   $5s^2 - 5s - 7$

4. $8a^3 + 7a^2 - 6a - 149$
   $-3a^3 - 7a^2 - 6a + 287$

5. $16b^3 - 12b - 196$
   $-12b^3 - 9b^2 - 684$

6. $21t^3 + 16t^2 - 5016$
   $-9t^3 - 64t + 3087$

8-7 E

Simplify:

1. $(x^2 + 9x + 8) + (7x^2 + 203x - 1076)$
2. $(7x^3 + 8x^2 + 16x - 29) + (216x^3 + 181x^2 - 175x - 633)$
3. $(8a^3 - 8a^2 - 16) + (165a^3 - 160a - 2147)$
4. $(16b^3 - 24b^2 + 48b - 408) - (21b^3 - 36b - 806)$
5. $(519x^2 - 803x + 977) - (-620x^2 - 603x + 677)$

8-7 F

Express each base six number as a polynomial in 6:

1. 25_{six}
2. 31_{six}
3. 52_{six}
4. 112_{six}
5. 524_{six}
6. 135_{six}
7. 1111_{six}
8. 1234_{six}
9. 2135_{six}
10. 3333_{six}
11. 4444_{six}
12. 5555_{six}

■ 8-8 MULTIPLICATION AND DIVISION OF POLYNOMIALS

Observe that 10^2 means 10×10 and 10^3 means $10 \times 10 \times 10$. Then it follows that

$$10^2 \times 10^3 = (10 \times 10) \times (10 \times 10 \times 10)$$
$$= 10^5.$$

If we add the exponents 2 and 3, we find the exponent 5. Similarly,

$$2^3 \times 2^4 = (2 \times 2 \times 2) \times (2 \times 2 \times 2 \times 2) = 2^7,$$

that is,

$$2^{3+4}.$$

The following law applies for multiplication of powers.

IX. $a^m \times a^n = a^{m+n}$

The following examples illustrate the law.

$$10^3 \times 10^4 = 10^{3+4} = 10^7; \text{ that is, } 10{,}000{,}000 \qquad (1)$$

$$10^{-3} \times 10^2 = 10^{-3+2} = 10^{-1}; \text{ that is, } 0.1 \qquad (2)$$

$$2^{-2} \times 2^3 \times 2^4 = 2^{-2+3+4} = 2^5; \text{ that is, } 32 \qquad (3)$$

$$x^2 \times x^3 \times x^{-4} = x^{2+3-4} = x^1; \text{ that is, } x \qquad (4)$$

The factors in each example are powers with the same base, and thus fit the pattern in IX. Now observe these examples.

$$3^2 \times 4^3 \neq 3^{2+3} \qquad (5)$$

and

$$3^2 \times 4^3 \neq 4^{2+3}$$

since the bases are not alike.

$$a^3 \times x^4 \neq a^{3+4} \qquad (6)$$

and

$$a^3 \times x^4 \neq x^{3+4}$$

since the bases are not alike.

Now consider some examples in division such as those given on the following page.

Example 1. Find $10^5 \div 10^2$.

$$\frac{10^5}{10^2} = \frac{10 \times 10 \times 10 \times 10 \times 10}{10 \times 10}$$

$$= 10 \times 10 \times 10 \times \frac{10 \times 10}{10 \times 10} \qquad \left(Note: \frac{10 \times 10}{10 \times 10} = 1\right)$$

$$= 10 \times 10 \times 10 = 1000$$

The answer can be expressed as 10^{5-2}. Note that

$$10^{5-2} = 10^3 = 1000.$$

Example 2. Find $10^2 \div 10^5$.

$$\frac{10^2}{10^5} = \frac{10 \times 10}{10 \times 10 \times 10 \times 10 \times 10}$$

$$= \frac{10 \times 10}{10 \times 10} \times \frac{1}{10 \times 10 \times 10}$$

$$= \frac{1}{10^3} = 0.001$$

The answer can be expressed as $10^{2-5} = 10^{-3}$. Note that

$$10^{-3} = \frac{1}{10^3} = 0.001.$$

The following law applies for division of powers.

$$\textbf{X.} \qquad \boldsymbol{a^m \div a^n = a^{m-n}}$$

The following examples illustrate the law.

Example 3. Find: (a) $\dfrac{x^7}{x^2}$ (b) $\dfrac{x^3}{x^5}$ (c) $\dfrac{14x^2}{2x^3}$.

(a) $\dfrac{x^7}{x^2} = x^{7-2} = x^5$

(b) $\dfrac{x^3}{x^5} = x^{3-5} = x^{-2} = \dfrac{1}{x^2}$

(c) $\dfrac{14x^2}{2x^3} = \dfrac{14}{2} \times \dfrac{x^2}{x^3} = 7x^{-1} = \dfrac{7}{x}$

Example 4. Simplify $\dfrac{14x^3 + 7x^2 + 28x}{-7x}$.

$$\frac{14x^3 + 7x^2 + 28x}{-7x} = \frac{14x^3}{-7x} + \frac{7x^2}{-7x} + \frac{28x}{-7x}$$

$$= -2x^2 - x - 4$$

Example 5. Estimate n, using scientific notation (see Section 3–9), if $n = 0.47 \times 612$.

$$0.47 = 4.7 \times 10^{-1},$$

that is, about

$$5 \times 10^{-1}.$$

$$612 = 6.12 \times 10^2,$$

that is, about

$$6 \times 10^2.$$

$$n \approx (5 \times 10^{-1}) \times (6 \times 10^2)$$

$$n \approx 30 \times 10^1$$

$$n \approx 3 \times 10^2$$

Thus $n \approx 300$.

Example 6. As in Example 5, estimate n: $n = 83.2 \div 0.039$.

$$n \approx \frac{8 \times 10}{4 \times 10^{-2}}, \quad \text{or} \quad \frac{8}{4} \times 10^{1-(-2)}$$

$$n \approx 2 \times 10^3$$

Thus $n \approx 2000$.

Example 7. Estimate n: $n = \dfrac{270 \times 0.08}{48,200}$.

$$n \approx \frac{(3 \times 10^2) \times (8 \times 10^{-2})}{5 \times 01^4}$$

$$n \approx \frac{24 \times 10^0}{5 \times 10^4}, \quad \text{or} \quad \frac{24}{5} \times 10^{0-4}$$

$$n \approx 5 \times 10^{-4}, \text{ since } \tfrac{24}{5} \approx 5$$

Thus $n \approx 0.0005$.

Exercises for Section 8-8

8-8 A

Simplify, giving each answer as a power:

1. $10^2 \times 10^4$ **2.** $3^2 \times 3^3$ **3.** $5^2 \times 5^3$
4. $6^2 \times 6^2$ **5.** $(\frac{1}{2})^2 \times (\frac{1}{2})^2$ **6.** $a^2 \times a^2$
7. $b^2 \times b^3$ **8.** $c^2 \times c^5$ **9.** $d^3 \times d^4$
10. $d^{10} \times d^{11}$ **11.** $5^4 \div 5^{-2}$ **12.** $8^5 \div 8^{-3}$
13. $x^6 \div x^4$ **14.** $x^{10} \div x^2$ **15.** $x^{-2} \div x^{-4}$

8-8 B

*Simplify:

1. $10 \times (10^2 + 10)$ **2.** $5 \times (5^2 + 5)$
3. $7 \times (7^2 + 7)$ **4.** $a \times (a^2 + a)$
5. $b \times (b^2 - 2b)$ **6.** $s \times (s - 10)$
7. $k \times (3 - k)$ **8.** $t \times (t^2 - 6t)$
9. $h \times (h + h^2)$ **10.** $p \times (p^2 - 6p)$

*Note: Apply the distributive law in each exercise. In Exercise 4 we have $(a \times a^2) + (a \times a)$; then simplify.

8-8 C

Simplify:

1. $x^3 \times x^4$ **2.** $a^3 \times a^2$

*__3.__ $7a^2 \times a^3$ *__4.__ $\dfrac{7a^4}{a^2}$

*__5.__ $\dfrac{8a^2b^3}{4ab}$ **6.** $\dfrac{16a^2b^4c^2}{4ab^2c}$

7. $\dfrac{25r^2s^3t^3}{5rs^2t^2}$ **8.** $\dfrac{7x^3 + 28x^2 + 420x}{7x}$

9. $\dfrac{8a^3b^2 + 16ab^3 + 800ab^4}{8ab}$ **10.** $\dfrac{245x^2y^2 + 595xy^3 + 600xy^4}{5xy}$

*Note: In Exercise 3, $7a^2 \times a^3 = (7 \times 1) \times (a^2 \times a^3)$. Simplify.

In Exercise 4, $\dfrac{7a^4}{a^2} = \dfrac{7}{1} \times \dfrac{a^4}{a^2}$.   Simplify.   In Exercise 5,

$\dfrac{8a^2b^3}{4ab} = \dfrac{8}{4} \times \dfrac{a^2}{a} \times \dfrac{b^3}{b}$. Simplify.

8-8 D

In Exercises 1–10 approximate:

1. 615×0.07

2. 240×0.0062

3. 139×27.5

4. 86.75×0.092

5. $(0.0723) \times (0.6991)$

6. $615 \div 0.07$

7. $240 \div 0.0062$

8. $139 \div 27.5$

9. $86.75 \div 0.092$

10. $(0.0723) \div (17.69)$

11. In Exercise 1 find the exact product.

12. In Exercise 6 find the quotient, correct to three digits.

8-8 E

Approximate:

1. $\dfrac{(600) \times (19.8)}{37.5}$

2. $\dfrac{(275) \times (0.067)}{0.62}$

3. $\dfrac{(1820) \times (0.0075)}{2400}$

4. $\dfrac{(17.8) \times (49.9)}{9600}$

5. $\dfrac{(246) \times (1000)}{5000}$

6. $\dfrac{(8.75) \times (0.087)}{87,500}$

7. $\dfrac{(4.9) \times (100)}{(2.7) \times (0.648)}$

8. $\dfrac{2600}{(1.3) \times (7.28)}$

9. $\dfrac{(55,000) \times (0.745)}{(16) \times (10^3)}$

10. $\dfrac{(0.657) \times (18.7) \times (210)}{(48.9) \times (16,480)}$

8-8 F

1. The sum of the test grades in a class of 49 students was 4275. Estimate the mean.

2. The area of a triangle can be found by multiplying one-half the product of the measures of two sides of the triangle by the sine of the angle between them. That is, $A = \frac{1}{2}ab \sin C$. Use $a = 167.5$, $b = 278.9$, and $m(\angle C) = 49$ to estimate the area of a triangle with these measures.

3. Use the formula from Exercise 2 to estimate the area of a triangle with $a = 2665$, $b = 3190$, and $m(\angle C) = 18$.

4. One horsepower is approximately equivalent to 0.7457 kilowatt. Estimate the number of kilowatts in 2375 horsepower.

Exercises 8–8 F continued on page 386.

5. Approximate the area of a circular pond with a radius 36.95 feet in length.

6. Find an estimate of the volume of a room in the shape of a rectangular solid. The dimensions of the room are 21.6 feet by 9.2 feet by 31.7 feet.

7. The formula for the volume of a sphere is $V = \frac{4}{3}\pi r^3$. Estimate the volume of the earth. Assume that the earth is spherical and has a radius of 3987 miles.

8. Estimate the distance around the earth at the equator. Use the data from Exercise 7.

9. Structural steel weighs about 490 pounds per cubic foot. Estimate the weight of a solid steel bar 12 feet long. It has a cross section rectangular in shape with dimensions of 6 inches by 3 inches.

10. Approximate the volume of a silo in the shape of a cylinder with a base radius of 7.85 feet and a height of 21.62 feet.

8-8 G

Find precise answers in Exercises 8–8 F and compare these with your estimates. For example, in Exercise 1 find $4275 \div 49$, correct to four digits.

■ 8-9 INEQUALITIES

In Section 5–9 graphs of inequalities were shown over the positive numbers and zero. Now that negative numbers have been introduced, it is possible to make such graphs over the set of real numbers. Consider the graphs in Figure 8–21. In (a) the graph of $x < -1$ is all of the number line to the left of point A. In (b) the graph of $-2 \leq x < 3$ is point A and all of the points between A and B; point B is not included.

In Section 5–9 a graph in the coordinate plane was shown only for quadrant I. Note in (c) and (d) that the graphs cover parts of each of the four quadrants.

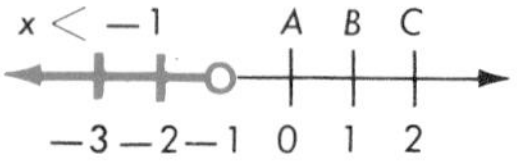

FIGURE 8–21(a)

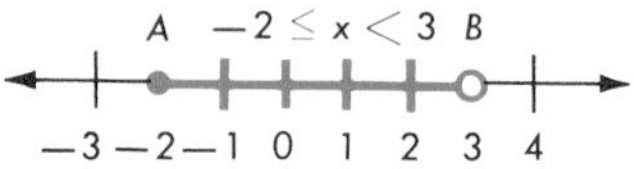

FIGURE 8–21(b)

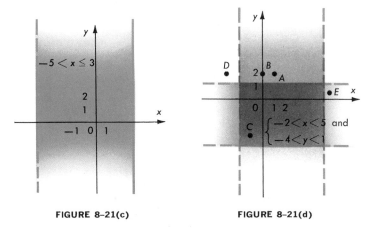

FIGURE 8–21(c)   FIGURE 8–21(d)

Example 1. Consider the inequality $x < -1$. State whether each number is a solution: (a) 1 (b) 0 (c) -1 (d) -50 (e) $-7\frac{1}{2}$.

(a) 1 is not a root

(b) 0 is not a root

(c) -1 is not a root

Note that points A, B, and C are not on the graph in Figure 8–21(a).

(d) -50 is a root

(e) $-7\frac{1}{2}$ is a root

See the graph in Figure 8–21(a).

Example 2. Consider the pair of inequalities:

$$\begin{cases} -2 < x < 5, \text{ and} \\ -4 < y < 1. \end{cases}$$

A number pair is a solution of these inequalities if the number pair satisfies both inequalities. State whether or not each number pair is a solution: (a) $(1, 2)$ (b) $(0, 2)$ (c) $(-1, -3)$ (d) $(-3, 2)$ (e) $(5\frac{1}{2}, \frac{1}{2})$.

(a) No; $-2 < 1 < 5$ but $-4 < 2 < 1$ is not true. See point A in Figure 8–21(d).

(b) No; $-2 < 0 < 5$ but $-4 < 2 < 1$ is not true. See point B in Figure 8–21(d).

(c) Yes; $-2 < -1 < 5$ and $-4 < -3 < 1$. See point C in Figure 8–21(d).

(d) No; $-2 < -3 < 5$ is not true and $-4 < 2 < 1$ is not true. See point D in Figure 8–21(d).

(e) No; $-4 < 5\frac{1}{2} < 1$ is not true, although $-4 < \frac{1}{2} < 1$ is true. See point E in Figure 8–21(d).

Example 3. On a number line make a graph of: (a) $x + 5 > 2$ (b) $x - 5 < -1$ (c) $2x > 6$ (d) $-2x < 6$.

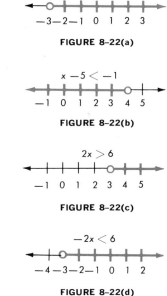

(a) Note that $-3 + 5$ is not greater than 2, but for any $x > -3$, the inequality is true. (See the graph.)

$x + 5 > 2$

FIGURE 8–22(a)

(b) Note that $4 - 5$ is not less than -1, but for any $x < 4$ the inequality is true. (See the graph.)

$x - 5 < -1$

FIGURE 8–22(b)

(c) The inequality is true for any $x > 3$.

$2x > 6$

FIGURE 8–22(c)

(d) The inequality is true for any $x > -3$.

$-2x < 6$

FIGURE 8–22(d)

In Example 3(d) note that the general solution for

$$-2x < 6 \quad \text{is} \quad x > -3.$$

We say that these are inequalities of the **opposite order,** since the symbols $<$ and $>$ are opposite in meaning. By checking several values greater than -3, you will find that the general solution, $x > -3$, is true.

In Examples 3(a), 3(b), and 3(c) note that each inequality and its general solution are of the **same order.**

Two inequalities which have the same set of roots are called **equivalent inequalities.** In Example 3(a), $x + 5 > 2$ and $x > -3$ are equivalent, since any number which satisfies one is a root of the other.

Exercises for Section 8–9

8–9 A

In each exercise an inequality and a set S are given.
(a) Are all members of set S solutions of the inequality?
(b) If not, write a set S' containing those members of S which are solutions. For example, consider

$$2x + 1 > 11, \quad S = \{-2, 0, 3, 5, 8, 10\}.$$

Try $x = -2$. Is $2(-2) + 1 > 11$? No. Now try $x = 0$. Is $2(0) + 1 > 11$? No. Try other members of S. *Answer:* No. $S' = \{8, 10\}$.

1. $x + 5 > 8,\ S = \{-1, 0, 3, 4, 20\}$
2. $x - 5 > 8,\ S = \{-8, 0, 5, 10, 15, 509\}$
3. $2x > -6,\ S = \{-3, -2, -1, 0, 604\}$
4. $4 < 2x < 8,\ S = \{-12, -6, -5, 0, 99, 203\}$
5. $-18 < 3x < 300,\ S = \{-12, -6, -5, 0, 99, 203\}$
6. $-2x < 8,\ S = \{-4, -3, 5, 0, 608\}$
7. $-5x > 10,\ S = \{0, 1, 2, -2, -3, -4, -80\}$
8. $-3x < -9,\ S = \{-5, -2, -1, 0, 3, 4, 5, 6\}$
9. $-5x < -10,\ S = \{-2, -1, 0, 1, 2, 3, 4, 5, 50\}$
10. $\dfrac{x}{-2} > 4,\ S = \{-16, -12, -10, -8, 0, 8, 16, 24\}$

8–9 B

Consider the inequality $8 > 5$. If we add $+3$ to both sides we have

$$8 + 3 > 5 + 3, \text{ that is, } 11 > 8.$$

We also see that $8 + (-3) > 5 + (-3)$, that is, $5 > 2$. If we start with the inequality $8 > 5$ and add $+3$ or -3 to each number, the result is an inequality of the same order.

In each exercise perform steps (a) and (b).
(a) Add $+13$ to each member, and determine whether the resulting inequality is of the same order as the one given.
(b) Add -13 to each member, and determine whether the resulting inequality is of the same order as the one given.

Exercises 8–9 B continued on page 390.

1. $4 > 3$ 2. $\frac{1}{2} > 0$
3. $-10 < 0$ 4. $-8 < 6$
5. $9 > -20$ 6. $8 > -15$
7. $-200 > -300$ 8. $-190 > -600$

9. From Exercises 1–8 does it appear that adding the same number to each side of an inequality produces an inequality of the same order?

8-9 C

In Figure 8–23 the colored part of the number line is the graph of certain equivalent inequalities. The "hole" at zero indicates that this point is not on the graph. Thus this is the graph of $x > 0$.

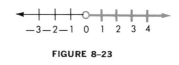

FIGURE 8-23

In Exercises 1–10 state whether Figure 8–23 is a graph of the inequality.

1. $x + 5 > 5$ 2. $x + 6 > 6$
3. $x + 8 > 8$ 4. $x + 10 > 10$
5. $\frac{1}{2} < x + \frac{1}{2}$ 6. $x - 5 > -5$
7. $x - 6 > -6$ 8. $x - 8 > +8$
9. $x + 10 > 9$ 10. $12 < x + 12$

8-9 D

Consider the inequality $12 > 10$. If we multiply each member by $+2$, we have

$$+2(12) > +2(10).$$

That is,

$$24 > 20.$$

If we multiply each member by $+\frac{1}{2}$, we have

$$+\tfrac{1}{2}(12) > +\tfrac{1}{2}(10).$$

That is,

$$6 > 5.$$

We have multiplied each member by $+2$ and then by $+\frac{1}{2}$, and the order in each inequality has remained the *same*.

In each exercise multiply both members by: (a) $+3$ (b) $+\frac{1}{3}$ (c) $+2$ (d) $+\frac{1}{2}$. In each case does the order remain the same?

1. $12 > 6$	**2.** $6 < 18$	**3.** $18 > 12$
4. $24 > 18$	**5.** $12 < 24$	**6.** $24 > 6$
7. $30 > 24$	**8.** $18 < 30$	**9.** $30 > 12$
10. $6 < 30$	**11.** $36 > 30$	**12.** $36 > 24$
13. $18 < 36$	**14.** $12 < 36$	**15.** $6 < 36$

16. In Exercises 1–15 does it appear that multiplying or dividing each member by the same positive number produces an inequality of the same order? (*Note:* We divide by 3 when we multiply by $\frac{1}{3}$. We divide by 2 when we multiply by $\frac{1}{2}$.)

8-9 E

In Figure 8–24 we have the graph of $x > 2$. In Exercises 1–10 state whether or not Figure 8–24 is the graph of the inequality.

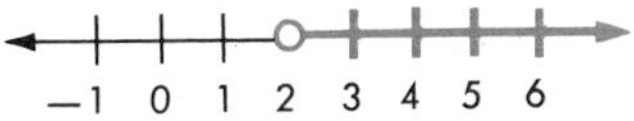

FIGURE 8-24

1. $3x > 6$	**2.** $4x > 8$
3. $6x > 12$	**4.** $8x > 16$
5. $10x > 20$	**6.** $\frac{1}{2}x > 1$
7. $\frac{1}{4}x > \frac{1}{2}$	**8.** $2\frac{1}{2}x > 5$
9. $\frac{1}{8}x > \frac{1}{4}$	**10.** $\frac{1}{10}x > \frac{1}{5}$

8-9 F

Consider the inequality $12 > 10$. If we multiply both sides by -2, we have

$$(-2)(12) < (-2)(10).$$

That is,

$$-24 < -20.$$

If we multiply each side by $-\frac{1}{2}$, we have

$$(-\tfrac{1}{2})(12) < (-\tfrac{1}{2})(10).$$

That is,

$$-6 < -5.$$

The order in $-6 < -5$ is *opposite* the order in $12 > 10$.

Exercises 8–9 F continued on page 392.

In each exercise multiply both members by: (a) -2 (b) $-\frac{1}{2}$
(c) -3 (d) $-\frac{1}{3}$.   Are the resulting orders opposite?

1. $12 > 6$ **2.** $-12 < 6$ **3.** $-12 < -6$
4. $-6 < 12$ **5.** $18 > 12$ **6.** $18 > 6$
7. $-18 < -12$ **8.** $-18 < 6$ **9.** $-6 > -18$
10. $24 > 6$ **11.** $-24 < -6$ **12.** $-24 < -12$

13. In Exercises 1–12 does it appear that multiplying or dividing
each side by a negative number produces an inequality of the
opposite order?   (*Note:* When we multiply by $-\frac{1}{2}$ we divide
by -2.   When we multiply by $-\frac{1}{3}$ we divide by -3.)

14. If $x > -2$, is $(-1)x < (-1)(-2)$?   Explain.

15. If $-2x > 6$, is $(-\frac{1}{2})(-2x) < (-\frac{1}{2})(6)$?   Explain.

8-9 G

In Exercises 1–14 match each inequality (or pair of inequalities) with
the correct graph in Figure 8–25.

1. $x < 2$ **2.** $x + 2 < 4$ **3.** $3x < 6$
4. $x > 3$ **5.** $2x > 6$ **6.** $x + 6 > 9$
7. $y > -2$ **8.** $y + 4 > +2$ **9.** $3y > -6$
10. $\begin{cases} y + 2 > 4 \\ x + 1 > 0 \end{cases}$ **11.** $\begin{cases} -2y < -4 \\ -3x < 3 \end{cases}$ **12.** $\begin{cases} -2 < x < 2 \\ 0 < y < 4 \end{cases}$

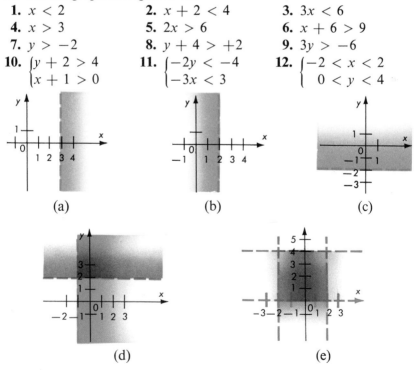

(a)   (b)   (c)

(d)   (e)

FIGURE 8-25

Vocabulary

The section in which each word appears is indicated in parentheses.

absolute value (8–2)
additive inverse (8–1)
coordinate plane (8–1)
equivalent inequalities (8–9)
negative numbers (8–1)
opposite order (8–9)
opposites (8–1)

ordered (Exercises 8–1 A)
positive numbers (8–1)
quadrants (8–1)
same order (8–9)
x-axis (8–1)
y-axis (8–1)

Chapter Review

A

If a statement is true, mark it true. If it is not true, write a replacement for the part underlined to make it true.

1. $(-5) + (-8) = \underline{-13}$
2. $(-5) - (-8) = \underline{+13}$
3. $(-8) \times (-5) = \underline{(+8) \times (+5)}$
4. $(-5) + (-6) = \underline{-(+11)}$
5. $(-5) \times (+7) = \underline{-(+35)}$
6. $(+5)[(-12) + (+12)] = \underline{-120}$
7. $(-5)^3 \times (+8) = \underline{+1000}$
8. $(-1)^5 \times (+1)^3 = \underline{+1}$
9. $(-8) \div (-2) = \underline{(-8) \times (-\frac{1}{2})}$
10. $(-8) \times (-2)(-5) = \underline{(-1) \times (+80)}$

B

Solve for x:

1. $-3x = 342$
2. $5x = -705$
3. $-15x = 634$
4. $-21x = 6300$
5. $7.5x = -1500$
6. $\frac{1}{2}x = -8$
7. $\frac{1}{4}x = -20$
8. $2\frac{1}{2}x = -60$
9. $3.1x = 930$
10. $0.021x = 84$
11. $-7x > 84$
12. $-7x + 3 > 94$
13. $\frac{x}{-5} < 30$
14. $\frac{3x}{-5} + (-8) < -42$

C

Perform the indicated operations:

1. $(-5)^2 \times (-1)^3$
2. $(-5)^2 \times (-5)^3$
3. $(-a)^2 \times (-a)^3$
4. $7x^2 \times (-8x^3y^2)$
5. $56x^4 \div 7x^3$
6. $(x^4 + 7x^2) \div x^2$
7. $-5x(x^3 + 3x^2 - x)$
8. $(a^2b^3 + ab^2 + ab) \div (-ab)$
9. (7 tens + 3 tens) ÷ 2 tens
10. (8 ones + 2 tens) ÷ 7 ones

D

1. Find the mean of: -8, -7, -143, $+278$, -50, $+3$, $+9$, and 0.
2. Find the sum of: $-7x^2 - 14x - 80.3$ and $-9x^2 + 6x + 50.7$.
3. In Exercise 2 subtract the first polynomial from the second.
4. On a number line make a graph of $3x > 7.5$.
5. On a number line make a graph of $-3x > 7.5$.
6. On a coordinate plane make a graph of $y = 3x - 6$.
7. On a coordinate plane make a graph of $3x < 9$.
8. On a coordinate plane make a graph of $-3x < 9$.

REVIEW OF CHAPTERS 1–8

A

In Exercises 1–5 solve for n:

1. $n = 28{,}730 + 19{,}406 + 105{,}273$
2. $n = (618.7)(2091)$
3. $n = 6\frac{3}{4} \div 3\frac{1}{8}$
4. $n = 12\frac{2}{3} \times 21\frac{1}{2}$
5. $n = 725\frac{1}{2} - 695.07$
6. Find $18\frac{1}{2}\%$ of $18,600.
7. A factory produced 950 watches in May and then produced 1150 in June. Find the percent of increase in production.
8. A certain worker's take-home pay of $585.00 represents 85% of his gross earnings for 1 month. Find his gross earnings, to the nearest cent.
9. Simplify:
   (a) $\dfrac{2\frac{1}{2} + \frac{2}{3}}{\frac{7}{12} + \frac{5}{6}}$
   (b) $\dfrac{\frac{2}{5} + \frac{7}{10} + 5}{\frac{13}{20} + 2\frac{3}{10}}$
10. Find the area of a triangle with a base of 13 feet and an altitude of 8 feet 6 inches.

11. A barrel in the shape of a cylinder is 3 feet 8 inches high. Its radius is 18 inches. Find its volume in cubic feet. The formula for volume is $V = \pi r^2 h$. (*Note:* Use 3.14 for π.)

12. Find the perimeter of a rectangle which is 17 meters 87 centimeters long and 6 meters 92 centimeters wide.

13. A family bought a house trailer on the installment plan. The cash price was $950. They paid $100 down and $37.20 per month for 25 months. Find the interest rate, to the nearest 1%.
$$\left(Note:\ r = \frac{24C}{B(n + 1)},\ \text{Section 6–3.} \right)$$

14. Find n if n is a whole number:
    (a) $n = \sqrt{16}$ (b) $n = \sqrt{49}$ (c) $n = \sqrt{244}$ (d) $n = \sqrt{256}$

15. Solve for n:
    (a) $\dfrac{n}{15} = \dfrac{1}{3}$ (b) $\dfrac{n}{85} = \dfrac{123}{255}$ (c) $\dfrac{48}{225} = \dfrac{n}{700}$

16. Find a: $a^2 + 12^2 = 13^2$.

17. Find c: $c^2 = 40^2 + 9^2$.

18. The hypotenuse of a right triangle is 60 feet and one of its legs is 48 feet. Find the length of the other leg.

19. Find the area of a 12-foot-long rectangle with a 15-foot diagonal.

20. Find the measure of the third angle of a triangle if the other two angles measure $37\frac{1}{2}°$ and $101\frac{1}{4}°$, respectively.

B

In Exercises 1–8 solve for y:

1. $2y - 5 = 18$
2. $3y + 75 = 84$
3. $\frac{1}{4}y = 16$
4. $\frac{1}{3}y - 8 = 7$
5. $2y + 6\frac{1}{2} = 284\frac{3}{4}$
6. $\frac{2}{3}y - 1 = 7$
7. $2\frac{1}{2}y + 6\frac{1}{4} = 32\frac{3}{8}$
8. $5y + 128 = 103$

9. Locate n between two consecutive whole numbers:
    (a) $n = \sqrt{7}$ (b) $n = \sqrt{39}$
    (c) $n = \sqrt{195}$ (d) $n = \sqrt{3475}$

10. What value or values of x will make $x^2 = 225$ a true equation?

11. Use the Table of Square Roots in the Appendix to find:
    (a) $\sqrt{89}$ (b) $\sqrt{107}$ (c) $\sqrt{129}$ (d) $\sqrt{7}$

12. We simplify $\sqrt{20}$: $\sqrt{20} = \sqrt{4}\sqrt{5} = 2\sqrt{5}$. Simplify:
    (a) $\sqrt{8}$ (b) $\sqrt{75}$ (c) $\sqrt{98}$ (d) $\sqrt{2400}$

C

1. Find the surface area of a spherical tank which has a radius of 3.4 feet.
2. The diagonal of a square is 14.14 feet long. Find the length of its side.
3. The area of a square field is 1 acre. Find the length of one side.
4. If $d = kt$ and $d = 75$ when $t = 6$, find d when $t = 9$.
5. Find the sum of the first 10 terms of the sequence 1, $4\frac{1}{2}$, 8, $11\frac{1}{2}$, ... Use the formula $S = (n/2)(a + l)$.
6. A box in the shape of a rectangular solid has the dimensions shown in Figure 8–26. Find its volume.
7. Find the total surface area of the box in Figure 8–26.

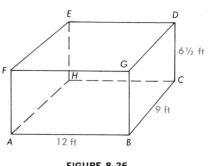

FIGURE 8–26

In Figure 8–26 find the length of:

8. AC
9. BD
10. AD
11. BE
12. AG

D

Mark each of the following true or false:

1. Two triangles having the same shape will have the same area.
2. The set of rational numbers is closed under addition.
3. The mean of 4, 7, and 10 is 7.
4. The mean of 4, 11, and 23 is $12\frac{2}{3}$.
5. A box contains 5 red balls and 3 white balls. The probability of drawing a red ball is $\frac{3}{8}$.
6. Three-fourths of $\frac{1}{2}$ is $\frac{3}{6}$.
7. If $n = \sqrt{759}$, then $27 < n < 28$.
8. If A represents the set of all numbers x for which $0 \leq x < 7.5$ and $B = \{2, 3.5, 0, \frac{49}{12}, \frac{75}{23}\}$, then $B \subseteq A$.
9. The sequence 2, 4, 7, 9, 12, 14, ... is an arithmetic sequence.
10. If $a = b$ and $b = c$, then $a = c$.
11. The sum of the measures of the angles of a triangle is 179°60′.
12. The area of a square of side 10 inches is greater than the area of a circle of radius 10 inches.

E

Use the Table of Trigonometric Ratios in the Appendix to find the value of:

1. sin 18°　　　　　　2. cos 46°　　　　　　3. tan 18°
4. tan 46°　　　　　　5. sin 44°　　　　　　6. cos 72°

7. Find the circumference of a circle with a radius of 6 feet.
8. Find the perimeter of a square whose side is 6 feet long.
9. A solid sphere is placed so that it just fits inside a cube of side 8 feet. Find the volume of space within the cube which is not occupied by the sphere. Give your answer to the nearest tenth of a cubic foot.

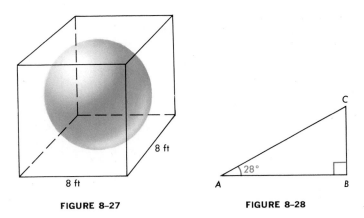

FIGURE 8–27　　　　　　　　　　　　　FIGURE 8–28

10. Use the tangent ratio to determine the measure of side *AB* in Figure 8–28.
11. Find the total surface area of a cylinder with radius 1 foot and height 14 inches. (*Note:* Use the formula $A = 2\pi r^2 + 2\pi rh$.)
12. The area of a circle is 144π square inches. Find the length of its radius.

Appendix

TABLE OF SQUARE ROOTS AND SQUARES

n	n^2	$\sqrt{n}$	n	n^2	$\sqrt{n}$	n	n^2	$\sqrt{n}$
1	1	1.000	51	2,601	7.141	101	10,201	10.050
2	4	1.414	52	2,704	7.211	102	10,404	10.099
3	9	1.732	53	2,809	7.280	103	10,609	10.149
4	16	2.000	54	2,916	7.348	104	10,816	10.198
5	25	2.236	55	3,025	7.416	105	11,025	10.247
6	36	2.449	56	3,136	7.483	106	11,236	10.296
7	49	2.646	57	3,249	7.550	107	11,449	10.344
8	64	2.828	58	3,364	7.616	108	11,664	10.392
9	81	3.000	59	3,481	7.681	109	11,881	10.440
10	100	3.162	60	3,600	7.746	110	12,100	10.488
11	121	3.317	61	3,721	7.810	111	12,321	10.536
12	144	3.464	62	3,844	7.874	112	12,544	10.583
13	169	3.606	63	3,969	7.937	113	12,769	10.630
14	196	3.742	64	4,096	8.000	114	12,996	10.677
15	225	3.873	65	4,225	8.062	115	13,225	10.724
16	256	4.000	66	4,356	8.124	116	13,456	10.770
17	289	4.123	67	4,489	8.185	117	13,689	10.817
18	324	4.243	68	4,624	8.246	118	13,924	10.863
19	361	4.359	69	4,761	8.307	119	14,161	10.909
20	400	4.472	70	4,900	8.367	120	14,400	10.954
21	441	4.583	71	5,041	8.426	121	14,641	11.000
22	484	4.690	72	5,184	8.485	122	14,884	11.045
23	529	4.796	73	5,329	8.544	123	15,129	11.091
24	576	4.899	74	5,476	8.602	124	15,376	11.136
25	625	5.000	75	5,625	8.660	125	15,625	11.180
26	676	5.099	76	5,776	8.718	126	15,876	11.225
27	729	5.196	77	5,929	8.775	127	16,129	11.269
28	784	5.292	78	6,084	8.832	128	16,384	11.314
29	841	5.385	79	6,241	8.888	129	16,641	11.358
30	900	5.477	80	6,400	8.944	130	16,900	11.402
31	961	5.568	81	6,561	9.000	131	17,161	11.446
32	1,024	5.657	82	6,724	9.055	132	17,424	11.489
33	1,089	5.745	83	6,889	9.110	133	17,689	11.533
34	1,156	5.831	84	7,056	9.165	134	17,956	11.576
35	1,225	5.916	85	7,225	9.220	135	18,225	11.619
36	1,296	6.000	86	7,396	9.274	136	18,496	11.662
37	1,369	6.083	87	7,569	9.327	137	18,769	11.705
38	1,444	6.164	88	7,744	9.381	138	19,044	11.747
39	1,521	6.245	89	7,921	9.434	139	19,321	11.790
40	1,600	6.325	90	8,100	9.487	140	19,600	11.832
41	1,681	6.403	91	8,281	9.539	141	19,881	11.874
42	1,764	6.481	92	8,464	9.592	142	20,164	11.916
43	1,849	6.557	93	8,649	9.644	143	20,449	11.958
44	1,936	6.633	94	8,836	9.695	144	20,736	12.000
45	2,025	6.708	95	9,025	9.747	145	21,025	12.042
46	2,116	6.782	96	9,216	9.798	146	21,316	12.083
47	2,209	6.856	97	9,409	9.849	147	21,609	12.124
48	2,304	6.928	98	9,604	9.899	148	21,904	12.166
49	2,401	7.000	99	9,801	9.950	149	22,201	12.207
50	2,500	7.071	100	10,000	10.000	150	22,500	12.247

TABLE OF TRIGONOMETRIC RATIOS

n	$\sin n°$	$\cos n°$	$\tan n°$	n	$\sin n°$	$\cos n°$	$\tan n°$
1	0.017	1.000	0.017	46	0.719	0.695	1.036
2	0.035	0.999	0.035	47	0.731	0.682	1.072
3	0.052	0.999	0.052	48	0.743	0.669	1.111
4	0.070	0.998	0.070	49	0.755	0.656	1.150
5	0.087	0.996	0.087	50	0.766	0.643	1.192
6	0.105	0.995	0.105	51	0.777	0.629	1.235
7	0.122	0.993	0.123	52	0.788	0.616	1.280
8	0.139	0.990	0.141	53	0.799	0.602	1.327
9	0.156	0.988	0.158	54	0.809	0.588	1.376
10	0.174	0.985	0.176	55	0.819	0.574	1.428
11	0.191	0.982	0.194	56	0.829	0.559	1.483
12	0.208	0.978	0.213	57	0.839	0.545	1.540
13	0.225	0.974	0.231	58	0.848	0.530	1.600
14	0.242	0.970	0.249	59	0.857	0.515	1.664
15	0.259	0.966	0.268	60	0.866	0.500	1.732
16	0.276	0.961	0.287	61	0.875	0.485	1.804
17	0.292	0.956	0.306	62	0.883	0.469	1.881
18	0.309	0.951	0.325	63	0.891	0.454	1.963
19	0.326	0.946	0.344	64	0.899	0.438	2.050
20	0.342	0.940	0.364	65	0.906	0.423	2.145
21	0.358	0.934	0.384	66	0.914	0.407	2.246
22	0.375	0.927	0.404	67	0.921	0.391	2.356
23	0.391	0.921	0.424	68	0.927	0.375	2.475
24	0.407	0.914	0.445	69	0.934	0.358	2.605
25	0.423	0.906	0.466	70	0.940	0.342	2.748
26	0.438	0.899	0.488	71	0.946	0.326	2.904
27	0.454	0.891	0.510	72	0.951	0.309	3.078
28	0.469	0.883	0.532	73	0.956	0.292	3.271
29	0.485	0.875	0.554	74	0.961	0.276	3.487
30	0.500	0.866	0.577	75	0.966	0.259	3.732
31	0.515	0.857	0.601	76	0.970	0.242	4.011
32	0.530	0.848	0.625	77	0.974	0.225	4.332
33	0.545	0.839	0.649	78	0.978	0.208	4.705
34	0.559	0.829	0.675	79	0.982	0.191	5.145
35	0.574	0.819	0.700	80	0.985	0.174	5.671
36	0.588	0.809	0.727	81	0.988	0.156	6.314
37	0.602	0.799	0.754	82	0.990	0.139	7.115
38	0.616	0.788	0.781	83	0.993	0.122	8.144
39	0.629	0.777	0.810	84	0.995	0.105	9.514
40	0.643	0.766	0.839	85	0.996	0.087	11.430
41	0.656	0.755	0.869	86	0.998	0.070	14.301
42	0.669	0.743	0.900	87	0.999	0.052	19.081
43	0.682	0.731	0.933	88	0.999	0.035	28.636
44	0.695	0.719	0.966	89	1.000	0.017	57.290
45	0.707	0.707	1.000				

Selected Answers

p. 2 Ex 1–1   **1.** (a), (c), and (d); (b), (e), and (f)
3. Pair nickels with dimes—one to one
5. One turn of the stile corresponds to one person.

p. 4 Ex 1–2 A   **1.** /////   **3.** ∩/////   **5.** ∩∩/////
7. ∩∩∩/////   **9.** ∩∩∩∩/////   **11.** ∩∩∩∩∩/////
13. ∩∩∩∩∩∩/////   **15.** ∩∩∩∩∩∩∩/////

p. 4 Ex 1–2 B   **1.** ∩/   **3.** ∩///   **5.** /////////   **7.** ∩∩∩/
9. ꝗꝗ∩

p. 4 Ex 1–2 C   **1.** 31   **3.** 211   **5.** 111   **7.** 120   **9.** 210   **11.** 216

p. 5 Ex 1–2 D   **1.** True   **3.** True   **5.** True   **7.** >   **9.** True   **11.** True

p. 5 Ex 1–2 E   **1.** True   **3.** True   **5.** //   **7.** True   **9.** True   **11.** True

p. 5 Ex 1–2 F   **1.** ∩∩∩//   **3.** ꝗ//   **5.** ////   **7.** ⌐⌐
9. ꝗꝗꝗ∩∩∩∩∩∩∩∩///

p. 5 Ex 1–2 G   **1.** ∩∩∩   **3.** ⧊⧊   **5.** ∩   **7.** ⚵   **9.** ꝗ

p. 6 Ex 1–2 H   **1.** 400   **3.** 2000   **5.** 10,310   **7.** 5   **9.** 20

p. 7 Ex 1–3 A   **1.** V   **3.** XV   **5.** XXV   **7.** XXXV   **9.** XLV   **11.** LV
13. LXV   **15.** LXXV

p. 8 Ex 1–3 B   **1.** IV   **3.** XII   **5.** XXIII   **7.** XXVIII   **9.** XXXVI
11. XLIV   **13.** LII   **15.** LXVII

p. 8 Ex 1–3 C   **1.** CXLII   **3.** CXLIX   **5.** CLVIII   **7.** CLXXXVII
9. CLXXXIX   **11.** CCCXCIX   **13.** DCCXCVIII   **15.** DCCCI

p. 8 Ex 1–3 D   **1.** CMIX   **3.** CMXXIX   **5.** CMXLIX   **7.** CMLXIX
9. CMLXXXIX   **11.** MIX   **13.** MXXIX   **15.** MXCIX

p. 8 Ex 1–3 E   **1.** CDXL   **3.** MCMXL   **5.** DCCCXL   **7.** CDXC
9. CMXC   **11.** CDL   **13.** DCCCLXXX   **15.** MMMDXX

p. 8 Ex 1–3 F   **1.** M   **3.** MMM   **5.** $\overline{\text{V}}$ **7.** $\overline{\text{VIII}}$ **9.** $\overline{\text{X}}$ **11.** $\overline{\text{LX}}$

p. 8 Ex 1–3 G   **1.** 24   **3.** 75   **5.** 92   **7.** 172   **9.** 340

p. 9 Ex 1–3 H   **1.** 400   **3.** 41   **5.** 900   **7.** 902   **9.** 1700   **11.** 6000

p. 9 Ex 1–3 I   **1.** True   **3.** >   **5.** True   **7.** True   **9.** <

p. 9 Ex 1–3 J   **1.** (a) 7; (b) 7; (c) 10   **3.** No; no   **5.** Four   **7.** Subtraction

p. 10 Ex 1–3 K   **1.** V + IV = IX or VI + IV = X
3. I = III − II   **5.** VI − II = IV

p. 13 Ex 1–4 A   **1.** $(3 \times 10) + (8 \times 1)$ **3.** $(9 \times 10) + (8 \times 1)$
5. $(3 \times 10^2) + (4 \times 10) + (5 \times 1)$
7. $(3 \times 10^3) + (4 \times 10^2) + (5 \times 10) + (9 \times 1)$
9. $(6 \times 10^3) + (0 \times 10^2) + (8 \times 10) + (4 \times 1)$
11. $(2 \times 10^4) + (6 \times 10^3) + (0 \times 10^2) + (5 \times 10) + (4 \times 1)$

p. 13 Ex 1–4 B   **1.** Forty-two   **3.** Eighty-seven   **5.** Three hundred nine
7. Four thousand five hundred thirty   **9.** Nine thousand six
11. Seventy-eight thousand five

p. 13 Ex 1–4 C   **1.** 67   **3.** 59   **5.** 47   **7.** 568   **9.** 3024   **11.** 5630

p. 14 Ex 1–4 D   **1.** 24   **3.** 56   **5.** 14   **7.** 112   **9.** 675   **11.** 2,040,050

p. 14 Ex 1–4 E   **1.** True   **3.** True   **5.** True   **7.** True   **9.** 110   **11.** True

p. 15 Ex 1–4 F   **1.** 48   **3.** 27   **5.** 26   **7.** 26   **9.** 160   **11.** 7

p. 19 Ex 1–5 A   **1.** {3,4,5}   **3.** A or {1,2,3,4,5}   **5.** A or {1,2,3,4,5}
7. ϕ or { }   **9.** {3,4,5}   **11.** B or {3,4,5,6,7}   **13.** B or {3,4,5,6,7}
15. ϕ or { }

p. 19 Ex 1–5 B   **1.** A **3.** B **5.** {3,4,5}   **7.** A **9.** B **11.** W

p. 20 Ex 1–5 C   **1.** 3   **3.** 5   **5.** 7   **7.** 9   **9.** 10   **11.** 12

p. 20 Ex 1–5 D   **1.** 7   **3.** 9   **5.** 10   **7.** 3

p. 20 Ex 1–5 E   **1.** True   **3.** True   **5.** True   **7.** True   **9.** False   **11.** True

p. 21 Ex 1–5 F   **1.** {1,2,4}   **3.** {1}   **5.** {1,3}   **7.** {1,2,4}   **9.** {1,3}   **11.** {1}

p. 25 Ex 1–6 A   **1.** 11   **3.** 19   **5.** 22   **7.** 24   **9.** 24   **11.** 27

p. 25 Ex 1–6 B   **1.** $x = 9, y = 9$ **3.** $x = 7, y = 8$ **5.** $x = 2, y = 6$
7. $x = 10, y = 8$ **9.** $x = 7, y = 9$ **11.** $x = 9, y = 9$

p. 25 Ex 1–6 C   **1.** 89   **3.** 192   **5.** 144   **7.** 245   **9.** 752   **11.** 1096

p. 25 Ex 1–6 D   **1.** 60; 57   **3.** 110; 111   **5.** 290; 285   **7.** 1000; 1052
9. 2150; 2129   **11.** 2600; 2550

p. 26 Ex 1–6 E   **1.** 69   **3.** 776   **5.** 1325   **7.** 196   **9.** 2295   **11.** 235

p. 26 Ex 1–6 F   **1.** 1300; 1253   **3.** 1600; 1610   **5.** 2100; 2001   **7.** 4000; 3900
9. 14,000; 13,945

p. 26 Ex 1–6 G   **1.** 1059   **3.** 3061   **5.** 21,482   **7.** 1109   **9.** 135,372

p. 26 Ex 1–6 H   **1.** 1415   **3.** 1814   **5.** 7862   **7.** 215,962   **9.** 24,497
11. 76,018

p. 27 Ex 1–6 I   **1.** 348   **3.** \$350   **5.** 882 mi   **7.** 167 hits   **9.** 98,703

p. 28 Ex 1–6 J   **1.** \$63   **3.** 73   **5.** 64

p. 28 Ex 1–6 K   **1.** 36   **3.** 76   **5.** 204

p. 29 Ex 1–6 L   **1.** 22   **3.** 20   **5.** 75   **7.** 110   **9.** 502   **11.** 1010

p. 29 Ex 1–6 M   **1.** Yes; yes   **3.** Yes   **5.** Associative property
7. The 4, 7, 5 in 4750 each have a value 10 times greater than their counterparts
in 475.   **9.** Yes; no; associative

p. 32 Ex 1–7 A   **1.** 96   **3.** 150   **5.** 108   **7.** 120   **9.** 100   **11.** 680
13. 480   **15.** 840   **17.** 660   **19.** 1400

p. 33 Ex 1–7 B   **1.** 400; 324   **3.** 1200; 1280   **5.** 1600; 1800   **7.** 2500; 2808
9. 400; 504   **11.** 120,000; 120,000   **13.** 4,000,000; 3,536,000   **15.** 18,000; 18,816

p. 33 Ex 1–7 C   **1.** 210,000; 241,060   **3.** 120,000; 99,324
5. 720,000; 756,000   **7.** 210,000; 185,250   **9.** 16,000,000; 16,875,000
11. 18,000,000; 17,854,375

p. 33 Ex 1–7 D   **1.** 87,217   **3.** 229,073   **5.** 328,416   **7.** 2,057,805
9. 7,425,000   **11.** 50,425,578

p. 33 Ex 1–7 E   **1.** 5100   **3.** 6040   **5.** 2040   **7.** 1920   **9.** 992   **11.** 1602

p. 34 Ex 1–7 F   **1.** 230   **3.** 980   **5.** 4560   **7.** 45,670   **9.** 13,450
11. 457,820

Rule: To multiply a whole number by 10, place a 0 at the right end of the numeral;
that is, "move" the decimal point one place to the right.

p. 34 Ex 1–7 G   **1.** 44,200   **3.** 54,300   **5.** 569,000   **7.** 354,000   **9.** 56,700
11. 750,000

Rule: To multiply a number by 10^p, where p is any whole number, "move" the
decimal point p places to the right.

p. 34 Ex 1–7 H   **1.** Commutative property of multiplication
3. Commutative property of multiplication
5. Commutative property of addition   **7.** Distributive

p. 34 Ex 1–7 I   **1.** 440 mi   **3.** 450 words   **5.** 100,750 cal   **7.** Yes   **9.** No

p. 35 Ex 1–7 J   **1.** $1,089,750   **3.** $504   **5.** $729   **7.** 1980 artichokes

p. 36 Ex 1–7 K   **1.** 144   **3.** 196   **5.** 387   **7.** 598   **9.** 1368   **11.** 3626

p. 36 Ex 1–7 L   **1.** 4165   **3.** 2961   **5.** 2304   **7.** 1100   **9.** 9872   **11.** 14,175

p. 36 Ex 1–7 M   **1.** 112   **3.** 138   **5.** 495   **7.** 676   **9.** 1100   **11.** 700

p. 36 Ex 1–7 N   **1.** 3   **3.** n = any whole number   **5.** 64   **7.** 7   **9.** 1

p. 37 Ex 1–7 O   **1.** 30   **3.** 72   **5.** 140   **7.** 200   **9.** 450   **11.** 384

p. 38 Ex 1–8 A   **1.** 6   **3.** 3   **5.** 3   **7.** 7   **9.** 10   **11.** 12   **13.** 5   **15.** 9
17. 11   **19.** 13

p. 39 Ex 1–8 B   **1.** 3   **3.** 6   **5.** 12   **7.** 40   **9.** 251   **11.** 3542   **13.** 227
15. 7989

p. 39 Ex 1–8 C   **1.** 25   **3.** 32   **5.** 16   **7.** 35   **9.** 91   **11.** 659   **13.** 24
15. 122

p. 39 Ex 1–8 D   **1.** 220   **3.** 333   **5.** 108   **7.** 1110   **9.** 2737   **11.** 629

p. 40 Ex 1–8 E   **1.** 500   **3.** 827   **5.** 3   **7.** 6024   **9.** 29,000   **11.** 4978

p. 40 Ex 1–8 F   **1.** 95   **3.** 110   **5.** 8   **7.** 697   **9.** 177   **11.** 3095

p. 40 Ex 1–8 G   **1.** 11   **3.** 2   **5.** 245   **7.** 81   **9.** 194   **11.** 116

p. 40 Ex 1–8 H   **1.** $6810   **3.** $773   **5.** $197   **7.** $4
9. 1, 2, 3, 4, 6, 8, 9, 12, 16, 18, 24, 36, 48, 72, 144; 144 has 9 more factors.

p. 41 Ex 1–8 I   **1.** 23   **3.** 35   **5.** 30   **7.** 57   **9.** 120   **11.** 958

p. 42 Ex 1–8 J   Exercise 10 is a counterexample.

p. 42 Ex 1–8 K   **1.** No; no

3. $\dfrac{834}{675} = \dfrac{800 + 30 + 4}{600 + 70 + 5} = \dfrac{700 + 130 + 4}{600 + 70 + 5} = \dfrac{700 + 120 + 14}{600 + 70 + 5}$

$\overline{159} \qquad\qquad\qquad\qquad\qquad\qquad\qquad\qquad 100 + 50 + 9$

5. $\dfrac{2047}{958} = \dfrac{2000 + 40 + 7}{900 + 50 + 8} = \dfrac{1900 + 140 + 7}{900 + 50 + 8} = \dfrac{1900 + 130 + 17}{900 + 50 + 8}$

$\overline{1089} \qquad\qquad\qquad\qquad\qquad\qquad\qquad\qquad 1000 + 80 + 9$

7. Yes

p. 43 Ex 1–8 L   **1.** True   **3.** True   **5.** True   **7.** True
9. (a) false; **(b)** true

p. 47 Ex 1–9 A   **1.** 8   **3.** 6   **5.** 9   **7.** 8   **9.** 13   **11.** 5   **13.** 5   **15.** 15
17. 8   **19.** 8

p. 47 Ex 1–9 B   **1.** 64   **3.** 31   **5.** 205   **7.** 415   **9.** 886   **11.** 2001

p. 47 Ex 1–9 C   **1.** 1779   **3.** 1621   **5.** 235   **7.** 3419   **9.** 10,208   **11.** 8055

p. 47 Ex 1–9 D   **1.** 10; 15   **3.** 30; 30   **5.** 20; 22   **7.** 60; 66   **9.** 40; 45
11. 90; 91

p. 47 Ex 1–9 E   **1.** 80; 97   **3.** 70; 68   **5.** 120; 160   **7.** 80; 79   **9.** 200; 198
11. 70; 76

p. 48 Ex 1–9 F   **1.** 2000; 2031   **3.** 800; 709   **5.** 500; 496   **7.** 200; 201
9. 70; 81   **11.** 95; 93

p. 48 Ex 1–9 G

1.
$$\begin{array}{r}97\\7\overline{)682}\\63\\\hline52\\49\\\hline\fbox{3}\end{array}$$

3.
$$\begin{array}{r}68\\5\overline{)342}\\30\\\hline42\\40\\\hline\fbox{2}\end{array}$$

5.
$$\begin{array}{r}29\\24\overline{)707}\\48\\\hline227\\216\\\hline\fbox{11}\end{array}$$

7.
$$\begin{array}{r}18\\126\overline{)2357}\\126\\\hline1097\\1008\\\hline\fbox{89}\end{array}$$

9.
$$\begin{array}{r}2\\495\overline{)1095}\\990\\\hline\fbox{105}\end{array}$$

11.
$$\begin{array}{r}64\\752\overline{)48703}\\4512\\\hline3583\\3008\\\hline\fbox{575}\end{array}$$

p. 48 Ex 1–9 H   **1.** Divisible; 99   **3.** Divisible; 74   **5.** Divisible; 130
7. Divisible; 1376   **9.** Divisible; 3834   **11.** Divisible; 14,712

p. 48 Ex 1–9 I   **1.** 20 mi/gal   **3.** 28 days   **5.** 3   **7.** 1050 mph
9. Son, $11,715; daughter, $11,715; servant, $3,905

p. 49 Ex 1–9 J   **1.** 75   **3.** 71   **5.** 161   **7.** 52 lb

p. 50 Ex 1–9 K   **1.** 68   **3.** 48   **5.** 49   **7.** 360   **9.** 120   **11.** 756

p. 50 Ex 1–9 L   **1.** 150   **3.** 112   **5.** 77   **7.** 117   **9.** 750   **11.** 900

p. 51 Ex 1–9 M   **1.** 4   **3.** 7   **5.** 2   **7.** 5   **9.** 3   **11.** 4

p. 51 Ex 1–9 N   **1.** 31   **3.** 32   **5.** 24   **7.** 3   **9.** 18   **11.** 45

p. 51 Ex 1–9 O   **1.** 11   **3.** 19   **5.** 7   **7.** 14   **9.** 30   **11.** 72

p. 51 Ex 1–9 P   **1.** Yes   **3.** No   **5.** Yes   **7.** No   **9.** Yes

p. 51 Ex 1–9 Q   **1.** True   **3.** True   **5.** True   **7.** Yes

p. 55 Ex 1–10 A   **1.** 12   **3.** 18   **5.** 24   **7.** 30   **9.** 49   **11.** 75   **13.** 86
15. 172

p. 55 Ex 1–10 B   **1.** 216   **3.** 252   **5.** 228   **7.** 612   **9.** 864   **11.** 3244

p. 56 Ex 1–10 C   **1.** 12   **3.** 24   **5.** 40   **7.** 52   **9.** 104   **11.** 120   **13.** 132
15. 144

p. 56 Ex 1–10 D   **1.** 1000   **3.** 1302   **5.** 2252   **7.** 5141   **9.** 20,432
11. 34,253

p. 56 Ex 1–10 E   **1.** 55   **3.** 34   **5.** 55   **7.** 54   **9.** 44   **11.** 45

p. 56 Ex 1–10 F   **1.** 55 **3.** 54 **5.** 50 **7.** 50 **9.** 53 **11.** 54

p. 57 Ex 1–10 G   **1.** 100 **3.** 110 **5.** 121 **7.** 103 **9.** 114 **11.** 112

p. 57 Ex 1–10 H   **1.** 53 **3.** 55 **5.** 50 **7.** 100 **9.** 100 **11.** 120

p. 59 Ex 1–11 A   **1.** 10 **3.** 20 **5.** 20 **7.** 30 **9.** 30 **11.** 40 **13.** 40 **15.** 50

p. 59 Ex 1–11 B   **1.** 130 **3.** 140 **5.** 200 **7.** 210 **9.** 220 **11.** 240 **13.** 1270 **15.** 1280

p. 60 Ex 1–11 C   **1.** 0 **3.** 100 **5.** 100 **7.** 100 **9.** 100 **11.** 200 **13.** 200 **15.** 200

p. 60 Ex 1–11 D   **1.** 300 **3.** 400 **5.** 400 **7.** 600 **9.** 600 **11.** 1200 **13.** 1400 **15.** 4600

p. 60 Ex 1–11 E   **1.** 850 **3.** 1930 **5.** 10,000 **7.** 110 **9.** 151,000

p. 60 Ex 1–11 F   **1.** 1580 mi **3.** 240,000 mi **5.** 40,000 **7.** $389,000,000 **9.** 6100

p. 62 Chapter Review A   **1. (a)** ℘ ℘℘ ∧∧∧ /////   **(b)** ℘℘ ///////
3. (a) 7 **(b)** $\{a,b,c,r,s,x,y\}$ **(c)** $\emptyset$ **(d)** no **5.** No. Subtraction is not commutative. **7.** 100_{six}; 36_{ten} **9. (a)** 210 **(b)** 21 **(c)** 30.4
 B **1.** 16,654 **3.** 1215 **5.** 121 **7.** $528 **9.** 5011_{six}
 C **1.** N **3.** Yes **5.** Yes **7.** Yes **9.** No

p. 67 Ex 2–1 A   **1.** $\frac{1}{4}$ **3.** $\frac{1}{4}$ **5.** $\frac{5}{8}$ **7.** $\frac{3}{4}$

p. 67 Ex 2–1 B   **1.** $\frac{3}{16}$ **3.** $\frac{19}{64}$ **5.** $\frac{1}{4}$ **7.** $\frac{35}{64}$ **9.** $\frac{23}{64}$ **11.** $\frac{39}{64}$

p. 68 Ex 2–1 C   **1.** $x = 2, y = 3$ **3.** $x = 2, y = 3$ **5.** $x = 2, y = 3$
7. $x = 4, y = 8$ **9.** $x = 4, y = 6$ **11.** $x = 6, y = 9$

p. 68 Ex 2–1 D   **1.** $x = 2, y = 8$ **3.** $x = 3, y = 12$ **5.** $x = 7, y = 28$
7. $x = 3, y = 6$ **9.** $x = 5, y = 15$ **11.** $x = 14, y = 49$

p. 68 Ex 2–1 E   **1.** $x = 6, y = 9$ **3.** $x = 8, y = 12$ **5.** $x = 10, y = 15$
7. $x = 18, y = 27, z = 36$ **9.** $x = 26, y = 39, z = 52$

p. 69 Ex 2–1 F   **1.** $\frac{1}{5}$ **3.** $\frac{2}{3}$ **5.** $\frac{3}{5}$ **7.** $\frac{3}{5}$ **9. (a)** $\frac{13}{360}$ **(b)** $\frac{13}{500}$

p. 69 Ex 2–1 G   **1.** No **3. (a)** $\frac{9}{12}$ **(b)** $\frac{10}{25}$ **(c)** $\frac{18}{20}$ **(d)** $\frac{16}{28}$ **(e)** $\frac{35}{40}$ **(f)** $\frac{18}{24}$
(g) $\frac{27}{6}$ **(h)** $\frac{91}{35}$ **(i)** yes

p. 70 Ex 2–1 H   **1.** $2\frac{1}{4}$ **3.** $3\frac{3}{5}$ **5.** $2\frac{1}{3}$ **7.** $3\frac{1}{2}$ **9.** $1\frac{1}{4}$ **11.** $1\frac{5}{8}$

p. 70 Ex 2–1 I   **1.** 4 **3.** 2 **5.** $1\frac{3}{5}$ **7.** $5\frac{1}{4}$ **9.** 2 **11.** 7

p. 70 Ex 2–1 J   **1.** $2\frac{1}{2}$ **3.** $6\frac{1}{4}$ **5.** $15\frac{2}{3}$ **7.** $5\frac{1}{4}$ **9.** $3\frac{3}{4}$ **11.** $9\frac{2}{3}$

p. 70 Ex 2–1 K   **1.** $\frac{4}{5}$ **3.** $\frac{3}{4}$ **5.** $\frac{3}{4}$ **7.** $\frac{2}{3}$ **9.** 2 **11.** $\frac{8}{3}$ **13.** $\frac{2}{7}$ **15.** $\frac{11}{25}$

p. 70 Ex 2–1 L   **1.** $\frac{4}{3}$ **3.** $\frac{7}{4}$ **5.** $\frac{52}{45}$ **7.** $\frac{73}{98}$

p. 73 Ex 2–2 A   **1.** 3 **3.** 7 **5.** $\frac{3}{4}$ **7.** 4 **9.** 11 **11.** 9

p. 74 Ex 2–2 B   **1.** 1 **3.** 4 **5.** 1 **7.** 8 **9.** 2 **11.** 8

p. 74 Ex 2–2 C   **1.** 2 **3.** 4 **5.** 6 **7.** 16 **9.** 6 **11.** 18

p. 74 Ex 2–2 D   **1.** $n = 6$ **3.** $n = 36$ **5.** $n = 15$ **7.** $n = 12$

9. $a = 1, n = 3$ **11.** $c = 2, n = 22$ **13.** Yes. $\dfrac{ac}{a} = \dfrac{a}{a} \times \dfrac{c}{1} = c$ where $a \neq 0$

p. 75 Ex 2–2 E   **1.** 3 **3.** 21 **5.** 13 **7.** 31 **9.** 19 **11.** 37

p. 75 Ex 2–2 F   **1.** 4 **3.** 7 **5.** 9 **7.** 9 **9.** 7 **11.** 23

p. 75 Ex 2–2 G   **1.** $\frac{1}{6}$ **3.** $\frac{1}{15}$ **5.** $\frac{2}{15}$ **7.** $\frac{3}{10}$ **9.** $\frac{2}{15}$ **11.** $\frac{5}{16}$

p. 76 Ex 2–2 H   1. $\frac{1}{2}$ 3. $\frac{1}{2}$ 5. $\frac{1}{3}$ 7. $\frac{2}{3}$ 9. $\frac{1}{2}$ 11. $\frac{3}{4}$

p. 76 Ex 2–2 I   1. $\frac{2}{3}$ 3. $\frac{1}{4}$ 5. $\frac{1}{3}$ 7. $\frac{3}{4}$ 9. $\frac{1}{2}$ 11. $\frac{1}{4}$

p. 76 Ex 2–2 J   1. $2\frac{1}{4}$ 3. $3\frac{15}{16}$ 5. $1\frac{1}{2}$ 7. $8\frac{1}{2}$ 9. $\frac{1}{2}$ 11. $1\frac{2}{3}$

p. 76 Ex 2–2 K   1. $\frac{1}{2}$ 3. $\frac{1}{4}$ 5. 6   7. 8   9. $\frac{1}{8}$ 11. 5

p. 76 Ex 2–2 L   1. $5\frac{5}{32}$ 3. $\frac{7}{12}$ 5. 3   7. $4\frac{3}{4}$ 9. 10   11. 6

p. 77 Ex 2–2 M   1. 12   3. $116   5. $\frac{1}{4}$ 7. $29.33   9. 475 lb

p. 77 Ex 2–2 N   1. (a) $\frac{8}{15}$ (b) $\frac{8}{15}$ 3. Yes   5. Yes; yes; closure property of multiplication   7. 1   9. (a) $\frac{5}{24}$ (b) $\frac{5}{24}$ (c) $\frac{4}{5}$ (d) $\frac{4}{5}$ (e) yes; yes

p. 78 Ex 2–2 O   1. $\frac{7}{16}$ 3. $\frac{1}{4}$ 5. $\frac{49}{150}$ 7. $34\frac{3}{8}$ 9. $19\frac{11}{16}$

p. 79 Ex 2–2 P   1. 12   3. 2000   5. 9207   7. 850 ft   9. 10,080 sec

p. 79 Ex 2–2 Q   1. 4   3. $7\frac{7}{8}$ 5. $1\frac{1}{2}$ 7. 8   9. $21\frac{2}{3}$ 11. $10\frac{1}{2}$

p. 79 Ex 2–2 R   1. $8   3. $46.50   5. $108   7. $150   9. $4.75   11. $1290

p. 80 Ex 2–2 S   1. 12 ft   3. 24 ft   5. 24 yd   7. 72 yd   9. 20 in.   11. 12 in.

p. 80 Ex 2–2 T   1. True   3. <   5. <   7. True   9. <

p. 82 Ex 2–3 A   1. 4; yes   3. 8; yes; yes   5. Yes; yes; yes   7. Yes; yes; yes   9. Yes; yes; yes   11. Yes

p. 83 Ex 2–3 B   1. Yes; yes   3. Yes; yes   5. Yes; yes   7. Yes; yes

p. 83 Ex 2–3 C   1. Yes   3. Yes   5. Yes   7. (a) yes   (b) yes   (c) yes   (d) yes   (e) yes   (f) yes

p. 83 Ex 2–3 D   1. $\frac{5}{2}$ 3. $\frac{9}{7}$ 5. $\frac{10}{9}$ 7. 1   9. $\frac{1}{5}$ 11. $\frac{4}{11}$

p. 84 Ex 2–3 E   1. $\frac{9}{8}$ 3. $\frac{3}{2}$ 5. 6   7. $\frac{4}{3}$ 9. $\frac{9}{8}$ 11. $\frac{3}{32}$

p. 84 Ex 2–3 F   1. $\frac{9}{4}$ or $2\frac{1}{4}$ 3. $\frac{33}{16}$ or $2\frac{1}{16}$ 5. $\frac{20}{7}$ or $2\frac{6}{7}$ 7. $\frac{5}{6}$ 9. $\frac{2}{3}$ 11. 2

p. 84 Ex 2–3 G   1. $\frac{2}{3}$ 3. $\frac{2}{5}$ 5. $\frac{1}{8}$ 7. 3   9. $\frac{1}{8}$ 11. $\frac{2}{9}$

p. 84 Ex 2–3 H   1. $\frac{4}{3}$ or $1\frac{1}{3}$ 3. $\frac{16}{13}$ or $1\frac{3}{13}$ 5. $\frac{24}{13}$ or $1\frac{11}{13}$ 7. $\frac{20}{9}$ or $2\frac{2}{9}$ 9. $\frac{3}{2}$ or $1\frac{1}{2}$ 11. $\frac{9}{4}$ or $2\frac{1}{4}$

p. 85 Ex 2–3 I   1. $\frac{4}{9}$ 3. $\frac{3}{2}$ or $1\frac{1}{2}$ 5. $\frac{7}{9}$ 7. $\frac{11}{8}$ or $1\frac{3}{8}$ 9. $\frac{11}{11}$ or $1\frac{1}{11}$ 11. $\frac{7}{10}$

p. 85 Ex 2–3 J   1. 2   3. $\frac{9}{8}$ or $1\frac{1}{8}$ 5. $\frac{2}{3}$ 7. $\frac{7}{6}$ or $1\frac{1}{6}$ 9. $\frac{11}{9}$ or $1\frac{2}{9}$ 11. $\frac{2}{3}$

p. 85 Ex 2–3 K   1. $\frac{2}{3}$ 3. $\frac{3}{8}$ 5. $\frac{33}{59}$ 7. $\frac{37}{40}$ 9. $\frac{1}{2}$ 11. 2

p. 85 Ex 2–3 L   1. $\frac{68}{33}$ or $2\frac{2}{33}$ 3. $\frac{1}{2}$ 5. $\frac{53}{11}$ or $4\frac{9}{11}$ 7. 2   9. $\frac{23}{40}$ 11. $\frac{3}{2}$ or $1\frac{1}{2}$

p. 85 Ex 2–3 M   1. 20   3. 20   5. 30   7. 72   9. 6   11. 8

p. 86 Ex 2–3 N   1. $21\frac{1}{3}$ urns   3. $9\frac{3}{11}$ lengths   5. 56 mph   7. $\$\frac{35}{48}$ 9. $2\frac{1}{2}$ hr

p. 86 Ex 2–3 O   1. 0. There is no number e such that $e \times 0 = 1$.   3. Yes   5. No. $\frac{5}{6} \neq \frac{6}{5}$ 7. No

p. 87 Ex 2–3 P   1. $21\frac{1}{3}$ 3. 76   5. $23,552   7. 40 windows   9. $7.75

p. 87 Ex 2–3 Q   1. 18 lb   3. 16 lb   5. 64 lb   7. 25 lb

p. 87 Ex 2–3 R   1. 64 mi

p. 90 Ex 2–4 A   1. 2×5 3. 3×5 5. 3×7 7. 5×7 9. 3×13 11. 5×13

p. 90 Ex 2–4 B   1. 2×2 3. 3×3 5. $3 \times 3 \times 3$ 7. $2 \times 2 \times 2 \times 2$ 9. $3 \times 3 \times 3 \times 3$ 11. $2 \times 2 \times 5 \times 5$

p. 91 Ex 2–4 C   1. $2 \times 3 \times 5$ 3. $2 \times 5 \times 7$ 5. $2 \times 2 \times 5$ 7. $2 \times 3 \times 3 \times 3$ 9. $2 \times 5 \times 5$ 11. $2 \times 2 \times 3 \times 3 \times 5$

405

p. 91 Ex 2–4 D   **1.** $2 \times 2 \times 3 \times 5$ **3.** $2 \times 2 \times 2 \times 2 \times 2 \times 3$
5. 2×17 **7.** 2×19 **9.** $2 \times 2 \times 2 \times 3 \times 5$ **11.** 5×41

p. 91 Ex 2–4 E   **1.** {(1,4), (2,2)} **3.** {(1,6), (2,3)} **5.** {(1,14), (2,7)}
7. {(1,25), (5,5)} **9.** {(1,42), (2,21), (3,14), (6,7)} **11.** {(1,50), (2,25), (5,10)}

p. 91 Ex 2–4 F   **1.** {(1,32), (2,16), (4,8)} **3.** {(1,45), (3,15), (5,9)}
5. {(1,54), (2,27), (3,18), (6,9)} **7.** {(1,72), (2,36), (3,24), (4,18), (6,12), (8,9)}
9. {(1,80), (2,40), (4,20), (5,16), (8,10)} **11.** {(1,110), (2,55), (5,22), (10,11)}

p. 91 Ex 2–4 G   **1.** {(1,112), (2,56), (4,28), (7,16), (8,14)}
3. {(1,124), (2,62), (4,31)}   **5.** {(1,125), (5,25)}
7. {(1,200), (2,100), (4,50), (5,40), (8,25), (10,20)}
9. {(1,212), (2,106), (4,53)} **11.** {(1,225), (3,75), (5,45), (9,25), (15,15)}

p. 92 Ex 2–4 H   **1.** Prime **3.** 3×17 **5.** Prime **7.** 3×13 **9.** Prime

p. 93 Ex 2–4 I   **1.** Prime **3.** Prime **5.** $3 \times 3 \times 13$ **7.** Prime **9.** Prime
11. 17×19

p. 93 Ex 2–4 J   In each of the following exercises, the number in parentheses
takes into account the multiplicity of a factor (i.e., the sum of the unique factors
of 4 is $1 + 2 + 4 = 7$, but the sum of the factors for each factorization of 4 is
$1 + 2 + 2 + 4 = 9$). **1.** 7(9) **3.** 15 **5.** 8 **7.** 24 **9.** 14 **11.** 36

p. 93 Ex 2–4 K   **1.** True **3.** False **5.** False **7.** False **9.** False

p. 93 Ex 2–4 L   **1.** 28 **3.** 12 **5.** 8 **7.** 20 **9.** 24 **11.** 24

p. 94 Ex 2–4 M   **1.** 12 **3.** 12 **5.** 60 **7.** 24 **9.** 6 **11.** 24

p. 94 Ex 2–4 N   **1.** 20 **3.** 30 **5.** 40 **7.** 24 **9.** 40 **11.** 120

p. 94 Ex 2–4 O   **1.** 30 **3.** 60 **5.** 30 **7.** 60 **9.** 120 **11.** 120

p. 94 Ex 2–4 P   **1.** 3 **3.** 5 **5.** 4 **7.** 1 **9.** 5

p. 94 Ex 2–4 Q   **1.** 1; relatively prime **3.** 1; relatively prime **5.** 3
7. 1; relatively prime **9.** 1; relatively prime **11.** 1; relatively prime **13.** 5

p. 97 Ex 2–5 A   **1.** 1 **3.** 1 **5.** $1\frac{1}{3}$ **7.** $1\frac{1}{2}$ **9.** 1 **11.** $\frac{4}{5}$

p. 97 Ex 2–5 B   **1.** $x = 3, y = 4, s = 1\frac{1}{6}$ **3.** $x = 21, y = 6, s = 1\frac{13}{14}$
5. $x = 9, y = 2, s = 3\frac{2}{3}$ **7.** $x = 20, y = 21, s = 1\frac{5}{36}$
9. $x = 20, y = 21, s = 1\frac{17}{24}$ **11.** $x = 25, y = 49, s = 2\frac{4}{35}$

p. 98 Ex 2–5 C   **1.** $\frac{5}{6}$ **3.** $\frac{4}{5}$ **5.** $1\frac{3}{14}$ **7.** $\frac{7}{12}$ **9.** $\frac{19}{24}$ **11.** $1\frac{4}{15}$

p. 98 Ex 2–5 D   **1.** $1\frac{1}{12}$ **3.** $1\frac{5}{12}$ **5.** $1\frac{23}{24}$ **7.** $1\frac{11}{12}$ **9.** $1\frac{7}{12}$ **11.** $1\frac{23}{24}$

p. 98 Ex 2–5 E   **1.** $2\frac{1}{4}$ **3.** $4\frac{5}{12}$ **5.** $2\frac{1}{9}$ **7.** $2\frac{3}{4}$ **9.** $6\frac{1}{4}$ **11.** $4\frac{1}{3}$

p. 98 Ex 2–5 F   **1.** $7\frac{7}{8}$ **3.** $5\frac{11}{16}$ **5.** $12\frac{17}{24}$ **7.** $11\frac{9}{20}$

p. 99 Ex 2–5 G   **1.** $11\frac{7}{12}$ **3.** $20\frac{5}{24}$ **5.** $10\frac{7}{24}$ **7.** $5\frac{11}{16}$

p. 99 Ex 2–5 H   **1.** $5\frac{1}{24}$ **3.** 14 **5.** $3\frac{19}{24}$ **7.** $28\frac{31}{60}$

p. 99 Ex 2–5 I   **1.** $16\frac{11}{24}$ ft **3.** $\$3661\frac{1}{2}$ **5.** $22\frac{1}{4}$ in. **7.** $20\frac{7}{30}$ hr **9.** $408\frac{3}{4}$ ft

p. 100 Ex 2–5 J   **1.** $8\frac{1}{8}$ ft **3.** $27\frac{7}{24}$ ft **5.** $7\frac{13}{16}$ ft **7.** $9\frac{5}{12}$ ft **9.** $7\frac{1}{16}$ ft

p. 100 Ex 2–5 K   **1.** $\$7\frac{1}{2}$ **3.** $\$4$ **5.** $\$8\frac{1}{24}$ **7.** $\$20\frac{1}{3}$ **9.** $\$69\frac{11}{20}$

p. 101 Ex 2–5 L   **1.** $1\frac{5}{9}$ **3.** $3\frac{1}{4}$ **5.** $1\frac{3}{7}$ **7.** $\frac{63}{64}$ **9.** $1\frac{9}{28}$ **11.** $4\frac{7}{11}$

p. 101 Ex 2–5 M   **1.** $\frac{11}{20}$ **3.** $1\frac{8}{13}$ **5.** $1\frac{11}{17}$ **7.** $3\frac{93}{170}$ **9.** $3\frac{9}{19}$ **11.** $4\frac{3}{7}$

p. 102 Ex 2–5 N   **1.** $4\frac{2}{3}$ **3.** 7 **5.** $\frac{31}{36}$ **7.** $3\frac{17}{75}$

p. 102 Ex 2–5 O   **1.** $3\frac{1}{6}$ **3.** $5\frac{11}{12}$ **5.** $6\frac{1}{8}$ **7.** $8\frac{5}{8}$
9. Yes; associative law of addition

p. 102 Ex 2–5 P   **1.** $\frac{15}{32}$ **3.** $4\frac{1}{2}$ **5.** $1\frac{7}{12}$ **7.** $\frac{91}{128}$ **9.** Yes; distributive law

p. 102 Ex 2–5 Q   1. $\frac{1}{8}$ 3. $\frac{1}{16}$ 5. $1\frac{3}{8}$ 7. $\frac{1}{24}$ 9. $1\frac{1}{4}$ 11. $1\frac{1}{12}$

p. 103 Ex 2–5 R   1. $1\frac{3}{8}$ 3. $\frac{7}{8}$ 5. $6\frac{2}{3}$ 7. $10\frac{1}{4}$ 9. $6\frac{1}{6}$ 11. $7\frac{3}{5}$

p. 104 Ex 2–6 A   1. $\frac{1}{2}$ 3. 0 5. $\frac{1}{2}$ 7. $\frac{1}{4}$ 9. $\frac{3}{4}$ 11. $1\frac{1}{4}$

p. 105 Ex 2–6 B   1. $\frac{1}{4}$ 3. $\frac{3}{8}$ 5. $\frac{7}{15}$ 7. $\frac{5}{24}$ 9. $\frac{2}{9}$ 11. $\frac{5}{16}$

p. 105 Ex 2–6 C   1. $\frac{5}{16}$ 3. $\frac{3}{10}$ 5. $\frac{1}{5}$ 7. $\frac{7}{20}$ 9. $\frac{2}{5}$ 11. $\frac{5}{12}$

p. 105 Ex 2–6 D   1. $1\frac{1}{4}$ 3. $1\frac{1}{8}$ 5. $3\frac{13}{24}$ 7. $3\frac{1}{6}$ 9. $1\frac{1}{6}$ 11. $8\frac{1}{12}$

p. 105 Ex 2–6 E   1. $\frac{3}{4}$ 3. $2\frac{1}{2}$ 5. $1\frac{2}{3}$ 7. $1\frac{1}{3}$ 9. $3\frac{1}{5}$ 11. $2\frac{1}{24}$

p. 105 Ex 2–6 F   1. $3\frac{3}{16}$ 3. $1\frac{13}{20}$ 5. $3\frac{17}{24}$ 7. $2\frac{21}{32}$ 9. $1\frac{1}{16}$ 11. $4\frac{23}{30}$

p. 106 Ex 2–6 G   1. $1\frac{5}{16}$ 3. $3\frac{1}{16}$ 5. $4\frac{19}{24}$ 7. $5\frac{2}{3}$ 9. $5\frac{11}{12}$ 11. $4\frac{19}{30}$

p. 106 Ex 2–6 H   1. $1\frac{9}{12}$ 3. $8\frac{11}{15}$ 5. $4\frac{11}{30}$ 7. $4\frac{131}{144}$ 9. $8\frac{43}{72}$ 11. $20\frac{19}{40}$

p. 106 Ex 2–6 I   1. $\$5\frac{7}{8}$ 3. $13\frac{3}{4}$ in. 5. $28\frac{3}{4}$ lb 7. $\frac{2}{125}$ 9. First; $\frac{7}{8}$ ft

p. 107 Ex 2–6 J   1. $6\frac{19}{24}$ lb 3. $1\frac{29}{30}$ lb 5. $11\frac{9}{16}$ lb 7. $9\frac{35}{48}$ lb 9. $64\frac{3}{8}$ lb

p. 107 Ex 2–6 K   1. $2\frac{5}{6}$ yd 3. $1\frac{2}{3}$ yd 5. $4\frac{23}{30}$ yd 7. $2\frac{5}{6}$ yd 9. $18\frac{1}{48}$ yd

p. 108 Ex 2–7 A   1. < 3. True 5. True 7. > 9. True 11. >

p. 109 Ex 2–7 B   1. True 3. > 5. True 7. < 9. < 11. >

p. 109 Ex 2–7 C   1. True 3. < 5. True 7. True 9. True 11. <

p. 109 Ex 2–7 D   1. $\frac{1}{4}, \frac{2}{4}, \frac{3}{4}$ 3. $\frac{1}{5}, \frac{1}{4}, \frac{1}{3}$ 5. $\frac{2}{9}, \frac{1}{3}, \frac{3}{7}$ 7. $\frac{13}{21}, \frac{19}{14}, \frac{5}{7}$
9. $\frac{69}{100}, \frac{7}{10}, \frac{19}{25}$ 11. $\frac{7}{12}, \frac{5}{8}, \frac{11}{16}$

p. 109 Ex 2–7 E   1. $\frac{1}{2}, \frac{7}{12}, \frac{5}{8}, \frac{3}{4}$ 3. $\frac{11}{10}, \frac{7}{5}, 1\frac{1}{2}, 2\frac{1}{10}$ 5. $1\frac{11}{12}, 2, 1\frac{13}{12}, 1\frac{7}{}$
7. $3\frac{3}{8}, 3\frac{5}{12}, 2\frac{19}{12}, 3\frac{2}{3}$ 9. $\frac{3}{10}, \frac{3}{8}, \frac{3}{5}, \frac{3}{4}, \frac{3}{2}$

p. 109 Ex 2–7 F   1. 4 3. 8 5. 2 7. 9 9. 4 11. 8

p. 110 Ex 2–7 G   1. 18 3. 18 5. 22 7. 25 9. 7 11. 25

p. 110 Ex 2–7 H   1. $2\frac{1}{3}$ ft 3. $19\frac{1}{5}$ ft 5. $4\frac{3}{8}$ ft 7. $\frac{15}{16}$ ft 9. $\frac{17}{9}$ ft

p. 110 Ex 2–7 I   1. > 3. True 5. > 7. True 9. True 11. >

p. 110 Ex 2–7 J   1. True 3. > 5. > 7. > 9. True

p. 111 Chapter Review A   1. $1\frac{23}{30}$ 3. $\frac{3}{8}$ 5. $\frac{9}{28}$ 7. 96 9. $\frac{11}{15}$

B 1. All 3. Yes. $\frac{3\frac{1}{2}}{3\frac{1}{2}} = 1$ 5. Yes 7. Yes, but only one l.c.d.; $\frac{1}{2}$ and

$\frac{1}{6}$ may be expressed with a common denominator of 6, 12, 18, 24, etc.

9. $\frac{a}{b}$. Given $a > r$, then $ab > rb$ and $\frac{a}{b} > \frac{r}{b}$.

p. 112 Review of Chapters 1–2 A   1. True 3. W 5. True 7. $\frac{4}{5}$
9. 60 11. True

B 1. $3(10^3) + 4(10^2) + 5(10) + 8$ 3. $\frac{91}{120}$ 5. 5423 7. $\$0.98$ 9. $\frac{516}{150}$
11. $\$65.00$

p. 115 Ex 3–1 A   1. $\frac{2}{10} + \frac{3}{100}$ 3. $\frac{6}{10} + \frac{2}{100} + \frac{5}{1000}$
5. $\frac{1}{10} + \frac{2}{100} + \frac{3}{1000} + \frac{4}{10,000}$ 7. $\frac{7}{100} + \frac{1}{1000} + \frac{2}{10,000}$
9. $\frac{4}{10} + \frac{7}{100} + \frac{3}{1000}$ 11. $\frac{2}{10} + \frac{3}{1000} + \frac{5}{10,000}$

p. 115 Ex 3–1 B   1. 0.7 3. 0.97 5. 0.75 7. 0.615 9. 0.088 11. 0.013

p. 115 Ex 3–1 C   1. 1.8 3. 3.7 5. 2.73 7. 8.75 9. 17.5 11. 1.365

p. 116 Ex 3–1 D   1. 1.6 3. 0.016 5. 0.00016 7. 37.5 9. 0.375 11. 0.00375

p. 116 Ex 3–1 E   1. Three tenths 3. Three thousandths

5. Three hundred thousandths   **7.** Two and six tenths
9. Two and six thousandths   **11.** Forty-five and ninety-three thousandths
p. 116 Ex 3–1 F   **1.** Twelve and seven tenths
3. Forty-six and five thousandths   **5.** Two hundred twenty and six hundredths
7. One and three hundred seventy-five ten thousandths   **9.** Four and six hundred
five ten thousandths   **11.** Two hundred forty-four and five hundredths

p. 116 Ex 3–1 G   **1.** 0.37   **3.** 0.297   **5.** 1.47   **7.** 0.61   **9.** 0.823   **11.** 0.1101

p. 116 Ex 3–1 H   **1.** 0.3   **3.** 0.06   **5.** 0.01   **7.** 0.206   **9.** 0.0091

p. 117 Ex 3–1 I   **1.** 1.3   **3.** 7000.1   **5.** 7.81   **7.** 19.19   **9.** 403.1

p. 117 Ex 3–1 J   **1.** $\frac{4}{5}$ **3.** $\frac{2}{5}$ **5.** $\frac{1}{4}$ **7.** $\frac{7}{20}$ **9.** $\frac{1}{10}$ **11.** $\frac{1}{5}$

p. 117 Ex 3–1 K   **1.** $\frac{9}{25}$ **3.** $\frac{3}{4}$ **5.** $\frac{1}{8}$ **7.** $\frac{19}{200}$ **9.** $\frac{9}{125}$ **11.** $\frac{37}{200}$

p. 117 Ex 3–1 L   **1.** $1\frac{3}{5}$ **3.** $\frac{151}{200}$ **5.** $25\frac{1}{4}$ **7.** $15\frac{2}{5}$ **9.** $8\frac{1}{8}$ **11.** $4\frac{29}{40}$

p. 118 Ex 3–1 M   **1.** 90   **3.** 1250   **5.** 130   **7.** 2500   **9.** 310

p. 118 Ex 3–1 N   **1.** 0.6   **3.** 0.44   **5.** 0.95   **7.** 0.5   **9.** 0.34   **11.** 0.26

p. 119 Ex 3–2 A   **1.** 2.8   **3.** 1.28   **5.** 6.0   **7.** 12.3   **9.** 1.4   **11.** 7.0
13. 0.6   **15.** 6.5   **17.** 1.001   **19.** 1.0

p. 119 Ex 3–2 B   **1.** 1.8   **3.** 1.35   **5.** 1.12   **7.** 1.061   **9.** 1.2642

p. 120 Ex 3–2 C   **1.** 13.73   **3.** 43.93   **5.** 137.16   **7.** 182.812   **9.** 103.661
11. 481.000

p. 120 Ex 3–2 D   **1.** 21.2   **3.** 67.39   **5.** 129.20   **7.** 190.47   **9.** 95.296
11. 38.000

p. 120 Ex 3–2 E   **1.** 253.54   **3.** 599.18   **5.** 43.884   **7.** 247.772   **9.** 554.675
11. 7887.475

p. 121 Ex 3–2 F   **1.** 0.885   **3.** 3.335   **5.** 23.747   **7.** 97.2   **9.** 128.73

p. 121 Ex 3–2 G   **1.** 93.3 ft   **3.** 7.21 in.   **5.** 33.0080   **7.** $989.57   **9.** $99.06

p. 122 Ex 3–2 H   **1.** 5.4   **3.** 75.9   **5.** 0.948   **7.** 16.515   **9.** 200.92
11. 246.00

p. 122 Ex 3–2 I   **1.** 5.89   **3.** 28.45   **5.** 11.100   **7.** 93.00   **9.** 99.90
11. 98.559

p. 122 Ex 3–2 J   **1.** 21.0 lb   **3.** 37.39 lb   **5.** 0.9890 lb   **7.** 12.42 lb
9. 48.35 lb

p. 124 Ex 3–3 A   **1.** 2.0   **3.** 4.4   **5.** 25.3   **7.** 2.0   **9.** 11.4   **11.** 5.14
13. 4.24   **15.** 18.03

p. 124 Ex 3–3 B   **1.** 15.5   **3.** 47.1   **5.** 26.5   **7.** 22.6   **9.** 31.9   **11.** 1.06
13. 3.12   **15.** 8.16

p. 124 Ex 3–3 C   **1.** 13.1   **3.** 6.18   **5.** 2.52   **7.** 7.92   **9.** 8.06

p. 124 Ex 3–3 D   **1.** 0.715   **3.** 1.098   **5.** 4.638   **7.** 31.156   **9.** 17.86

p. 125 Ex 3–3 E   **1.** 4.56   **3.** 2.28   **5.** 2.65   **7.** 40.92   **9.** 1188.49

p. 125 Ex 3–3 F   **1.** 6.54   **3.** 13.91   **5.** 8.14   **7.** 2.831   **9.** 4.542
11. 123.7801

p. 125 Ex 3–3 G   **1.** 23.6   **3.** 8.26   **5.** 2.57   **7.** 5.84   **9.** 7.709   **11.** 52.036

p. 125 Ex 3–3 H   **1.** 79.6 yd   **3.** $ 0.31   **5.** $84.25
7. Food, $97.10; clothing, $25.50   **9.** No; correct change is $2.52.

p. 126 Ex 3–3 I   **1.** 4.85, 5.15   **3.** 18.25, 19.75   **5.** 8.475, 8.525
7. 8.745, 8.755   **9.** 27.310, 27.360   **11.** 96.875, 97.125

p. 127 Ex 3–3 J   **1.** 7.3   **3.** 18.4   **5.** 13.5   **7.** 7.76   **9.** 13.4   **11.** 175.38

p. 127 Ex 3–3 K   **1.** 0.079 ft   **3.** 0.0002 ft   **5.** 1.45 ft   **7.** 49.8 ft
9. 107.37 ft

p. 129 Ex 3–4 A   **1. (a)** yes   **(b)** yes   **3. (a)** yes   **(b)** yes   **5.** Yes   **7.** Yes

p. 130 Ex 3–4 B   **1.** 3000; 3956.4   **3.** 30; 39.564   **5.** 30; 39.564
7. 300; 395.64   **9.** 0.3; 0.39564   **11.** Yes

p. 130 Ex 3–4 C   **1.** 0.5   **3.** 12.6   **5.** 2130.5   **7.** 0.18   **9.** 10   **11.** 2.1
13. 32   **15.** 8.4   **17.** 5.6   **19.** 100   **21.** 9

p. 130 Ex 3–4 D   **1.** 0.045   **3.** 0.1024   **5.** 3.75   **7.** 9   **9.** 4.096   **11.** 2.704

p. 131 Ex 3–4 E   **1.** 10.86   **3.** 206.25   **5.** 4.576   **7.** 0.1225   **9.** 4.34456

p. 131 Ex 3–4 F   **1. (a)** 21; **(b)** 18.7   **3. (a)** 2000; **(b)** 2278.08
5. (a) 6; **(b)** 6.7175   **7. (a)** 117; **(b)** 116.754   **9. (a)** 4500; **(b)** 4267.6
11. (a) 4; **(b)** 4.78125

p. 131 Ex 3–4 G   **1.** 56.4   **3.** 501.6   **5.** 32   **7.** 160.55   **9.** 576.9
11. 1154.4

p. 131 Ex 3–4 H   **1. (a)** 0.67; **(b)** 0.87217   **3. (a)** 450; **(b)** 437.4732
5. (a) 160; **(b)** 142.1847   **7. (a)** 900; **(b)** 1082.75   **9. (a)** 36; **(b)** 35.39646
11. (a) 80; **(b)** 89.5635

p. 132 Ex 3–4 I   **1.** 237   **3.** 57.13   **5.** 251.33   **7.** 81,075.2   **9.** 81,075.2

p. 132 Ex 3–4 J   **1.** 693.55 lb   **3.** 59.84 gal   **5.** $49.00   **7.** $23.75
9. $550.725 or $550.73

p. 133 Ex 3–4 K   **1.** 2720 lb   **3.** 22,176 lb   **5.** 6480 lb   **7.** 1825 ft   **9.** 35 ft

p. 133 Ex 3–4 L   **1.** 63 man-hr   **3.** $41.03   **5.** 44.092 lb   **7.** 337 in.
9. 77.5775 lb

p. 134 Ex 3–4 M   **1.** 0.0   **3.** 0.8   **5.** 0.2   **7.** 0.0   **9.** 5.1   **11.** 17.0
13. 90.1   **15.** 25.0

p. 134 Ex 3–4 N   **1.** 0.6   **3.** 6   **5.** 6.9   **7.** 21   **9.** 98.7   **11.** 3841.2

p. 134 Ex 3–4 O   **1.** 43.75   **3.** 0.45   **5.** 91.96   **7.** 476.71   **9.** 387.19125
11. 1057.16

p. 134 Ex 3–4 P   **1.** $135.00   **3.** $597.21   **5.** $16.13   **7.** $4.01
9. $875.00   **11.** $201.30   **13.** $199.77   **15.** $465.75

p. 136 Ex 3–5 A   **1.** 3.1   **3.** 0.9   **5.** 0.4   **7.** 36   **9.** 24   **11.** 100   **13.** 50
15. 35

p. 136 Ex 3–5 B   **1.** 42   **3.** 1600   **5.** 3.3   **7.** 2.11   **9.** 40   **11.** 2.4

p. 137 Ex 3–5 C   **1. (a)** 8000; **(b)** 9000   **3. (a)** 17; **(b)** 18.5
5. (a) 25; **(b)** 32   **7. (a)** 11; **(b)** 12.3   **9. (a)** 90; **(b)** 108   **11. (a)** 7; **(b)** 7.5

p. 137 Ex 3–5 D   **1. (a)** 3; **(b)** 3.2   **3. (a)** 4; **(b)** 4   **5. (a)** 23; **(b)** 20.8
7. (a) 4; **(b)** 3.9   **9. (a)** 0.3; **(b)** 0.28   **11. (a)** 14; **(b)** 13.8

p. 137 Ex 3–5 E   **1.** $0.81   **3.** $2.413   **5.** $37.65   **7.** 15.5 gal   **9.** $9750

p. 138 Ex 3–5 F   **1.** 5.5   **3.** 6.9   **5.** 3.9   **7.** 5.0   **9.** 4.4   **11.** 0.8

p. 138 Ex 3–5 G   **1. (a)** 2; **(b)** 2.01   **3. (a)** 0.1; **(b)** 0.12   **5. (a)** 2.5;
(b) 2.56   **7. (a)** 0.06; **(b)** 0.06   **9. (a)** 0.4; **(b)** 0.45   **11. (a)** 0.3; **(b)** 0.37

p. 138 Ex 3–5 H   **1.** 0.165   **3.** 0.0625   **5.** 2.91073   **7.** 0.18007
9. 0.005507   **11.** Move decimal point p places to the left.

p. 138 Ex 3–5 I   **1.** 0.130   **3.** 3.229   **5.** 0.120   **7.** 10.132   **9.** 0.073   **11.** 0.222

p. 141 Ex 3–6 A   **1.** 2   **3.** 125   **5.** 25   **7.** 625

p. 141 Ex 3–6 B   **1.** 0.25   **3.** 0.4   **5.** 0.5   **7.** 0.125   **9.** 0.625   **11.** 0.4375
13. 0.7   **15.** 0.6875

p. 141 Ex 3–6 C   **1.** $\frac{2}{5}$ **3.** $\frac{1}{2}$ **5.** $\frac{4}{5}$ **7.** $\frac{2}{25}$ **9.** $\frac{6}{25}$ **11.** $\frac{17}{20}$ **13.** $\frac{1}{50}$
15. $\frac{99}{100}$

p. 141 Ex 3–6 D   **1.** 0.333   **3.** 0.667   **5.** 0.294   **7.** 0.429   **9.** 0.647
11. 0.556   **13.** 0.778   **15.** 0.714.

p. 142 Ex 3–6 E   **1.** $1\frac{1}{2}$ **3.** $11\frac{13}{20}$ **5.** $2\frac{3}{40}$ **7.** $10\frac{1}{100}$ **9.** $9\frac{1}{8}$ **11.** $5\frac{7}{8}$
13. $4\frac{3}{80}$ **15.** $12\frac{5}{8}$

p. 142 Ex 3–6 F   **1.** 0.28 > 0.279   **3.** 0.650 > 0.64   **5.** 0.04 > 0.004
7. 0.143 > 0.1399   **9.** 1.21 > 1.2075   **11.** 9.011 > 9.002

p. 142 Ex 3–6 G   **1.** True   **3.** >   **5.** <   **7.** True   **9.** True   **11.** =

p. 142 Ex 3–6 H   **1.** 2.5 ft   **3.** 7.006 ft   **5.** 0.25 ft   **7.** 0.518 ft   **9.** 2.9925 ft

p. 142 Ex 3–6 I   **1.** 0.125   **3.** 0.2525   **5.** 0.1625   **7.** 0.625   **9.** 2.13275
11. 0.0075   **13.** 0.1256   **15.** 0.0175875

p. 143 Ex 3–6 J   **1.** $\frac{1}{9}$ **3.** $\frac{41}{333}$ **5.** $\frac{17}{99}$

p. 145 Ex 3–7 A   **1.** 5%   **3.** 23%   **5.** 75%   **7.** 93%   **9.** 125%   **11.** 150%
13. 62.5%   **15.** 12.5%

p. 145 Ex 3–7 B   **1.** 12.5%   **3.** 50%   **5.** 37.5%   **7.** 87.5%   **9.** 100%
11. 28%   **13.** 130%   **15.** 141.7%

p. 146 Ex 3–7 C   **1.** 33.3%   **3.** 11.1%   **5.** 6.2%   **7.** 544.4%   **9.** 66.7%
11. 55.6%   **13.** 166.7%   **15.** 42.9%

p. 146 Ex 3–7 D   **1.** (a) 0.01; (b) $\frac{1}{100}$ **3.** (a) 0.05; (b) $\frac{1}{20}$
5. (a) 0.35; (b) $\frac{7}{20}$ **7.** (a) 0.75; (b) $\frac{3}{4}$ **9.** (a) 0.1; (b) $\frac{1}{10}$
11. (a) 1.15; (b) $1\frac{3}{20}$ **13.** (a) 0.125; (b) $\frac{1}{8}$ **15.** (a) 2; (b) 2

p. 146 Ex 3–7 E   **1.** (a) 0.005; (b) $\frac{1}{200}$ **3.** (a) 0.375; (b) $\frac{3}{8}$
5. (a) 0.0025; (b) $\frac{1}{400}$ **7.** (a) 0.875; (b) $\frac{7}{8}$ **9.** (a) 0.225; (b) $\frac{9}{40}$
11. (a) $0.66\frac{2}{3}$; (b) $\frac{2}{3}$ **13.** (a) $0.16\frac{2}{3}$; (b) $\frac{1}{6}$ **15.** (a) 0.7225; (b) $\frac{289}{400}$

p. 146 Ex 3–7 F   **1.** 20%   **3.** 75%   **5.** 33%   **7.** 52%, 48%   **9.** 75%

p. 148 Ex 3–8 A   **1.** 5.5   **3.** 38.4   **5.** 5.4   **7.** 18.5   **9.** 21.6   **11.** 851

p. 148 Ex 3–8 B   **1.** $87.48   **3.** 4673.6 lb   **5.** 42   **7.** 4212 people
9. $31.34

p. 148 Ex 3–8 C   **1.** 400   **3.** 100   **5.** 104   **7.** 200   **9.** 28   **11.** 2700

p. 149 Ex 3–8 D   **1.** 400   **3.** $850 + $34 = $884   **5.** $1250.22
7. $1020   **9.** $65.86

p. 149 Ex 3–8 E   **1.** 25%   **3.** 37.5%   **5.** 3.75%   **7.** 5%   **9.** 2.5%
11. 12,200%

p. 149 Ex 3–8 F   **1.** 12%   **3.** 35%   **5.** 40%   **7.** $83\frac{1}{3}$%   **9.** 37.5%

p. 150 Ex 3–8 G   **1.** Yes   **3.** Yes   **5.** (a) 1 (b) 1 (c) 2 (d) 36   **7.** $787.50
9. 80 fps

p. 152 Ex 3–9 A   **1.** 1×10^3 **3.** 7×10 **5.** 9×10^2 **7.** 7×10^3
9. 8.05×10^2 **11.** 1.9×10^3 **13.** 3.5×10^3 **15.** 1.6×10^6

p. 153 Ex 3–9 B   **1.** 1×10^{-2} **3.** 1×10^{-4} **5.** 6.5×10^{-2}
7. 1.01×10^{-2} **9.** 4.4×10^{-4} **11.** 3.74×10^{-4} **13.** 1.72×10^{-5}
15. 1.13×10^{-5}

p. 153 Ex 3–9 C   **1.** 170   **3.** 7,000,000   **5.** 4570   **7.** 362   **9.** 183
11. 81,200

410

p. 153 Ex 3–9 D   **1.** 0.03   **3.** 0.016   **5.** 0.000606   **7.** 0.000475
9. 0.00000139   **11.** 0.0004713

p. 153 Ex 3–9 E   **1.** 1.86×10^5 **3.** 1.083×10^3 **5.** $\$4.3 \times 10^4$
7. 7.457×10^{-1} **9.** 1.4×10^{-2}

p. 155 Ex 3–10 A   **1.** 3.25   **3.** 25.13   **5.** 20.23   **7.** 232.5   **9.** 3003.25

p. 155 Ex 3–10 B   **1.** $4 \times \frac{1}{6}$ **3.** $(3 \times \frac{1}{6}) + (2 \times \frac{1}{36})$
5. $(2 \times \frac{1}{6}) + (4 \times \frac{1}{216})$ **7.** $(2 \times \frac{1}{6}) + (3 \times \frac{1}{36}) + (2 \times \frac{1}{216})$
9. $(3 \times 1) + (5 \times \frac{1}{6}) + (2 \times \frac{1}{216})$
11. $(4 \times 1) + (1 \times \frac{1}{6}) + (5 \times \frac{1}{36}) + (3 \times \frac{1}{216})$

p. 156 Ex 3–10 C   **1.** 0.3   **3.** 1.0   **5.** 1.4   **7.** 4.0   **9.** 4.2   **11.** 10.5

p. 156 Ex 3–10 D   **1.** 3.35   **3.** 10.03   **5.** 41.03   **7.** 204.01   **9.** 41.331
11. 50.343

p. 156 Ex 3–10 E   **1.** 0.1   **3.** 2.1   **5.** 20.1   **7.** 0.5   **9.** 2.4   **11.** 0.5

p. 156 Ex 3–10 F   **1.** 1.05   **3.** 3.04   **5.** 4.05   **7.** 10.50   **9.** 23.04
11. 4.115

p. 156 Ex 3–10 G   **1.** 0.4   **3.** 1.2   **5.** 1.3   **7.** 2.3   **9.** 2.4   **11.** 4.1

p. 157 Chapter Review A   **1.** 0.537   **3.** 0.0589   **5.** 1.073   **7.** 0.461
9. 0.7215
  B   **1.** 270   **3.** 25,100   **5.** 60   **7.** 200   **9.** 680
  C   **1.** True   **3.** True   **5.** True   **7.** True   **9.** True
  D   **1.** $n > 3$ or $n < 3.2$ **3.** True   **5.** True   **7.** True   **9.** $p = 2.53$
  E   **1.** 3   **3.** 0.51   **5.** 0.0068   **7.** 0.0081   **9.** 0.403   **11.** 400   **13.** 810
       15. 2%   **17.** 125   **19.** 1200

p. 162 Ex 4–1 A   **1.** Floor, wall, ceiling, etc.
3. **(a)** $\overline{AB} \parallel \overline{CD} \parallel \overline{EF} \parallel \overline{GH}$; $\overline{AC} \parallel \overline{BD} \parallel \overline{HF} \parallel \overline{GE}$
(b) $\overline{AC}$ intersects $\overline{AB}, \overline{AG}, \overline{CD}, \overline{CE}$; $\overline{BD}$ intersects $\overline{AB}, \overline{BH}, \overline{CD}, \overline{DF}$;
$\overline{HF}$ intersects $\overline{BH}, \overline{GH}, \overline{DF}, \overline{EF}$; $\overline{GE}$ intersects $\overline{AG}, \overline{GH}, \overline{CE}, \overline{EF}$.
(c) E; A; B; B **(d)** no; no; no; no   **5. (a)** east   **(b)** south   **(c)** west

p. 163 Ex 4–1 B   **1.** $\angle ABC$, $\angle B$, $\angle CBA$ **3.** $\angle GHI$, $\angle H$, $\angle IHG$
5. $\angle MNP$, $\angle N$, $\angle PNM$

p. 165 Ex 4–2 A   **1.** Right   **3.** Acute   **5.** Obtuse   **7.** Obtuse   **9.** Acute
11. Obtuse

p. 165 Ex 4–2 B   **1.** Acute   **3.** Obtuse   **5.** Obtuse

p. 165 Ex 4–2 C   **1.** 33°   **3.** 122°   **5.** 131°

p. 166 Ex 4–2 E   **1.** 135°55′   **3.** 103°58′   **5.** 91°20′   **7.** 81°44′   **9.** 180°

p. 166 Ex 4–2 F   **1.** 360°   **3.** 45°; 135°   **5.** 81°   **7.** 113°   **9.** 360°

p. 169 Ex 4–3 A   **1.** $x = 4$; $3(4) = 12$ **3.** $x = 7\frac{1}{7}$; $7(7\frac{1}{7}) = 50$
5. $x = 5$; $13(5) = 65$ **7.** $x = 19.4$; $3.75(19.4) = 72.750$
9. $x = 20$; $45(20) = 900$

p. 169 Ex 4–3 B   **1.** $n = 21$; $\frac{1}{3}(21) = 7$ **3.** $n = 1\frac{2}{3}$; $\frac{1}{5}(1\frac{2}{3}) = \frac{1}{3}$
5. $n = 1$; $\frac{1}{5}(1) = \frac{1}{5}$ **7.** $n = 49$; $\frac{1}{7}(49) = 7$ **9.** $n = 270$; $\frac{1}{15}(270) = 18$

p. 170 Ex 4–3 C   **1.** $y = 8$; $\frac{3}{4}(8) = 6$ **3.** $y = 1\frac{3}{5}$; $\frac{5}{8}(1\frac{3}{5}) = 1$
5. $y = 300$; $\frac{4}{15}(300) = 80$ **7.** $y = 8$; $2\frac{3}{4}(8) = 22$ **9.** $y = 819$; $\frac{5}{9}(819) = 455$

p. 170 Ex 4–3 D   **1.** $x = \dfrac{6}{a}$ **3.** $x = \dfrac{d}{c}$ **5.** $x = 17d$ **7.** $x = \dfrac{ad}{c}$

9. $x = \dfrac{ac}{b}$

p. 170 Ex 4–3 E   **1.** 200   **3.** 400   **5.** $2\frac{1}{2}$ hr   **7.** 90°   **9.** $164

p. 170 Ex 4–3 F   **1.** A, 2; B, 6; C, 10   **3.** G, 22; H, 10; I, 28
5. J, $1\frac{1}{5}$; K, 3; L, $4\frac{1}{5}$; M, 6

p. 173 Ex 4–4 A   **1.** 9   **3.** 30   **5.** $4\frac{1}{2}$ **7.** $16\frac{9}{12}$ **9.** $10\frac{1}{2}$ **11.** 59

p. 173 Ex 4–4 B   **1.** 7.5   **3.** 33.9   **5.** 52,800   **7.** 54.9   **9.** 1770.45
11. 659.175

p. 173 Ex 4–4 C   **1.** 2   **3.** 9   **5.** $6\frac{2}{3}$ **7.** 16   **9.** $9\frac{2}{3}$ **11.** $81\frac{2}{3}$

p. 173 Ex 4–4 D $(i/12) = f$ **1.** 3   **3.** 4   **5.** $1\frac{2}{3}$ **7.** $3\frac{1}{4}$ **9.** 9   **11.** 36

p. 174 Ex 4–4 E   **1.** 36   **3.** 81.6   **5.** 33   **7.** 114   **9.** 219   **11.** 165

p. 174 Ex 4–4 F   **1.** $\frac{1}{2}$ **3.** 33   **5.** $12\frac{3}{8}$ **7.** $1\frac{1}{5}$ **9.** 1   **11.** $\frac{1}{2}$

p. 174 Ex 4–4 G   **1.** $5\frac{1}{2}$ yd > 16 ft > 190 in. $> \frac{2}{3}$ rd
3. 7 yd, 1 ft, 3 in. $> 7\frac{1}{3}$ yd > 21.75 ft > 249 in.
5. $AB = \frac{7}{8}$; $CD = 1\frac{1}{8}$; $EF = 1\frac{3}{8}$ **7. (a)** $2\frac{3}{4}$, 1, $1\frac{1}{4}$ **(b)** 33, 12, 15   **9.** 1.5 mi

p. 177 Ex 4–5 A   **1.** 1   **3.** 2   **5.** 4   **7.** 19.5   **9.** 14.96

p. 177 Ex 4–5 B   **1.** 25.4   **3.** 91.44   **5.** 152.4   **7.** 44.45   **9.** 100.965

p. 177 Ex 4–5 C   **1.** 1 yd < 1 m < 105 cm   **3.** $1\frac{1}{2}$ km < 1 mi < 6000 ft
5. 20 cm $= \frac{1}{5}$ m < 10 in.   **7.** $\frac{1}{3}$ m < 350 mm < 14.5 in.
9. 20,000 fathoms < 40 mi < 70 km

p. 177 Ex 4–5 D   **1.** 20.1125 km/hr   **3.** 6.21 mi   **5.** 1.38 in./hr
7. 385.826 in./sec/sec   **9.** 100 mi; by 337 in.

p. 178 Ex 4–5 E   **1.** True   **3.** False (≈ 1.5 mm)   **5.** False   **7.** False
9. True

p. 179 Ex 4–6 A   **1.** 17   **3.** $7\frac{1}{2}$ **5.** $11\frac{1}{6}$ **7.** 1.05   **9.** $56\frac{3}{4}$

p. 180 Ex 4–6 B   **1.** 0   **3.** $3\frac{3}{5}$ **5.** 4.3   **7.** 675   **9.** 12.825

p. 180 Ex 4–6 C   **1.** 19.5   **3.** 75.5   **5.** 45   **7.** 66   **9.** 81

p. 180 Ex 4–6 D   **1.** 3   **3.** 11   **5.** 9   **7.** 42   **9.** 1936

p. 180 Ex 4–6 E   **1.** 18   **3.** $27\frac{1}{2}$ **5.** $4\frac{4}{7}$ **7.** $70\frac{5}{12}$ **9.** $46\frac{31}{33}$

p. 180 Ex 4–6 F   **1.** $C + M = T$; $C = T - M$ **3.** $w + p = g$; $p = g - w$
5. $c + s = t$; $c = t - s$ **7.** $T = p + 0.005p$ **9.** 112

p. 183 Ex 4–7 A   **1.** 46 ft   **3.** 107.5 ft   **5.** 64 in.   **7.** 25 m 4 cm   **9.** 72 rd

p. 183 Ex 4–7 B   **1.** 60 in.   **3.** 87 yd   **5.** 96 rd   **7.** 27 ft   **9.** 33 m 88 cm

p. 184 Ex 4–7 C   **1.** 25 in.   **3.** 40 m   **5.** 25 ft 5 in.   **7.** 20.5 yd
9. $p = a + b + c$

p. 184 Ex 4–7 D   **1.** 5.338 mi   **3.** 10.99 yd   **5.** 14.13 cm   **7.** 50.24 ft
9. 3.14 in.

p. 184 Ex 4–7 E   **1.** 37.68 ft   **3.** 1475.8 in.   **5.** 50.24 cm   **7.** 753.6 ft
9. 2512 yd

p. 184 Ex 4–7 F   **1.** 374 ft   **3.** 55 yd 2 ft   **5.** $60.75   **7.** 29 ft   **9.** $17\frac{1}{2}$ in.

p. 185 Ex 4–7 G   **1.** 14 in.   **3.** 5.84×10^8 mi   **5.** 15.7 in.   **7.** 4 in.
9. 2.87 in.

p. 186 Ex 4–7 H   **1.** 13°   **3.** 99°   **5.** 72°   **7.** 22°   · **9.** 20°   **11.** 179°

p. 189 Ex 4–8 A   **1.** 50 sq ft   **3.** 10 sq yd   **5.** 84 sq m   **7.** 250 sq cm
9. 66,625 sq yd

p. 189 Ex 4–8 B   **1.** 35 sq ft   **3.** 95 sq in.   **5.** 12.49 sq ft   **7.** 1200 sq cm

p. 189 Ex 4–8 C   **1.** 24 sq ft   **3.** $1\frac{11}{16}$ sq ft   **5.** 279 sq ft   **7.** 10 sq m

p. 189 Ex 4–8 D   **1.** 113.04 sq in.   **3.** 706.50 sq m   **5.** 19.625 sq ft
7. 1298.22 sq ft   **9.** 275.98 sq cm

p. 190 Ex 4–8 E   **1.** 9360 sq ft   **3.** 120 ft   **5.** 4840 sq yd   **7.** 284 sq ft
9. 640 acres

p. 190 Ex 4–8 F   **1.** 21.5 sq in.   **3.** 160.14 sq in.

p. 191 Ex 4–8 G   **1.** 40 sq in.
3. The whole circle is equal to the sum of its sectors.
Or, $A = \frac{1}{2}r(b_1 + b_2 + b_3 + b_4 + b_5 + b_6)$
$\qquad = \frac{1}{2}r(C) \qquad (b_1 + b_2 + \cdots + b_6) = C$ (circumference)
$\qquad = \frac{1}{2}r(2\pi r) \qquad C = \pi d \quad d = 2r$
$\qquad = \frac{1}{2}(2\pi r^2)$
$\qquad = \pi r^2 \qquad$ (formula for area of a circle)
5. $A = \frac{1}{2}r \times C \qquad C = 2\pi r$
$\quad A = \frac{1}{2}r \times (2\pi r) \qquad$ Substitute $2\pi r$ for C.
$\quad A = \pi r^2 \qquad \frac{1}{2}(2\pi r) = \pi r; \pi r \times r = \pi r^2$

p. 195 Ex 4–9 A   **1.** 864 sq ft   **3.** 312 sq in.   **5.** 143 sq yd   **7.** 82.1 sq m
9. 45 sq ft   **11.** $150\frac{1}{2}$ sq mm

p. 195 Ex 4–9 B   **1.** (a) $251\frac{3}{7}$ sq in.   (b) $408\frac{4}{7}$ sq in.
3. (a) $1885\frac{5}{7}$ sq in.   (b) $7542\frac{6}{7}$ sq in.   **5.** (a) $62\frac{6}{7}$ sq ft   (b) $69\frac{1}{7}$ sq ft
7. (a) $18,857\frac{1}{7}$ sq cm   (b) $19,083\frac{3}{7}$ sq cm   **9.** (a) 968 sq in.   (b) 2200 sq in.
11. (a) 110 sq mm   (b) 1342 sq mm

p. 196 Ex 4–9 C   **1.** 8 sq ft   **3.** 32.97 sq in.   **5.** 648 sq ft
7. Cube; by 129 sq in.

p. 199 Ex 4–10 A   **1.** 500 sq in.   **3.** 351 sq in.   **5.** 175 sq in.   **7.** 11.25 sq in.

p. 199 Ex 4–10 B   **1.** 942 sq in.   **3.** 678.24 sq in.   **5.** 351.68 sq in.
7. 21.195 sq in.

p. 200 Ex 4–10 C   **1.** 616 sq ft   **3.** 2464 sq ft   **5.** 61,600 sq mi
7. 50,000,000 sq mi

p. 200 Ex 4–10 D   **1.** 200.96 sq ft   **3.** 2.0096×10^8 sq mi   **5.** 20.41 sq ft
7. Sphere; by 314 sq in.

p. 203 Ex 4–11 A   **1.** 36 cu ft   **3.** 10 cu yd   **5.** 1920 cu ft

p. 203 Ex 4–11 B   **1.** 96 cu ft   **3.** 1728 cu in.   **5.** 1920 lb   **7.** 39.25 cu in.
9. 476.67 cu in.

p. 204 Ex 4–11 C   **1.** (a) yes   (b) yes   (c) yes   (d) $V = hB$; yes
3. (a) yes   (b) $V = \frac{1}{3}hB$; yes   **5.** (a) yes   (b) yes   (c) yes   (d) yes
(e) $V = \frac{4}{3}\pi r^3$; yes

p. 207 Chapter Review A   **1.** True   **3.** True   **5.** True   **7.** True   **9.** True
   B   **1.** $n = 2.5; 13 \times 2.5 = 32.5$ **3.** $n = 51; \frac{1}{3} \times 51 = 17$
     5. $n = 40; 2.8 \times 40 = 112$
     7. $x = 9; 3 \times 9 + 41 = 68, 27 + 41 = 68$
     9. $x = 1000; 1.6 \times 1000 - 900 = 700, 1600 - 900 = 700$
   C   **3.** 4427.41 km   **5.** 40   **7.** 264 cu ft   **9.** 31.4 cu in.; no
   D   **1.** True   **3.** $f > y$ **5.** True   **7.** True   **9.** True

p. 209 Review of Chapters 1–4 A   **1.** $9\frac{7}{20}$ **3.** $12\frac{3}{5}$ **5.** 233   **7.** 63   **9.** 9
11. 11
   B   **1.** Yes; 7 hundredths equals 70 thousandths and by the distributive
   property   **3.** Yes; properties for addition of fractions   **5.** Yes;
   property for multiplication of fractions by 1   **7.** 14.4   **9.** 6   **11.** 10.8 lb

C **1.** 0.27 **3.** 0.98 **5.** 0.024 **7.** 1.50 **9.** 41% **11.** 250% **13.** 80%
15. 20,400% **17.** 11.7 lb **19.** 5000 **21.** (a) 4 (b) 2 (c) 4 (d) 5

p. 214 Ex 5–1 A **1.** ~2:1 **3.** ~18:1 **5.** ~13:1 **7.** ~17.5 billion dollars

p. 214 Ex 5–1 B **1.** 50° **3.** Yes; upward **5.** 55°

p. 218 Ex 5–2 A **1.** 6 farmers = 25%

3 mechanics = $12\frac{1}{2}$%

2 electricians = $8\frac{1}{3}$%

4 carpenters = $16\frac{2}{3}$%

9 laborers = $37\frac{1}{2}$%

24   100%

p. 220 Ex 5–3 A **1.** (a) 7.5 (b) 15 (c) 27.5 (d) 45
3. (a) 5 (b) 5 (c) 5 **5.** $E = 5R$

p. 221 Ex 5–3 B **9.** (a) yes; (b) yes; (c) yes; (d) yes;
(e) An ordered pair identifies one specific point; a change in order would identify another specific point.

p. 221 Ex 5–3 C **7.** Yes **9.** (0, 1)

p. 222 Ex 5–3 D **1.** $d = 60t$

p. 222 Ex 5–3 E **1.** $(\frac{1}{2}, 3)$, (1, 6), (2, 12), $(1\frac{1}{2}, 9)$
3. (0, 2), (1, 4), (2, 6), (3, 8) **5.** (0, 32), (5, 41), (10, 50), $(2, 35\frac{3}{5})$

p. 222 Ex 5–3 F **3.** Yes

p. 224 Ex 5–4 A **1.** 1 **3.** $1\frac{3}{4}$ **5.** 3 **7.** 14 **9.** 20° **11.** 58° **13.** 80°
15. 70°

p. 225 Ex 5–4 B **1.** 0 **3.** 12 **5.** 48 **7.** 108

p. 225 Ex 5–4 C **1.** 0 **3.** 146.25 **5.** 374.4 **7.** 1625

p. 225 Ex 5–4 E

1.

x	0	1	2	3	4	5	6	7	8	9	10	11	12	13
y	0	1	4	9	16	25	36	49	64	81	100	121	144	169

14	15	16	17	18	19	20
196	225	256	289	324	361	400

3. (a) 6.5 (b) 8.5 (c) yes (d) yes (e) yes **5.** 3.5 **7.** 9.5 **9.** 12.5
11. 15.5 **13.** 11 ft

p. 228 Ex 5–5 A **1.** $\frac{1}{6}$ **3.** $\frac{1}{6}$ **5.** $\frac{1}{2}$ **7.** $\frac{1}{2}$ **9.** 0

p. 228 Ex 5–5 B **1.** $\frac{1}{2}$ **3.** $\frac{5}{14}$ **5.** $\frac{6}{7}$ **7.** 1

p. 228 Ex 5–5 C **1.** 748 **3.** $\frac{1}{2}$ **5.** $\frac{1}{4}$ **7.** 3 **9.** $\frac{1}{13}$

p. 229 Ex 5–5 D **1.** (a) 5% (b) 50 **3.** $\frac{73}{100}$
5. The grocer would know which brand to stock more of.
7. (a) 2:5 (b) 11:20 **9.** Yes; to regain lost sales

p. 232 Ex 5–6 A

	Mean	Median	Mode	Range
1.	16.8	16	16	6
3.	68.25	73	50	37
5.	7.2	7	6.5	4

p. 232 Ex 5–6 B **1.** $12\frac{15}{19}$ sec **3.** 10.6 sec **5.** Mean
7. No; this range indicates only that the times were all very close.

414

p. 233 Ex 5–6 C   **1.** One-half are greater than $5800 and one-half are less than $5800. **3.** No. **5.** 6 ft $\frac{2}{7}$ in. **7.** 104.94 sq ft **9.** 2.38
11. Yes, it would benefit the manager by increasing earlier shopping; or no, afternoon shoppers would miss the opportunity to win a door prize.

p. 234 Ex 5–6 D   **3.** 9–10, 10–11, 11–12, 12–1, 1–2

p. 235 Ex 5–6 E   **1.** $m = \dfrac{S}{n} = \dfrac{314}{33} = 9.52$ gal **3.** 10

5. $m = \dfrac{S}{n} = \dfrac{21.7}{35} = 0.6$ lb **7.** 0.5 lb

9. (a) 5.7% (b) 14.3% (c) (0.6–0.8) 25.7% (0.4–0.6) 42.9%, (0.2–0.4) 11.4%

p. 239 Ex 5–7 A   **1.** 33° **3.** 20° **5.** 88°40′ **7.** 51°3′

p. 239 Ex 5–7 B   **1.** 31° **3.** 58° **5.** 29°2′ **7.** 41°5′43″

p. 239 Ex 5–7 C   **1.** 660 **3.** 514 **5.** 1950 **7.** 2760

p. 240 Ex 5–7 D   **1.** 90° N; 90° S **3.** 0° N or S of the equator
5. 40°45′ N **7.** 38° W

p. 240 Ex 5–7 E   **1.** 171°52′ **3.** 17° **5.** 261°40′ **7.** 127°10′

p. 240 Ex 5–7 F   Distances measured in nautical miles **1.** 2520 **3.** 2260
5. 3040 **7.** 4500 **9.** 3800

p. 243 Ex 5–8 A   **1.** 10 A.M.; noon; 11 A.M. **3.** 11 A.M. **5.** 90° E
7. 1 P.M. **9.** 8 P.M. Friday

p. 244 Ex 5–8 B   **1.** None **3.** 5 hr **5.** 9 hr **7.** 9 hr

p. 244 Ex 5–8 C   **1.** 4:04 **3.** 3:50 **5.** 4:10

p. 248 Chapter Review A   **5.** c; r

B 1.

n	1	2	3	4	5	6	7	8	9	10	11	12
C	1	2	4	8	16	32	64	128	256	512	1024	2048

13	14	15	16
4096	8192	16,384	32,768

3. $\frac{1}{80}$ **5.** (a) $\frac{79}{200}$ (b) $\frac{93}{200}$ (c) $\frac{7}{50}$
7. (a) $15\frac{1}{2}$ (b) 23.92 (c) 3 and 4 (d) 63

p. 253 Ex 6–1 A   **1.** $40 **3.** $180 **5.** $460 **7.** $14.58 **9.** $12.50

p. 253 Ex 6–1 B   **1.** $53.13 **3.** $69.34 **5.** $3\frac{1}{2}$% **7.** $7000 **9.** $699.57

p. 254 Ex 6–1 C   **1.** $6.81 **3.** $12.10 **5.** $14.04

p. 254 Ex 6–1 D   **1.** $6 **3.** $22.70 **5.** $186 **7.** $4.75
9. (1) $12 (2) $31.50 (3) $45.40 (4) $19.50 (5) $372 (6) $169
(7) $9.50 (8) $15.30 $I = .02p$

p. 254 Ex 6–1 E   **1.** $2.50 **3.** $15.00 **5.** (a) yes; (b) yes; (c) yes

p. 255 Ex 6–1 F   **3.** (a) $1\frac{1}{3}$ (b) $1\frac{1}{3}$ (c) $1\frac{1}{3}$ (d) $1\frac{1}{3}$ **5.** (a) yes; (b) yes

p. 257 Ex 6–2 A   **1.** 30 **3.** 72 **5.** 138 **7.** 70 **9.** 84

p. 258 Ex 6–2 B   **1.** 2 **3.** $S = \frac{7}{2}(a + l)$ **5.** Yes

p. 258 Ex 6–2 C   **1.** (a) yes; (b) yes, by the division axiom

p. 260 Ex 6–3 A   **1.** (a) $62 (b) 12.8% **3.** 33.6% **5.** 40% **7.** 21.4%
9. 28.8%

p. 261 Ex 6–3 B   **1.** 53.3%   **3.** 10.4%   **5.** 55.9%   **7.** 13.1%
9. A, 7.1%; B, 10.6%

p. 262 Ex 6–3 C   **1.** 15   **3. (a)** Yes, by the multiplication axiom; **(b)** yes, by the division axiom   **5. (a)** 0.4   **(b)** 0.6   **(c)** 0.8   **7.** Same

p. 263 Ex 6–3 D   **1.** $p = \dfrac{B(n+1)}{2}$

p. 267 Ex 6–4 A   **1.** $77.40   **3.** $117.00   **5.** $128.40   **7.** $150.15

p. 267 Ex 6–4 B   **1.** $3.25   **3.** $4.91   **5.** $5.39   **7.** $6.31

p. 267 Ex 6–4 C   **1.** $3.36   **3.** $3.79   **5.** $6.18   **7.** $3.52

p. 267 Ex 6–4 D   **1. (a)** $57.00   **(b)** $2.39   **(c)** $6.25   **(d)** $48.36
3. (a) $73.00   **(b)** $3.07   **(c)** $8.97   **(d)** $60.96   **5. (a)** $122.65   **(b)** $5.15
(c) $13.77   **(d)** $103.73   **7. (a)** $103.08   **(b)** $4.33   **(c)** $9.49   **(d)** $89.26

p. 268 Ex 6–4 E   **1.** $787.50   **3.** $107.61   **5. (a)** $98.38   **(b)** $4.13
(c) $9.92   **(d)** $84.33   **7.** $182.42

p. 269 Ex 6–5 A   **1. (a)** $15,720   **(b)** $13,800   **(c)** $16,500   **3.** $70.80
5. $35.40   **7.** $18.35

p. 270 Ex 6–5 B   **1.** $323.40   **3.** $88.90   **5.** 18 squares   **7.** $196.88
9. $253.50   **11.** $140.76

p. 272 Ex 6–5 C   **1.** $1344   **3. (a)** $4.20   **(b)** $16.80   **(c)** $84   **5.** 3.1¢

p. 273 Ex 6–5 D   **1.** $936; $323.40; total, $1259.40   **3.** 15%   **5.** $4703.40
7. Yes; by $1006.80

p. 274 Ex 6–5 E   **1.** Tax, home costs, auto costs, $4704; food, $1680; clothing, $504; health and recreation, $420; education, $252; savings, $672; miscellaneous, $168.   **3.** $\frac{1}{2}$ or 50%

p. 274 Ex 6–5 F   **1. (a)** $x = 0.56i$; **(b)** $y = 0.26i$; **(c)** $z = 0.18i$
(d) $i = x + y + z$ **3. (a)** false; **(b)** true
5. The answer depends upon the student's experience.

p. 278 Ex 6–6 A   **1.** $1080   **3.** $1259.71   **5.** $520.30

p. 278 Ex 6–6 B   **1.** $179.59; $79.59   **3.** $527.80; $127.80
5. $1280.10; $280.10   **7.** $1149.50; $149.50   **9.** $112.68; $12.68

p. 279 Ex 6–6 C   **1.** In 9 yr   **3.** $2232.31   **5.** $3.10   **7.** Yes   **9.** $207.56

p. 280 Ex 6–6 D   **1. (a)** $1.50   **(b)** $3.40   **(c)** $5.10   **3.** 14 yr
5. $4.30; $8.00

p. 281 Ex 6–7 A   **1.** $5.93   **3.** $9.48

p. 283 Ex 6–7 B   **1.** $510.10   **3.** $2045.45   **5.** $2928.52   **7.** $924.95
9. $1322.64

p. 286 Ex 6–7 C   **1. (a)** $1656.00   **(b)** $3312.00   **(c)** $7452.00
3. Open for class discussion   **5. (a)** $1550.00   **(b)** $2667.00   **(c)** $4075.00
(d) $13,110.00   **7. (a)** $2446.00   **(b)** $4892.00   **(c)** $7338.00   **(d)** $9784.00
9. $12,966.00; $360.17   **11. (a)** $2042.00   **(b)** $4888.00   **(c)** $8392.00
(d) $12,962.00

p. 288 Ex 6–7 D   **1. (a)** 64\frac{7}{8}$ **(b)** 37\frac{1}{8}$ **(c)** 27\frac{3}{4}$ **(d)** 45\frac{3}{4}$ **(e)** 12,300
3. 1.78%   **5. (a)** $$\frac{7}{8}$ **(b)** 2\frac{5}{8}$ **(c)** 1\frac{1}{4}$ **(d)** 1\frac{1}{2}$ **7.** $7,079,400
9. $5,600,000

p. 290 Chapter Review A   **1.** $5   **3.** 1071   **5.** $273   **7.** $5119.40   **9.** $224.98
   B   **1.** 204   **3.** 10%   **7.** No; it would be more realistic if it were a smaller percentage of a smaller income.   **9.** $1321.14

416

p. 291 Review of Chapters 1–6 A   **1.** 418.16   **3.** 5.12   **5.** 217
7. $3\frac{11}{19}$ or 3.6   **9.** 129.843   **11.** 641   **13.** 3065.086   **15.** 137.16 cm   **17.** 2.5 yr
19. (0,3), (1,5), (2,7), (3,9)
    B   1. 76.2   **3.** $\frac{3}{10}$ or 30%   **5.** $556.51   **7.** 83.33%   **9.** 7.065 ft
    C   1. 14.435   **3.** 12   **5.** $2\frac{1}{3}$ **7.** $28\frac{7}{3}$, $30\frac{1}{4}$, 30.24, 29, 27.99
    9. (a) 3   **(b)** 3   **(c)** 3   **(d)** 4   **11.** Approximately 2¢ per oz
    D   1. Commutative property for multiplication   **3.** Commutative property
    for addition   **5.** Distributive property   **7.** Associative property for
    multiplication   **9. (a)** prime   **(b)** not prime   **(c)** not prime
    (d) not prime   **11.** {2,3,5}

p. 297 Ex 7–1 A   **1.** Yes   **3.** Yes   **5.** No   **7.** Yes   **9.** Yes   **11.** No

p. 297 Ex 7–1 B   **1.** Yes   **3.** Yes   **5.** No   **7.** Yes   **9.** Yes   **11.** Yes

p. 298 Ex 7–1 C   **1.** Yes   **3.** Yes   **5.** Yes   **7. (a)** yes; **(b)** yes; **(c)** $62\frac{6}{7}$

p. 298 Ex 7–1 D   **1.** Yes   **3.** Yes   **5.** Yes   **7.** Yes   **9.** Yes
11. (a) yes; yes; yes   **(b)** yes; yes; yes   **(c)** yes; yes; yes; yes

p. 299 Ex 7–1 E   **1. (a)** $x = 40$; **(b)** $y = 32$; **(c)** $z = 24$ **3.** 96 ft
5. 64 ft   **7.** 72 ft   **9.** 60 ft   **11.** 124 ft

p. 300 Ex 7–1 F   **1.** Each side of an equation may be multiplied by the same
number without changing the answer.   Associative and commutative properties.
Each side of an equation may be multiplied by 1 without changing the answer.
3. 10   **5.** 12   **7.** 16   **9.** 30

p. 304 Ex 7–2 A   **1.** Yes; theorem III   **3.** Yes; theorem IV
5. Yes; theorem IV

p. 305 Ex 7–2 B   **1.** 6   **3.** $21\frac{3}{5}$ **5.** 4   **7.** 10   **9.** 36   **11.** 69.696

p. 305 Ex 7–2 C   **1.** Yes, by theorem III   **3.** 12 in.   **5.** Yes, by theorem IV
7. $\overline{BA}$; $\overline{BC}$; $\overline{AC}$ **9.** Yes, by theorem III

p. 307 Ex 7–2 D   **1. (a)** $16\frac{2}{3}$ ft   **(b)** 30 ft   **3.** $102\frac{6}{7}$ ft
5. Yes; $\overline{AD} = \frac{5}{14} \times \overline{AE}$ **7.** 12 in.
9. Yes, by theorem VI and then by theorems III, IV, or V

p. 311 Ex 7–3 A   **1. (a)** 0.38   **(b)** 0.92   **(c)** 0.42   **3. (a)** 0.27   **(b)** 0.6
(c) 1   **(d)** 1.7   **5.** Yes; if $m(\angle A) > m(\angle B)$, then the side opposite $\angle A$ is
larger than the side opposite $\angle B$, and hence tan $\angle A >$ tan $\angle B$.
7. (a) true   **(b)** true   **(c)** true   **(d)** true   **(e)** true
9. (a) false   **(b)** false   **(c)** false   **(d)** false   **(e)** true

p. 313 Ex 7–3 B   **1. (a)** yes; **(b)** yes; **(c)** yes; **(d)** yes, because when the same
number is divided by two different numbers, the larger number yields the middle
quotient.   **3.** Yes; the larger the angle, the larger the ratio of the side opposite
to the side adjacent.   **5. (a)** yes;   **(b)** yes, because the larger the angle, the
larger the ratio of the side opposite to the hypotenuse.

p. 316 Ex 7–4 A (using 5-place tables)   **1.** 0.087   **3.** 0.466   **5.** 1.000
7. 2.145   **9.** 11.430

p. 316 Ex 7–4 B   **1.** 2°   **3.** 28°   **5.** 44°   **7.** 62°   **9.** 87°

p. 316 Ex 7–4 C   **1.** 14°   **3.** 21°   **5.** 73°   **7.** 59°   **9.** 30°

p. 317 Ex 7–4 D   **1.** 2.55   **3.** 34.4   **5.** 71.2   **7.** 54°

p. 317 Ex 7–4 E   **1.** 86.6 ft   **3.** 93.7 ft   **5.** 245 sq yd   **7.** 32.8 yd   **9.** 28°

p. 320 Ex 7–5 A   **1.** 0.087   **3.** 0.500   **5.** 0.707   **7.** 0.946   **9.** 1.000

p. 320 Ex 7–5 B   **1.** 26°   **3.** 49°   **5.** 62°   **7.** 30°

p. 320 Ex 7–5 C 1. 1° 3. 30° 5. 80° 7. 47°

p. 320 Ex 7–5 D 1. 6 3. 242.47 5. 20 7. 31°

p. 321 Ex 7–5 E 1. 54.5 ft 3. 67° 5. 1426.8 ft 7. 19.0 m 9. 77°

p. 324 Ex 7–6 A 1. 0.999 3. 0.951 5. 0.707 7. 0.500 9. 0.035

p. 324 Ex 7–6 B 1. 6° 3. 43° 5. 60° 7. 79°

p. 324 Ex 7–6 C 1. 88° 3. 60° 5. 38° 7. 20°

p. 324 Ex 7–6 D 1. 12.99 3. 100 5. 10 7. 20°

p. 325 Ex 7–6 E 1. True 3. $>$ 5. True 7. True 9. $>$ 11. False
13. False 15. True 17. True

p. 326 Ex 7–6 F 1. 88.3 ft 3. 28° 5. 23° 7. 51°, 1.94 in., 1.57 in.
9. 131.2 ft

p. 327 Ex 7–6 G 1. (a) yes; (b) yes; (c) yes; (d) yes 3. Yes; yes
5. $\frac{1}{2}$; exact

p. 331 Ex 7–7 A 1. 4 3. 11 5. 1 7. 6 9. 16 11. 10

p. 331 Ex 7–7 B 1. 2 3. 5 5. 17 7. 10 9. $\frac{3}{2}$ 11. $\frac{5}{2}$

p. 331 Ex 7–7 C 1. $2 < \sqrt{5} < 3$ 3. $4 < \sqrt{19} < 5$ 5. $5 < \sqrt{35} < 6$
7. $7 < \sqrt{55} < 8$ 9. $9 < \sqrt{88} < 10$ 11. $12 < \sqrt{157} < 13$

p. 332 Ex 7–7 D 1. 4.58 3. 1.73 5. 5.48 7. 5.92 9. 10.25 11. 19.36

p. 332 Ex 7–7 E 1. 2.72 3. 3.54 5. 2.80 7. 4.25 9. 10.45 11. 6.38

p. 332 Ex 7–7 F 1. 2.83 3. 5.74 5. 10.49 7. 14.14 9. 76.16 11. 72.11

p. 333 Ex 7–7 G 1. 22.36 3. 15.81 5. 22.134 7. 26.46 9. 25.296
11. 15.492 13. 72.11 15. 76.16 17. 23.916 19. 18.76

p. 336 Ex 7–8 A 1. 5 3. 30 5. 9.8 7. 25 9. 9.5

p. 336 Ex 7–8 B 1. 6 3. 40 5. 10.4 7. 7 9. 24

p. 336 Ex 7–8 C 1. 81.5 3. 26 5. 19.2 7. 18.8 9. 16.5

p. 336 Ex 7–8 D 1. 12 ft 3. 24 yd 5. 50 ft 7. 41 ft 9. 97.5 sq in.
11. 13.3

p. 338 Ex 7–8 E 1. 26 in. 3. 23° 5. 12.8 in. 7. 1024 sq in.

p. 339 Ex 7–9 A 1. 10 ft 3. 26.0 ft 5. 20 in. 7. 40 in. 9. 14.1 ft
11. 31.8 ft

p. 340 Ex 7–9 B 1. $2\sqrt{3}$ 3. $20\sqrt{3}$ 5. $10\sqrt{2}$ 7. $10\sqrt{5}$ 9. 41.23

p. 341 Ex 7–9 C 1. $b = 1$ ft; $c = 1.414$ ft 3. Yes 5. $b = 3$, $c = 4.243$
7. $b = 5$, $c = 7.071$ 9. Yes 11. Yes

p. 341 Ex 7–9 D 1. $a = 1.732$, $c = 2$ 3. Yes 5. $a = 5.196$, $c = 6$
7. $a = 8.66$, $c = 10$ 9. Yes 11. Yes

p. 342 Ex 7–9 E 1. 40 ft 3. $CD = 40$ ft, $AD = 69.28$ ft 5. 181.7 ft
7. (a) 30° (b) $x = 8$ in., $y = 16$ in. (c) 13.9 in. (d) 41° (e) 49° (f) 21.2 in.

p. 345 Ex 7–10 A 1. (a) It rains; (b) the street will be wet.
3. (a) Two angles of a triangle are congruent; (b) the sides opposite these angles
will have the same measure. 5. (a) The number is 16; (b) it is divisible by 8.
7. (a) It is an even number; (b) it is divisible by 2. 9. (a) A rectangle has sides of
length 8 feet and 6 feet; (b) it has an area of 48 square feet. 11. (a) The airline
strike is settled; (b) the flight schedules will at last be met.

p. 346 Ex 7–10 B 1. If the streets are wet, then it has rained. False

3. If the sides opposite 2 angles of a triangle have the same measure, then the angles are congruent. True **5.** If a number is divisible by 8, then it is 16. False. **7.** If a number is divisible by 2, then it is an even number. True **9.** If a rectangle has an area of 48 square feet, then it has sides of length 8 feet by 6 feet. False **11.** If the flight schedules are at last met, then the airline strike will be settled. False

p. 346 Ex 7–10 C   **1.** Right **3.** Right **5.** Not right **7.** Not right
9. Right **11.** Right

p. 346 Ex 7–10 D   **1.** They probably drove 3 stakes into the ground so that the taut rope formed a triangle whose dimensions were $3 \times 4 \times 5$.
3. 30°, 60°, 90° **5.** 30° **7.** Yes **9.** Yes

p. 348 Chapter Review A   **1.** (a) 68 (b) 220 (c) 1
3. $\frac{16}{18} = 24/x$; $x = 27$ days **5.** $48\frac{3}{4}$ min **7.** (a) 0.292 (b) 0.956 (c) 0.306
    B **1.** 12 **3.** 15 **5.** 84 sq ft **7.** 13°
    9. Two perpendicular lines which intersect form congruent angles.
    C **1.** 32 **3.** 9.85 **5.** 2.89 **7.** 39 ft **9.** one side = 10 m;
    diagonal = 14.11 m
    D **1.** sine ratio $= \dfrac{\text{side opposite}}{\text{hypotenuse}}$ **3.** tangent ratio $= \dfrac{\text{side opposite}}{\text{side adjacent}}$
    5. $\frac{1}{2}$ **7.** 2, $\frac{2}{4}$, $\frac{3}{2}$; $\sqrt{2}$, $\sqrt{3}$, $\sqrt{5}$ **9.** cosine ratio $= \dfrac{\text{side adjacent}}{\text{hypotenuse}}$
    E **1.** True **3.** = **5.** True **7.** = **9.** True **11.** <

p. 354 Ex 8–1 A   **1.** $-5, +3, -2\frac{1}{2}, +7.3, +16, -1$ **5.** Right **7.** Right
9. Left **11.** (a) true (b) true (c) true (d) true **13.** 6 integers
15. (a) $+5$ (b) -15 (c) $+10$ (d) -5 (e) -4 (f) -12

p. 355 Ex 8–1 B   **1.** True **3.** < **5.** True **7.** > **9.** True **11.** True
13. True **15.** True

p. 355 Ex 8–1 D   **1.** Straight line **3.** 16 square units **5.** 5
7. (a) IV (b) on y-axis (c) on y-axis (d) III

p. 356 Ex 8–1 E   **9.** Yes

p. 359 Ex 8–2 A   **1.** (a) 9 (b) 15 (c) 15 (d) 14 (e) 12 (f) 105
3. = **5.** = **7.** True **9.** = **11.** = **13.** >

p. 359 Ex 8–2 B   **1.** $+14$ **3.** -14 **5.** 0 **7.** -603 **9.** -91
11. $-22\frac{1}{6}$

p. 359 Ex 8–2 C   **1.** $+28$ **3.** $+20$ **5.** -6 **7.** -8 **9.** $+204$

p. 360 Ex 8–2 D   **1.** (a) yes (b) yes (c) yes (d) yes
3. (a) yes (b) yes (c) yes (d) yes

p. 360 Ex 8–2 E   **1.** $5 **3.** $+15$ yd **5.** $+2°$ **7.** Yes

p. 363 Ex 8–3 A   **1.** $+6$ **3.** $+30$ **5.** $+24\frac{1}{4}$ **7.** $+9.9$ **9.** -52.3
11. $+25.5$

p. 363 Ex 8–3 B   **1.** $+2$ **3.** 0 **5.** $+30$ **7.** $+40.8$ **9.** $+400$ **11.** 120

p. 363 Ex 8–3 C   **1.** 25° **3.** $125 **5.** $11 **7.** 695 points
9. (a) 2 (b) 7 (c) 5 (d) 25 (e) 16 (f) 24 (g) 13 (h) 178

p. 366 Ex 8–4 A   **1.** -48 **3.** -48 **5.** $+48$ **7.** $+24$ **9.** -24
11. $+225$ **13.** -360 **15.** $-8\frac{3}{4}$

p. 367 Ex 8–4 B   **1.** $+36$ **3.** -140 **5.** -96 **7.** $+36$ **9.** $+216$

p. 367 Ex 8–4 C   **1.** $+6$ **3.** $+24$ **5.** $+60$ **7.** Yes; yes

p. 367 Ex 8-4 D **1.** -8 **3.** -5 **5.** -3 **7.** $+4$ **9.** $+8$ **11.** -1
13. 0 **15.** -1

p. 368 Ex 8-4 E **1.** -10 **3.** $+15$ **5.** $+2\frac{1}{2}$ **7.** $-\frac{18}{25}$ **9.** -8

p. 368 Ex 8-4 F **1.** $+1$ **3.** $+16$ **5.** -8 **7.** $+1$ **9.** $+625$ **11.** -32

p. 368 Ex 8-4 G **1.** Yes; $(+5)$ is a distance of 5 in the positive direction, so by adding a distance of 5 in the negative direction (-5), we end with 0.
3. Yes; $[(+5) + (-5)]$ equals 0 for Exercise 1. **5.** $+30$

p. 370 Ex 8-5 A **1.** 6 **3.** 0 **5.** 0 **7.** -4 **9.** 4 **11.** $-14\frac{3}{4}$

p. 370 Ex 8-5 B **1.** 9 **3.** -9 **5.** 0 **7.** 9 **9.** -45 **11.** -25

p. 370 Ex 8-5 C **1.** 19 **3.** 84 **5.** $\frac{8}{15}$ **7.** $5\frac{1}{6}$ **9.** -2 **11.** -102

p. 371 Ex 8-5 D **1.** $8\frac{8}{9}°$ C **3.** $100°$ C **5.** $-10°$ C **7.** $-17\frac{7}{9}°$ C
9. $-30\frac{5}{9}°$ C **11.** $-55\frac{5}{9}°$ C

p. 371 Ex 8-5 E **1.** 144 **3.** -2 **5.** 16 **7.** -96 **9.** 14

p. 371 Ex 8-5 F **1.** $-1, 0, 1$ **3.** -300 **5.** -410 **7.** -11 **9.** 144

p. 372 Ex 8-5 G **1.** ±2 **3.** ±5 **5.** ±10 **7.** ±2.24 **9.** ±10.68 **11.** ±8
13. 24

p. 374 Ex 8-6 A **1.** $(1, 5), (0, 0), (-1, -5)$ **3.** $(4, 3), (-4, -1), (0, 1)$
5. $(5, 0), (2, -6), (4, -2)$ **7.** $(3, -8), (5, 0), (7, 8)$
9. $(32, 0), (16, -8\frac{8}{9}), (0, -17\frac{7}{9})$

p. 374 Ex 8-6 B **1.**

C	-40	-20	-5	0	5	10	40
F	-40	-4	23	32	41	50	104

3. 212 **5.** (a) 77 (b) 14 (c) 5 (d) -13 (e) 86 (f) 45 (g) 35 (h) -35

p. 375 Ex 8-6 C **1.**

t	-1	0	1	2	3	4	5
d	-60	0	60	120	180	240	300

3.

t	-3	-2	-1	0	$+1$	$+2$	$+3$	$+4$	$+5$
d	-54	-35	-28	-27	-26	-19	0	37	98

5. No.

p. 379 Ex 8-7 A **1.** 9 tens **3.** 12 tenths **5.** 16 ones **7.** $12x$ **9.** $130a$

p. 379 Ex 8-7 B **1.** 123 **3.** 48 **5.** 313 **7.** 7 **9.** -95

p. 380 Ex 8-7 C **1.** $3x^3 + 4x^2 + 4x - 5$ **3.** $10a^3 + 11a^2 - a + 7$
5. $8c^4 + c^3 + c^2 + 8c - 5$

p. 380 Ex 8-7 D **1.** $5x^2 + 6x + 15$ **3.** $s^2 + 8s + 5$
5. $28b^3 + 9b^2 - 12b + 488$

p. 380 Ex 8-7 E **1.** $8x^2 + 212x - 1068$ **3.** $173a^3 - 8a^2 - 160a - 2163$
5. $1139x^2 - 200x + 300$

p. 380 Ex 8-7 F **1.** $(2 \times 6) + 5$ **3.** $(5 \times 6) + 2$
5. $(5 \times 6^2) + (2 \times 6) + 4$ **7.** $(1 \times 6^3) + (1 \times 6^2) + (1 \times 6) + 1$
9. $(2 \times 6^3) + (1 \times 6^2) + (3 \times 6) + 5$
11. $(4 \times 6^3) + (4 \times 6^2) + (4 \times 6) + 6$

p. 384 Ex 8-8 A **1.** 10^6 **3.** 5^5 **5.** $(\frac{1}{2})^4$ **7.** b^5 **9.** d^7 **11.** 5^6 **13.** x^2
15. x^2

p. 384 Ex 8-8 B **1.** $10^3 + 10^2 = 1100$ **3.** $7^3 + 7^2 = 392$ **5.** $b^3 - 2b^2$
7. $3k - k^2$ **9.** $h^2 + h^3$

p. 384 Ex 8-8 C **1.** x^7 **3.** $7a^5$ **5.** $2ab^2$ **7.** $5rst$ **9.** $a^2b + 2b^2 + 100b^3$

p. 385 Ex 8-8 D **1.** 42 **3.** 3900 **5.** 0.05 **7.** 40,000 **9.** 1000 **11.** 43.05

p. 385 Ex 8-8 E **1.** 300 **3.** 0.008 **5.** 50 **7.** 300 **9.** 2

p. 385 Ex 8–8 F   **1.** 80   **3.** 1,300,000   **5.** 4800 sq ft   **7.** 2.6×10^{11} cu mi
9. 750 lb

p. 386 Ex 8–8 G   **1.** 87.24   **3.** 1,313,458.575   **5.** 4287.05 sq ft
7. 265,584,108,126.86 cu mi   **9.** 735 lb

p. 389 Ex 8–9 A   **1.** No; $S' = \{4, 20\}$
3. No; $S' = \{-2, -1, 0, 604\}$ **5.** No; $S' = \{-5, 0, 99\}$
7. No; $S' = \{-3, -4, -80\}$ **9.** No; $S' = \{3, 4, 5, 50\}$

p. 389 Ex 8–9 B   **1.** (a) $17 > 16$; yes   (b) $-9 > -10$; yes   **3.** (a) $3 < 13$;
yes (b) $-23 < -13$; yes   **5.** (a) $22 > -7$; yes   (b) $-4 > -33$; yes
7. (a) $-187 > -287$; yes   (b) $-213 > -313$; yes   **9.** Yes

p. 390 Ex 8–9 C   **1.** Yes   **3.** Yes   **5.** Yes   **7.** Yes   **9.** No

p. 390 Ex 8–9 D   **1.** (a) $36 > 18$; yes   (b) $4 > 2$; yes   (c) $24 > 12$; yes
(d) $6 > 3$; yes   **3–15.** In each case the order remains the same.

p. 391 Ex 8–9 E   **1.** Yes   **3.** Yes   **5.** Yes   **7.** Yes   **9.** Yes

p. 391 Ex 8–9 F   **1.** (a) $-24 < -12$; yes (b) $-6 < -3$; yes
(c) $-36 < -18$; yes   (d) $-4 < -2$; yes   **3–11.** In each case the order becomes
opposite.   **13.** Yes   **15.** Yes; multiplying or dividing an inequality by a negative
number produces an inequality of the opposite order.

p. 392 Ex 8–9 G   **1.** (b)   **3.** (b)   **5.** (a)   **7.** (c)   **9.** (c)   **11.** (d)   **13.** (e)

p. 393 Chapter Review A   **1.** True   **3.** True   **5.** True   **7.** -1000 **9.** True

B   **1.** -114 **3.** $-42\frac{4}{15}$ **5.** -200 **7.** -80 **9.** 300   **11.** $x < -12$
13. $x > -150$

C   **1.** -25 **3.** $(-a)^5$ **5.** $8x$ **7.** $-5x^4 - 15x^3 + 5x^2$ **9.** 5

D   **1.** 10.25   **3.** $-2x^2 + 20x + 131$

p. 394 Review of Chapters 1–8 A   **1.** 153,409   **3.** $2\frac{4}{5}$ **5.** 30.43   **7.** 21.05%
9. (a) $2\frac{4}{17}$ (b) $2\frac{4}{59}$ **11.** 25.905 cu ft   **13.** 9%   **15.** (a) 5   (b) 41   (c) $149\frac{1}{3}$
17. ±41 **19.** 108 sq ft

B   **1.** $11\frac{1}{2}$ **3.** 64   **5.** $139\frac{1}{8}$ **7.** $10\frac{9}{20}$
9. (a) $2 < n < 3$ (b) $6 < n < 7$ (c) $13 < n < 14$
(d) $58 < n < 59$ **11.** (a) 9.434   (b) 10.344   (c) 11.358   (d) 2.646

C   **1.** 145.19 sq ft   **3.** 208.71 ft   **5.** 167.5   **7.** 489 sq ft   **9.** 11.1 ft
11. 16.3 ft

D   **1.** False   **3.** True   **5.** False   **7.** True   **9.** False   **11.** True

E   **1.** 0.309   **3.** 0.325   **5.** 0.695   **7.** 37.7 ft   **9.** 243.8 cu ft   **11.** 13.61 sq ft

Index